# STRUCTURED WIRING DESIGN MANUAL

## Second Edition

Author: Robert N. Bucceri

Published By: Silent Servant, Inc.

©**Copyright 2004** Silent Servant, Inc.

E-mail: swdbook4@aol.com

Library Of Congress
Bucceri, Robert N.
Silent Servant, Inc.
ISBN 0-9700057-1-7

# CONTENTS

# INTRODUCTION

This Manual will provide you information on how to pre-wire a home during the construction stage and how to ultimately build a Structured Wiring System to support sub-systems that include an Ethernet Network, Integrated Security System, Automated Audio & Video System, Automated Lighting System, Automated Heating & Cooling System, Automated Water Systems, Automated Motorized Systems, PBX Telephone System, and much more.

Chapter One concentrates on the overall wiring infrastructure of the home, 'step-by-step' system design procedures, cable pulling and termination procedures along with how the structured wiring distribution panel and hubs are configured. The structured wiring distribution panel is the central point of any structured wiring system. This panel is where the majority of cables are connected to distribute data and control signals to sub-system components throughout the home. The remaining chapters provide information on each of the sub-systems mentioned above, what their specific wiring requirements are, what system components are used, and how the cables are terminated to each component.

Also included in this manual is information on how to automate these sub-systems to provide the user with a great deal of convenience, entertainment, safety, security and energy management features. Most Structured Wiring Systems provide a wiring infrastructure for some of the sub-systems listed above, but will generally not offer much in the way of automation capability as least not at the level that this manual provides. In other words, we take a step beyond the conventional structured wiring system and introduce a multitude of automated control features. This will greatly increase the usefulness of these sub-systems while maximizing system benefits to make the most out of your Structured Wiring System. Automated control features can be incorporated into the overall home control system by using a home controller like *Stargate*. *Stargate* provides the system designer with the ability to program Events used to control sub-systems automatically and conditionally through 'scheduled time' Events and other 'IF conditions'. 'IF conditions' may include time of day, Digital Inputs, Analog Inputs, IR, RF, X-10 and ASCII Text. *Stargate* along with other control components are discussed at length in Chapter Three. The ease of programming these Events used by *Stargate* are demonstrated so you can get familiar with how to program automated control functions that can be tailored for specific family lifestyles. As sub-systems are added or changed to keep up with advances in technology, *Stargate* can be reprogrammed to support these changes as required.

This Manual is written in an 'Example Home' format that will help you to understand how a system is designed, installed and programmed. As you read through this manual, you will find a wide range of figures that contain highly detailed diagrams illustrating wiring and termination information that the text will not be able to furnish. Most chapters also include floor plans that illustrate how cables are configured for each sub-system and the locations of the sub-system equipment where cables are terminated. There are also diagrams that illustrate sub-systems in greater detail as a whole or in part. It is important to read this manual from 'cover-to-cover' and study the diagrams in order to understand how the 'Example Home' puts it all together. With all of the information provided by this manual at hand, you will be able to apply the same design concepts and installation procedures to create a system for your own home or for your customers.

The equipment illustrated in the 'Example Home' system is used for example purposes only and it is not our intentions to promote this equipment. There are many other brands of distribution panels and home control components that can provide similar results.

# DEDICATION

I dedicate the Structure Wiring Design Manual to my wife Elizabeth,
my daughter Debra, family and friends who have supported
me during the creation of this publication.

# Structured Wiring System Design

**1-1 Structured Wiring Introduction:** A residential *Structure Wiring System* is defined as the in-home physical wiring infrastructure with the primary function to connect various electronic, multimedia and household devices in a logical organized and well managed configuration. With the explosion of the computer age, more and more households now have multiple computers. With a *Structured Wiring System* in place an *Ethernet System* can be configured to network all of the computers, printers, scanners and other associated equipment for the purpose of sharing system resources.

The Internet has developed into a powerful tool for everyone in the household and has become almost as common as television in most homes. The power and convenience of this *service* is demonstrated when it places the world's information at one's fingertips and provides worldwide communications right from the home. An *Ethernet System* supported by a *Structured Wiring System* allows all computers in the home to access the Internet through one network computer that acts as a *Server*. This allows the system to operate with only one modem contained by the *Computer/Server* for the purpose of minimizing hardware requirements.

There are also digital telephone systems and security systems that benefit from *Structured Wiring*. Whole house audio/video systems and multimedia entertainment rooms use *Structured Wiring* to share system resources. This is made possible through the use of a *Structure Wiring System* that supports the capability of displaying DVD and VCR programs in all rooms of the home for the purpose of shared entertainment.

Audio/video equipment can be controlled automatically as well as remotely by utilizing infrared (IR) control that is supported by *Structured Wiring*. Video cameras that provide security surveillance images, video of the infant's room as well as video images of the pool area benefit from *Structured Wiring*. These TV images can be triggered ON automatically using motion detectors that are part of the security system. Utilizing these motion detectors contained by an entirely separate subsystem from the audio/video (IR) control system is an example of system integration. This is made possible by the support of a *Structured Wiring System*.

When considering all of the benefits of a *Structure Wiring System*, a significant advantage is the ability to simplify system modifications so when the customer's requirements change over

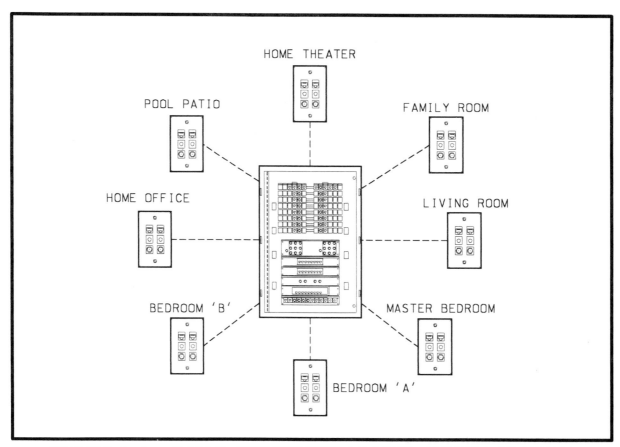

FIGURE 1-1   BASIC STRUCTURED WIRING SYSTEM DIAGRAM

the years, the proper wiring and distribution capabilities will be available. This means that adding telephone lines, computers, printers, scanners, TVs, audio/video equipment, and other components is greatly simplified. System problems are less likely to occur with a *Structured Wiring System* and trouble shooting the system is much easier to perform when the 'Home Run' topology is utilized. Being able to support the latest equipment and subsystems in the future will also benefit the customer and will increase the value of the home while making it more desirable to potential buyers.

A typical *Structure Wiring System* will include a *Signal Distribution Panel* with the required *Hubs, Service Outlets* and cabling as shown in Figure 1-1. A signal *Distribution Panel* acts much like a telephone switchboard that dispatches *services* such as Cable TV (CATV), telephone communications, Ethernet, Internet, whole house audio/video, security communications and others. These services are linked at the *Distribution Panel* (via patch cables) to the desired *Interactive Receptacles*

and/or *Service Outlets* located in each room.

There are basically two types of wall mounted service jack arrangements used to connect an assortment of equipment in each room. *Interactive Receptacles* are used in each room to provide *services* that the homeowner needs today and in the future. *Service Outlets* provide *services* that the customer needs for today's requirements and does not necessarily consider what the requirements may be in the future. *Service Outlets* are also used in addition to an *Interactive Receptacle* or when a smaller quantity of services are required in a location.

Each *Interactive Receptacle* will generally consist of one telephone jack, one Ethernet jack, two coaxial cable jacks, and two fiber optic connectors as shown in Figure 1-2. The coaxial jacks are normally used for Video Input and Video Output signals while the fiber optic cables are available to ensure future system capabilities. All of the conductors terminated to an *Interactive Receptacle* to support these standard services are furnished by a versatile wire 'Bundle' that is very popular within the *Structured Wiring Industry*.

2

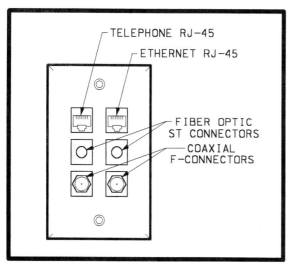

FIGURE 1-2  INTERACTIVE RECEPTACLE

**1-2 Wire Bundle:** A wire 'Bundle' consists of three different types of conductors all wrapped together to form one bundle of cables. This configuration makes it easier to pull cables through the attic and inside walls when compared to routing six separate cables. (See 'Bundle' shown in Figure 1-5). This 'Bundle' consists of two high capacity telephone/data (CAT 5, 4 UTP) cables that contain four pairs of conductors each. The 'Bundle' also contains two Quad-Shield copper core RG-6 coaxial cables, and two Multi-Mode glass-lined fiber optic cables. There are also wire 'Bundles' that consist of RG-6 coaxial cables and (CAT 5, 4 UTP) cables without the fiber optic cables. Some 'Bundles' even have speaker wires in place of the fiber optic cables; however, in most cases the speaker locations are no where near the *Interactive Receptacles* to take advantage of them. Besides providing quality conductors in a group that is more convenient to install, 'Bundles' offer standard fire protection and are available in 500-foot rolls. All cables must comply with **EIA/TIA specifications** when installing either 'Bundles' or individual cables.

**1-3 Coaxial Cable:** Coaxial cables can be pulled as a part of the wire 'Bundle' or as individual cables. The designer has the option of pulling coaxial cable as well as other types of cables in place of a 'Bundle' or in addition to a 'Bundle' as required. RG-6 cable should be specified as part of any 'Bundle' and in situations where individual

coaxial cables are pulled instead, RG-6 cables are also recommended. RG-59 coaxial cable is commonly used in residential construction; however, is does not have the bandwidth that is necessary for future home automation standards and does not provide the best quality picture for high-definition digital TV or satellite. RG-6 coaxial cable (standard foil shield with braid) is recommended for most multimedia applications. These applications include; Cable TV (CATV), TV antennas, satellite, CCTV cameras and in some cases Internet *service* through a CATV computer modem. Only use RG-6 coaxial cable and preferably (RG-6 Quad Shield) coaxial cable whenever possible.

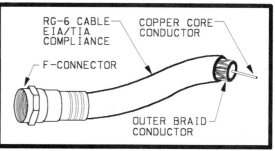

FIGURE 1-3  RG-6 COAX CABLE

**1-4 CAT 5, 4 UTP Cable:** In any home that incorporates a *Structured Wiring System*, we recommend using (CAT 5, 4 UTP) cable for the majority of data communications and low voltage applications. (CAT 5, 4 UTP) cable consists of four pairs (8 conductors) of 24 GA twisted copper wire that was originally developed for 100Base-T (Fast Ethernet) networks. Since then (CAT 5, 4 UTP) has become a very good general-purpose cable for data communication purposes and for applications that require data speeds of up to 100

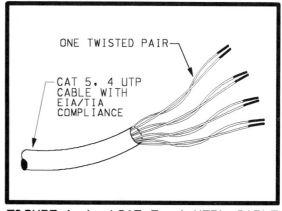

FIGURE 1-4  (CAT 5, 4 UTP)  CABLE

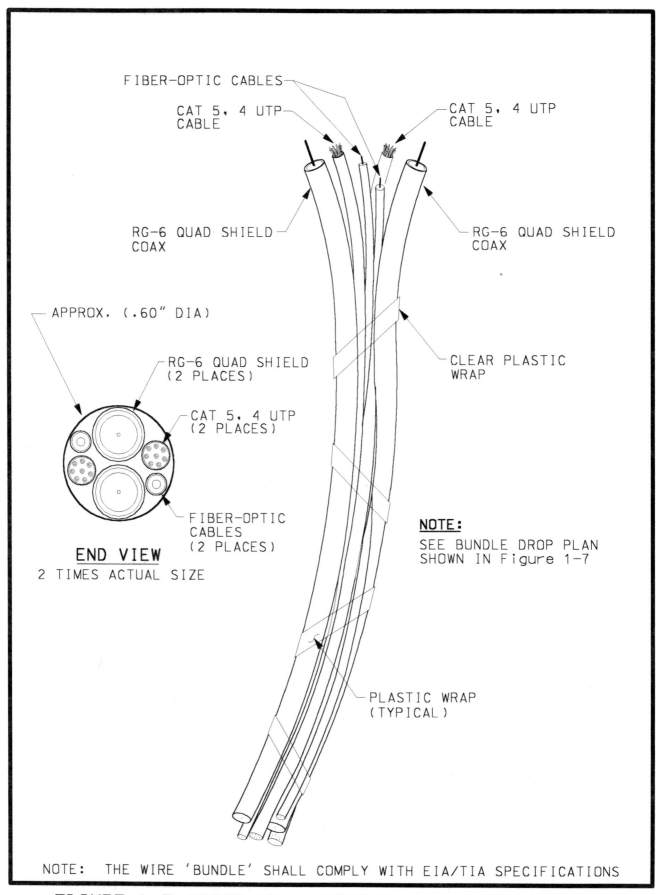

FIBER-OPTIC CABLES

CAT 5, 4 UTP CABLE

CAT 5, 4 UTP CABLE

RG-6 QUAD SHIELD COAX

RG-6 QUAD SHIELD COAX

CLEAR PLASTIC WRAP

APPROX. (.60" DIA)

RG-6 QUAD SHIELD (2 PLACES)

CAT 5, 4 UTP (2 PLACES)

FIBER-OPTIC CABLES (2 PLACES)

**END VIEW**
2 TIMES ACTUAL SIZE

**NOTE:**
SEE BUNDLE DROP PLAN SHOWN IN Figure 1-7

PLASTIC WRAP (TYPICAL)

NOTE:   THE WIRE 'BUNDLE' SHALL COMPLY WITH EIA/TIA SPECIFICATIONS

## FIGURE 1-5 SPEED WRAP BUNDLE WITH FIBER OPTICS

Mps. The tight twists of each pair of wires contained by this cable is a very good method of avoiding signal interference and cross talk. In addition to Ethernet, Internet and telephone *service*, (CAT 5, 4 UTP) cable is often used to support security system sensors, audio/video IR control, intercom systems, touch screens, temperature sensors, *JDS* Keypads, general purpose sensors, Digital & Analog Inputs and other data and low voltage applications. In cases where only four conductors are needed to provide the desired *services*, the additional conductors contained by the (CAT 5, 4 UTP) cable are available in case one or more conductors are damaged over the life of the system. By using (CAT 5, 4 UTP) cable for all telephone, data networks and other applicable systems, there will most likely be a sufficient quantity of conductors left over to upgrade systems in the future.

**1-5 Fiber Optic Cable**: Fiber Optic technology converts video, data and voice signals into light and then beams this light through optical fiber to transport information from one location to another. The fiber itself consists of a thin glass filament that allows the light to travel over long distances due to low resistance. There are three types of fiber optic cable: Single-Mode, Multi-Mode and Plastic Optical Fiber. Single-Mode is an optical fiber that propagates one light mode while Multi-Mode fiber propagates multiple modes of light. Each fiber that makes-up a Multi-Mode cable is designed to carry a different signal independent from the other fibers within the same cable. Plastic Optical Fiber is fairly new technology that is designed to perform in a similar manner to Single-Mode cable while being more economical. The type of fiber optic cable contained by the wire 'Bundle' previously described in Section 1-2, is Multi-Mode Fiber.

Light is introduced into a fiber optic cable using a light emitting diode (LED) or a laser. Light is pulsed ON & OFF by the light source to a light sensitive receiver located on the other end of the cable. This receiver converts these light pulses into digital signals that are equal to the original signals introduced by the light source. Analog TV sets can receive program signals through a fiber optic cable in the sequence described as follows: Analog TV signals are converted to digital signals by using an analog/digital converter. An LED is pulsed ON & OFF in response to the digital input signals and converts these signals to an LED light signal. Once the light travels to the other end of the cable, light shines on a light sensitive receiver and converts the light back into digital signals. Digital signals are then converted back into the original analog signals by a digital/analog converter before being received by the TV. Now that Digital TVs are available, converting from analog to digital and vise versa will no longer be necessary.

Compared to copper conductors, one glass fiber can perform the job of hundreds of copper conductors. Fiber has the capability of carrying more data at higher speeds while occupying less space. Signals that are carried by fiber optic cable can travel long distances without having to be amplified. Fiber also allows optic networks to operate at much higher speeds and has a larger bandwidth while providing greater signal carrying capacity. The larger bandwidth has plenty of capacity for current demands and will provide capabilities well beyond present technologies. Fiber optic cable also has greater resistance to electromagnetic noise or interference from motors, radio signals, power surges and other interference. There is no possibility of a short circuit when using fiber optic cable because there is no electrical current carried by the fiber. It can not produce electrical sparks that can cause fires. It is relatively small in size and lighter in weight than copper conductors.

An increase in demand for fiber optic cable has brought the price down to a competitive level with copper cable; however, the fiber optic connectors, transmitters and converters required to support this type of system are considerably more expensive than the supporting copper wire components. The disadvantage of a fiber optic system is the high installation cost because it takes longer to make system connections compared to copper conductors and also requires skilled labor and specialized tools.

Applications for fiber optic cable are increasing all the time. Telephone companies have been using fiber optic systems for over twenty years. Cable TV companies are also beginning to use fiber optic technology in their cable systems and in some cases have run fiber up to residential homes for testing purposes. In select residential locations, an optical receiver may soon be used to integrate fiber and coaxial cable. The optical receiver converts fiber optic light pulses back into digital signals that could be sent into homes over coaxial cable. A home that has fiber optic capabilities could avoid copper conductors all together by having the Telephone and/or Cable Company route fiber optic *service* cable right up to the home. This will allow fiber to be used up to the *Service Input Hub* in the *Distribution Panel*. From there the signals could be distributed to the appropriate rooms over the fiber optic cables provided by each *Zone* 'Bundle' that is terminated to an *Interactive Receptacle*.

Fiber optics has become the industry standard for telecommunications. Fiber optics is certainly expected to replace copper conductors completely. This is why 'future proofing' residential homes today will be very useful in the years to come.

**1-6 Speaker Cable:** Speaker cable used to support a *Whole House Audio/Video System* should be routed to each room of the home, to the patio area, and even to the garage in cases where the homeowner desires entertainment while working on home projects. Good quality wire

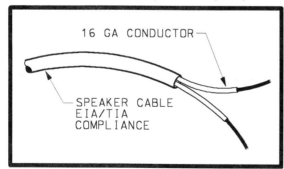

FIGURE 1-6 SPEAKER CABLE

should always be installed because it will be very difficult to replace in the future. Poor quality speaker cable or thin gauge wire can be the cause of poor quality sound. In applications where speaker wire is routed over long distances through a home, it will become more susceptible

to resistance losses and signal interference. Two or four conductor 14 GA to 16 GA speaker wire should be used for most speaker applications. 12 GA wire maybe required for long lengths of speaker wire or for high-powered speaker applications. Please consult with specific audio and video equipment manufacturers or suppliers for recommended wire types and size.

All other cable types that are generally used in residential *Structured Wiring Systems* are described in the appropriate subsystem chapters that follow.

**1-7 The Equipment Room:** When the designer begins to develop the design of a *Structured Wiring System,* a drawing or sketch of the home should be completed. This drawing should be a *Plan View* similar in concept to the drawing that illustrates the 'Example Home' design shown in Figure 1-7. This drawing should identify where the *Equipment Room* is located. It should also identify where the *Interactive Receptacles* and/or *Service Outlets* are located and what type of cables need to be pulled from the *Equipment Room* to each *Interactive Receptacle* and/or *Service Outlet.* This drawing should also identify what the *Service Inputs* are, where each *service* entrance enclosure is located on the exterior walls of the home and the cable types that needs to be pulled from the *Equipment Room* to each *service* entrance enclosure.

The location of the *Equipment Room* is actually the first part of the system to identify on the drawing. This room is ideally a centralized room or closet that houses all of the main control equipment used to receive and distribute signals throughout the home. A centralized location is desirable to minimize the length of cable pulled from the *Equipment Room* to most areas of the home. The *Equipment Room* is also the location where all *Service Input* cables feed the *Distribution Panel* to provide the home with *services* such as telephone, Internet, Cable TV, TV antenna, satellite, CCTV, and infrared (IR) control of the audio/video equipment functions. It is also the location where all of the cables are pulled from to provide *services* to the *Interactive Receptacles* and/or *Service Outlets* in each room or area of the home.

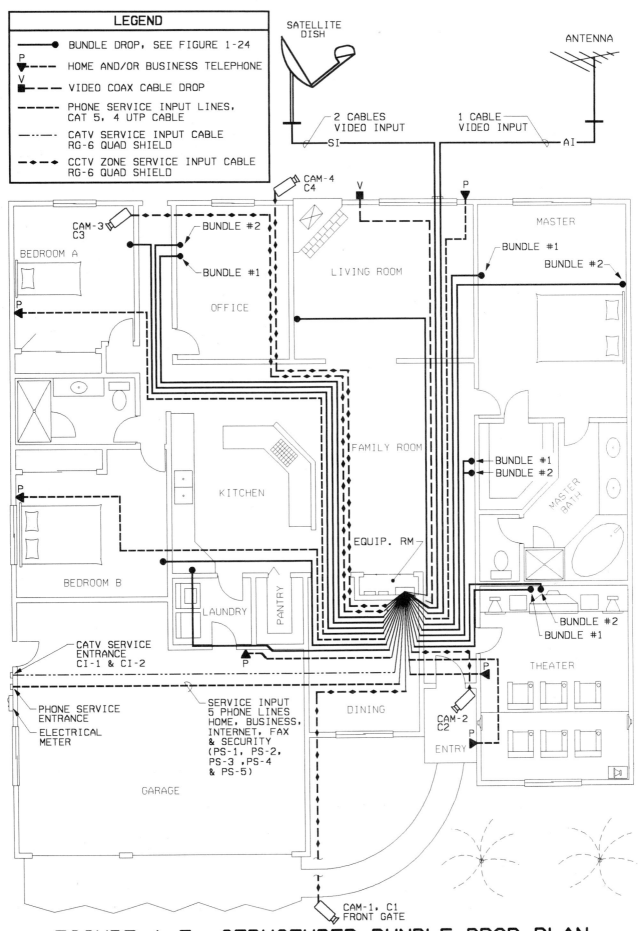

FIGURE 1-7 STRUCTURED BUNDLE DROP PLAN

Another ideal location for an *Equipment Room* is near the *Whole House Audio/Video Equipment*. This is because coaxial cables, IR control cables and other conductors may be routed from the audio/video equipment to the *Distribution Panel* before the output signals are routed to each room. The close proximately would also minimize cable lengths and installation costs while allowing system modifications to be made with less difficulty.

Notice where the *Equipment Room* is located in the *Structured Bundle Drop Plan* shown in Figure 1-7. This is as close as possible to a centralized location in this particular home and the *Whole House Audio/Video Equipment* is also shown near by. In some homes the *Equipment Room* may need to be located in one corner of the home or in a location that is not at all centralized. This is OK because the system will work just the same except the cables will take longer to pull and the total cost of the cable will be higher.

Home floor plans that make it difficult to locate the *Equipment Room*, leaves the homeowner with the option of using a closet in an extra bedroom or possibly an unused linen closet when room permits. Sometimes there is extra space on a wall inside a large Master Bedroom closet that can be partially used as an *Equipment Room*. The amount of space needed depends on the system requirements and type of equipment selected. When designing a system, it is always best to plan ahead and incorporate the *Equipment Room* into the house plans from the beginning.

An important consideration to make when selecting a location for the *Equipment Room* is to first find out if there is adequate access space above the ceiling for the installer to pull the cables. Access space must be considered because some areas of the home have low rooflines that may not provide sufficient space. The *Equipment Room* should not be located in the garage because during certain months of the year the equipment may need to be cooled or heated. An *Equipment Room* that contains electronic equipment should ideally be kept between 75°F and 90°F during the summer months and at a minimum of 40°F during the winter months. Most electronic equipment manufacturers state that ambient temperatures in excess of 105°F for prolonged periods of time will reduce the life of the equipment. Furthermore, excess moisture in the air will eventually corrode electronic boards and cause equipment failures. The relative humidity should be kept between 30% and 60%. Relative humidity levels below 30% can damage electronic components because static discharge is more prevalent in this environment.

Electronic equipment that is often housed in the *Equipment Room* include: The *Distribution Panel*, *Stargate* Home Controller, PBX Telephone Controller, Hardwired Lighting Controller, Multi-Zone HVAC Controller, Audio/Video IR-Controller, Security System Panel, continuous 12V DC power supply, AC power strips, local surge suppressor, and other associated home control equipment similar to what is illustrated in the 'Example Home' *Equipment Room* in Figure 1-8. In addition to the control equipment, the 'Example Home' uses a relay panel to control the motorized window coverings and the security/hurricane shutters. This room also houses video camera modulators and a vehicle detection console. Optional equipment may include an uninterrupted power supply (UPS) for the 12V DC control power and for critical 120V AC electrical loads such as emergency lighting and the motorized security/hurricane shutters.

The *Equipment Room* should have a dedicated power receptacle on a 120V AC, 20 amp circuit. Additional power may be required depending on the total electrical power needed to operate the equipment; however, 20 amps is generally more than sufficient to operate most home control systems.

The interior walls in the *Equipment Room* should be covered with sheets of high-grade 1/2" thick plywood to provide a hard surface to mount the electronic equipment on. Plywood should be fastened to the wall studs and painted with semi-gloss latex paint before mounting the equipment. The hard surface of the plywood will also allow the installer to easily support cables using loop type cable hangers and wire ties. A strip of plywood can also be installed on the ceiling of the *Equipment Room* where cables can penetrate the ceiling in order to access the attic space for distribution purposes. These holes are

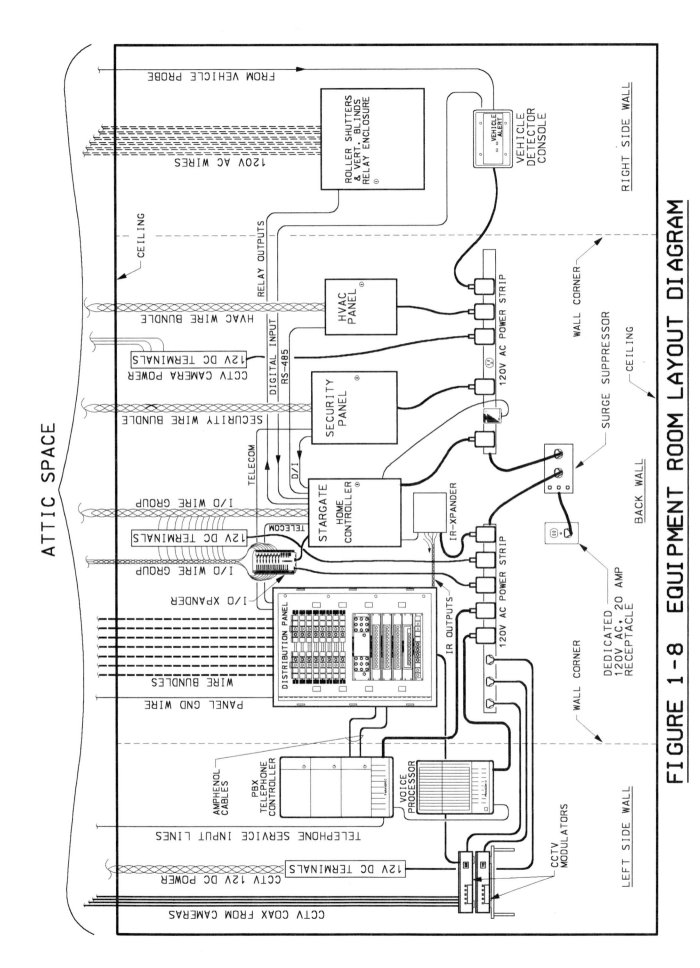

FIGURE 1-8   EQUIPMENT ROOM LAYOUT DIAGRAM

drilled through the plywood approximately 1/2" larger in diameter than each cable group diameter. After the cables are pulled, expandable foam sealer is used to provide a tight seal between the cables and the holes. This will help keep insects from entering the home and avoid the loss of conditioned air. Escutcheon plates can also be used around the cable penetrations to maintain a clean looking installation.

The installer may elect to route most of the cables from the attic and down through the *Equipment Room* walls to the appropriate equipment for an extra clean looking installation. To accommodate this approach the installer must pre-drill holes in the top plate of the framed wall to allow cables to be pulled down between the wall studs to each piece of equipment. This approach is normally used when a control enclosure is recessed into the drywall. If the control enclosure is surface mounted and has knockout holes in the back panel, this approach will also work. If there are no knockout holes in the back of the panel this approach will in most cases not be practical.

All electronic equipment should be arranged in the room to allow easy access for servicing and troubling shooting purposes. To minimize the length of cables routed between components within the *Equipment Room*, associated equipment should be mounted next to each other. An example of proper equipment placement is illustrated in Figure 1-8. Notice that the PBX Telehone Controller and Voice Processor are mounted together right next to the *Distribution Panel* in order to feed the telephone extension lines to the *Telephone Hubs*. Also notice that the *Stargate, IR-Xpander* and the *Distribution Panel* are mounted close together for wiring purposes.

Sufficient lighting should be provided in the *Equipment Room* in order to service, troubleshoot or modify the whole house control system in the future. Fluorescent lighting is not recommended because fluorescent ballast's can cause electrical noise on the power lines, which could interfere with data communication cables and/or certain types of home control components. Incandescent lighting is preferable.

Most of the electronic equipment in the *Equipment Room* will give off heat. Depending on the total amount of heat rejected to the room and whether the room is well ventilated or not will determine if cooling is required. A small amount of conditioned air may be needed to maintain the temperature equal to or below 90°F. This heat is measured either in Watts or BTU per hour. This heat rate can be determined by looking at the equipment specifications or by reading the sticker on the back of each component. This sticker will often list the Kilowatt (kW) power consumption. Sometimes only the voltage and amperage are indicated. To determine the amount of heat rejected from each electronic component using the voltage and amperage figures, one would multiply the (voltage) x (amperage) x 3.4 BTU per hour per watt to find the heat rejected in BTU per hour.

**\* (Volts x Amps ) = Watts or Power**

**Example Problem:**
The total rate of heat rejected by all electronic components in an *Equipment Room* is 300 watts. If the conditioned supply air temperature is 55°F and 90°F is the maximum temperature that the *Equipment Room* will be allowed to reach, find the total CFM required to properly cool the room.

**Find:  Cubic Feet Per Minute = CFM**
300 watts x 3.4 BTU/hr/watt = 1,020 Btu/hr
**Q = 1.08 x CFM x ($T_R$ - Ts)**
Q = 1,020 BTU/hr
1.08 is a constant
$T_R$ = Required *Equipment Room* Temp. = 90°F
Ts  = Air supplied to the *Equip. Room* = 55°F

**CFM = Q/1.08 x ($T_R$ - Ts)**
**CFM = 1,020 Btuh / 1.08 x (90 – 55)**

**\* 27 CFM \***

27 CFM can; for instance, be easily supplied to the *Equipment Room* through a 4" diameter duct and a small supply air diffuser.

The entrance door to the *Equipment Room* may provide sufficient ventilation to remove the excess heat if a bifold type door with ventilation slates is used. In some cases, an air transfer grille can be installed in a standard type door to provide the required ventilation as well.

**1-8 Distribution Panel:** The heart of the 'Example Home' *Structured Wiring System* is the *FutureSmart® Pro 8 Distribution Panel* that is located in the *Equipment Room* as previously shown in Figure 1-8. The *Distribution Panel* is the common point of wire origination, distribution and termination. The *Distribution Panel* contains a collection of products designed to distribute and manipulate telephone, data, entertainment and control signals originating from within the home or from outside the home. The *Distribution Panel* is designed to allow changes to be made to the configuration of the low voltage wiring network in a home by simply rearranging the appropriate patch cables (*jumpers*) or by adding additional Hubs.

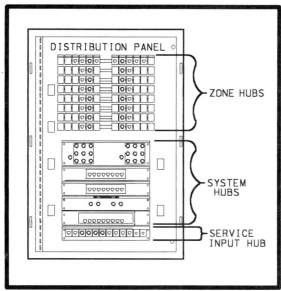

# FIGURE 1-9 HUB SECTIONS

In Figure 1-7, notice how all of the wire 'Bundles' are routed in a 'Home Run' topology originating from the *Distribution Panel*. Also notice that the *Service Inputs* are routed to the *Distribution Panel* as well, making this device the centerpiece of the *Structure Wiring System*.

The *Distribution Panel* is made up of three major sections. As shown in Figure 1-9, the bottom section of the panel contains the *Service Input Hub*. The middle section of the panel consists of a number of *System Hubs* and the upper section of the panel houses 8 *Zone Hubs*.

Each portion of the *Distribution Panel* will be discussed in detail in the following sections.

**1-9 Service Input Hub:** The *Service Input Hub* is the gateway that is used to connect outside telephone *service*, Internet *service*, Fax *service*, Cable TV *service*, TV antenna *service*, CCTV Camera inputs and more. Each *Service Input* interfaces the home from inside a dedicated enclosure called a *service* entrance. Each enclosure is generally mounted on an exterior wall of the home. These enclosures provide a means of terminating the appropriate *service* cable(s) from the street to the *Service Input* cables in the home.

## SERVICE INPUT HUB

In the 'Example Home', *Service Input* cables are pulled from the *Equipment Room* to each *service* entrance enclosure and are terminated to the rear of the *Service Input Hub*. This will provide the customer with *services* wherever they are needed in the home. When using a surface mounted *Distribution Panel* such as the *FutureSmart® Pro 8*, *Service Input* cables are connected to the rear of the *Service Input Hub* as shown in Figures 1-10. In this configuration, conductors are routed from the attic and down inside the *Equipment Room* wall in order to penetrate the wall behind the *Distribution Panel* before terminating the cables. Once the cable connections are made, *service* signals are allowed to travel to the front connectors of the *Service Input Hub* shown in Figure 1-11. These *services* will then be allowed to travel to the *System Hubs* for distribution to the appropriate *Zone Hubs*.

Notice how each *service* such as, Cable TV (CATV), TV antenna, and CCTV camera inputs are allowed to travel to the *Video Input Hub* with the use of four RG-6 coaxial patch cables. Once these *services* are connected to the *Video Input Hub*, signals can be *jumpered* to the appropriate *Zone Hub(s)* described in Section 1-10.

Four IR Outputs from the *JDS IR-Xpander* (Infrared Audio/Video Controller) are shown connected to the rear of the *Service Input Hub* as

# OFFICE HUB REAR CONNECTIONS

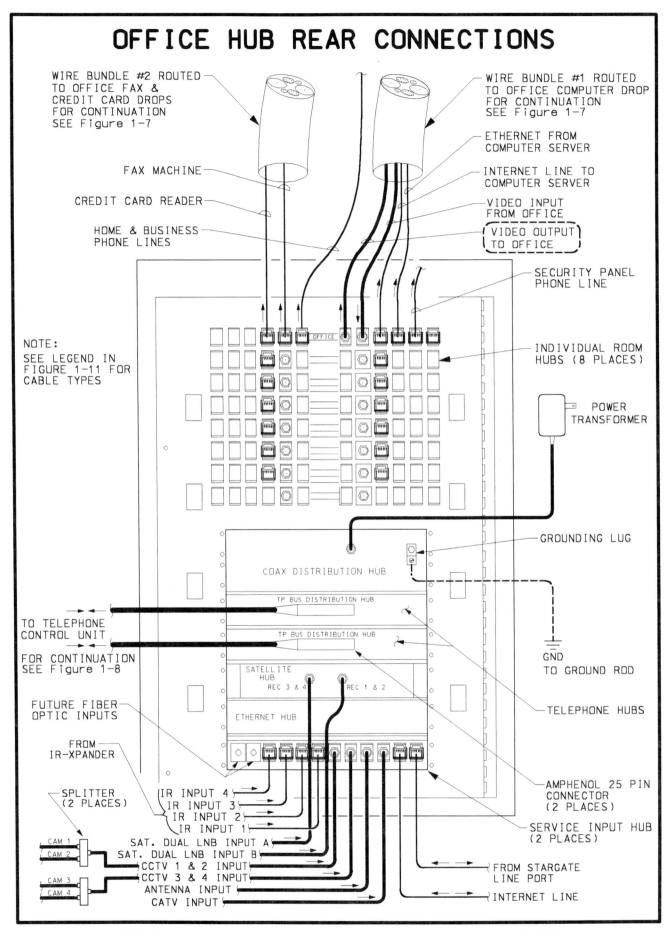

WIRE BUNDLE #2 ROUTED TO OFFICE FAX & CREDIT CARD DROPS FOR CONTINUATION SEE Figure 1-7

WIRE BUNDLE #1 ROUTED TO OFFICE COMPUTER DROP FOR CONTINUATION SEE Figure 1-7

FAX MACHINE

CREDIT CARD READER

HOME & BUSINESS PHONE LINES

ETHERNET FROM COMPUTER SERVER

INTERNET LINE TO COMPUTER SERVER

VIDEO INPUT FROM OFFICE

VIDEO OUTPUT TO OFFICE

SECURITY PANEL PHONE LINE

NOTE:
SEE LEGEND IN FIGURE 1-11 FOR CABLE TYPES

INDIVIDUAL ROOM HUBS (8 PLACES)

OFFICE

POWER TRANSFORMER

COAX DISTRIBUTION HUB

GROUNDING LUG

TP BUS DISTRIBUTION HUB

TO TELEPHONE CONTROL UNIT

FOR CONTINUATION SEE Figure 1-8

TP BUS DISTRIBUTION HUB

GND
TO GROUND ROD

SATELLITE HUB

REC 3 & 4          REC 1 & 2

TELEPHONE HUBS

FUTURE FIBER OPTIC INPUTS

ETHERNET HUB

FROM IR-XPANDER

SPLITTER (2 PLACES)

IR INPUT 4
IR INPUT 3
IR INPUT 2
IR INPUT 1
SAT. DUAL LNB INPUT A
SAT. DUAL LNB INPUT B
CCTV 1 & 2 INPUT
CCTV 3 & 4 INPUT
ANTENNA INPUT
CATV INPUT

CAM 1
CAM 2
CAM 3
CAM 4

AMPHENOL 25 PIN CONNECTOR (2 PLACES)

SERVICE INPUT HUB (2 PLACES)

FROM STARGATE LINE PORT

INTERNET LINE

## FIGURE 1-10   PANEL HUBS - REAR VIEW

# OFFICE HUB CONNECTIONS

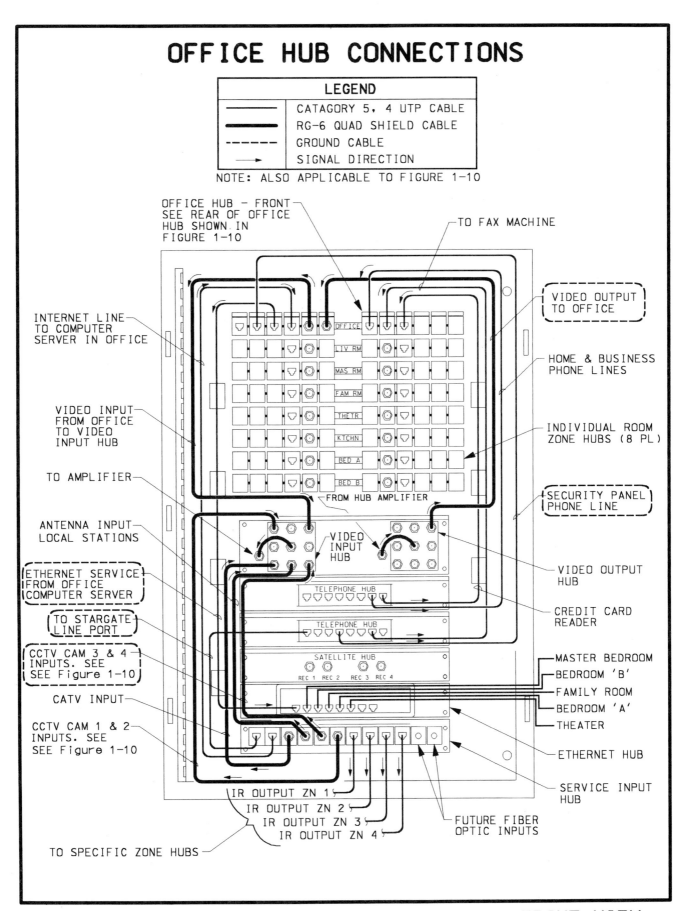

**LEGEND**

| | |
|---|---|
| ——— | CATAGORY 5, 4 UTP CABLE |
| ▬▬▬ | RG-6 QUAD SHIELD CABLE |
| - - - - - | GROUND CABLE |
| → | SIGNAL DIRECTION |

NOTE: ALSO APPLICABLE TO FIGURE 1-10

OFFICE HUB - FRONT
SEE REAR OF OFFICE
HUB SHOWN IN
FIGURE 1-10

TO FAX MACHINE

VIDEO OUTPUT
TO OFFICE

INTERNET LINE
TO COMPUTER
SERVER IN OFFICE

HOME & BUSINESS
PHONE LINES

VIDEO INPUT
FROM OFFICE
TO VIDEO
INPUT HUB

INDIVIDUAL ROOM
ZONE HUBS ( 8 PL )

TO AMPLIFIER

SECURITY PANEL
PHONE LINE

ANTENNA INPUT
LOCAL STATIONS

VIDEO OUTPUT
HUB

ETHERNET SERVICE
FROM OFFICE
COMPUTER SERVER

CREDIT CARD
READER

TO STARGATE
LINE PORT

MASTER BEDROOM

BEDROOM 'B'

CCTV CAM 3 & 4
INPUTS. SEE
SEE Figure 1-10

FAMILY ROOM

BEDROOM 'A'

CATV INPUT

THEATER

CCTV CAM 1 & 2
INPUTS. SEE
SEE Figure 1-10

ETHERNET HUB

SERVICE INPUT
HUB

IR OUTPUT ZN 1
IR OUTPUT ZN 2
IR OUTPUT ZN 3
IR OUTPUT ZN 4

FUTURE FIBER
OPTIC INPUTS

TO SPECIFIC ZONE HUBS

OFFICE   LIV RM   MAS RM   FAM RM   THETR   KTCHN   BED A   BED B

FROM HUB AMPLIFIER

VIDEO INPUT HUB

TELEPHONE HUB

TELEPHONE HUB

SATELLITE HUB

REC 1   REC 2   REC 3   REC 4

# FIGURE 1-11   DISTRIBUTION PANEL HUBS - FRONT VIEW

IR inputs in Figure 1-10. IR Outputs are shown at the rear panel of the *IR-Xpander* in Figure 3-7 on page 76. When audio/video *Zone* control is required, IR signals will travel to the front of the *Service Input Hub* before being *jumpered* directly to the appropriate *Zone/Room Hubs* located on the top half of the panel. These patch cables can be fabricated from standard (CAT 5, 4 UTP) cable with RJ-45 plug connectors. The patch cable configuration shown in Figure 1-11, bypasses the *System Hubs*. This is because the individual *Zone* IR Inputs must remain separate from all others to avoid premature control responses from audio/video equipment located in other areas of the home. In the 'Example Home', an audio/video IR control output is *jumpered* directly from the *Service Input Hub* to the Family Room *Zone Hub* as shown in Figure 1-12.

The *Service Input Hub* will generally have a standard configuration of two coaxial *Source Inputs* from CATV, TV antenna, etc., four CAT 5 twisted pair inputs for communication *services* and two fiber optic inputs. These services will include entertainment, satellite, Internet, communications, etc. Fiber optic connectors are available on the *Service Input Hub* to support system upgrades in the future when the appropriate *services* become available and economical. The *Service Input Hub* also includes four expansion slots for adding extra inputs, which makes it easy to customize or re-configure as system requirements change over time.

Satellite Input cables do not connect to the *Service Input Hub,* but instead connect directly to the F-connectors on the rear of the *Satellite Hub* as shown in Figure 1-10. There are two (RG-6 Quad Shield) coaxial cables routed from the satellite dish. This is because the satellite is equipped with a dual LNB (Input A & Input B). A dual LNB allows 'Occupant A' to watch a different program in another room than Occupant 'B' because they each have their own satellite input and satellite receiver. A single LNB satellite dish forces the whole family to watch what ever channel is selected for the TV with the satellite receiver. The *Satellite Hub* will be discussed further in Section 1-13.

Telephone *service* input cables for most homes will normally connect to the *Service Input Hub* for distribution to each room; however, in the 'Example Home', a Panasonic KX-TD1232 Digital Hybrid telephone system is incorporated and requires the telephone *service* to enter the system at the KX-TD1232 Telephone Controller. The telephone *Service Input* cables from the *service* entrance can be seen connected to the Telephone Controller shown in Figure 1-8. Also see Chapter Eight for more on this hybrid telephone system.

**1-10 System Hubs:** As shown in Figure 1-9, all *System Hubs* are mounted in the *Distribution Panel* above the *Service Input Hub* and below the *Zone Hubs*. *System Hubs* include, the *Coax Distribution Hub* (Video Hub), *Telephone Hub*, *Satellite Hub*, and the *Ethernet Hub*. The main purpose of a *System Hub* is to provide a means of sharing *Service Input* signals and to provide a means of distributing these *services* to the appropriate rooms in the home. Some of the *System Hubs* are designed to condition, amplify and manipulate the signals before being distributed to the appropriate rooms. *Service* distribution through the home is accomplished by using patch cables (*jumpers*) to bridge signals from the appropriate *System Hubs* to the desired *Zone Hub*. An example of this is illustrated in Figure 1-11. Find the *Video Output Hub* located in the middle of the panel. Notice the patch cable that is connected from this *System Hub* to the Office *Zone Hub* at the top of the *Distribution Panel*. From here the signals are carried to the back of the *Zone Hub* as shown in Figure 1-10, and through the connected conductor before reaching the wall outlet in the Office.

*System Hubs* are also used to receive input signals from within the home for the purpose of sharing these inputs with occupants in other areas of the home. For instance; output signals originating from the Theater VCR can be received by the *Video Input Hub* and redistributed to the Family Room, Master Bedroom, pool patio, etc. This is accomplished by connecting a patch cable between the Theater *Zone Hub* and the *Video Input Hub* shown in Figure 1-17.

Signals from a *System Hub* can be easily diverted to a different *Zone Hub* by reconfiguring the patch cables between the appropriate *System Hub* and the desired *Zone Hub*. This is very

# FAMILY ROOM HUB CONNECTIONS

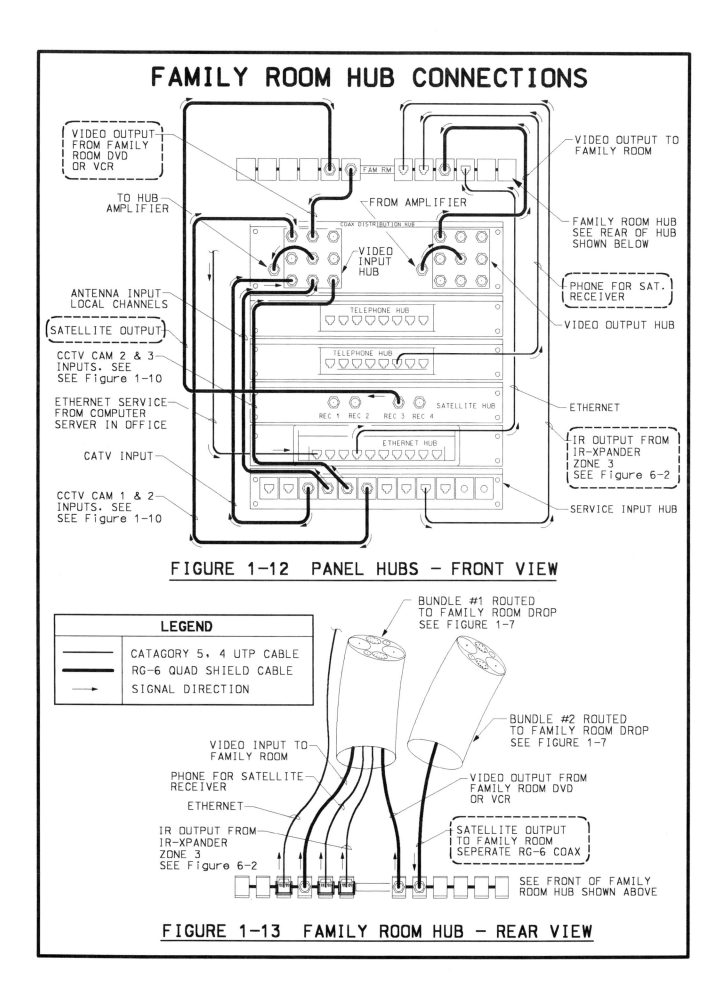

VIDEO OUTPUT FROM FAMILY ROOM DVD OR VCR

TO HUB AMPLIFIER

FROM AMPLIFIER

VIDEO INPUT HUB

COAX DISTRIBUTION HUB

VIDEO OUTPUT TO FAMILY ROOM

FAMILY ROOM HUB SEE REAR OF HUB SHOWN BELOW

ANTENNA INPUT LOCAL CHANNELS

PHONE FOR SAT. RECEIVER

SATELLITE OUTPUT

VIDEO OUTPUT HUB

CCTV CAM 2 & 3 INPUTS. SEE SEE Figure 1-10

TELEPHONE HUB

TELEPHONE HUB

ETHERNET SERVICE FROM COMPUTER SERVER IN OFFICE

SATELLITE HUB
REC 1   REC 2   REC 3   REC 4

ETHERNET

CATV INPUT

ETHERNET HUB

IR OUTPUT FROM IR-XPANDER ZONE 3 SEE Figure 6-2

CCTV CAM 1 & 2 INPUTS. SEE SEE Figure 1-10

SERVICE INPUT HUB

## FIGURE 1-12   PANEL HUBS - FRONT VIEW

### LEGEND

| | |
|---|---|
| —————— | CATAGORY 5, 4 UTP CABLE |
| ▬▬▬▬▬ | RG-6 QUAD SHIELD CABLE |
| → | SIGNAL DIRECTION |

BUNDLE #1 ROUTED TO FAMILY ROOM DROP SEE FIGURE 1-7

BUNDLE #2 ROUTED TO FAMILY ROOM DROP SEE FIGURE 1-7

VIDEO INPUT TO FAMILY ROOM

PHONE FOR SATELLITE RECEIVER

ETHERNET

VIDEO OUTPUT FROM FAMILY ROOM DVD OR VCR

IR OUTPUT FROM IR-XPANDER ZONE 3 SEE Figure 6-2

SATELLITE OUTPUT TO FAMILY ROOM SEPERATE RG-6 COAX

SEE FRONT OF FAMILY ROOM HUB SHOWN ABOVE

## FIGURE 1-13   FAMILY ROOM HUB - REAR VIEW

useful; for instance, when a system component such as a fax machine or other device is moved to another room in the home.

**1-11 Zone Hubs:** There are a total of eight *Zone Hubs* available on the *Pro 8 Distribution Panel.* These Hubs are located at the top half of the *Panel* shown in Figure 1-9. These Hubs include: The Office, Living Room, Master Bedroom, Family Room, Theater, Kitchen, Bedroom 'A', and Bedroom 'B'. Each *Zone Hub* is capable of receiving *Service Input Signals* from a verity of *System Hubs* that were previously discussed in Section 1-10.

On the Office *Zone Hub* shown at the top of the *Panel* in Figure 1-11, a number of *services* are available to this room, which include Video Inputs, Video Outputs, Internet, Ethernet, fax machine, credit card reader and telephone. All of these signals are allowed to enter the Office *Zone* by connecting individual patch cables to bridge the signals from the appropriate *System Hubs* to the Office *Zone Hub* as shown. Some of these signals such as telephone communications actually travel in both directions; however, for simplicity purposes it is easier to think of them as moving in one direction towards the *Zone Hubs* and out to the rooms to visualize how these signals are distributed.

## ZONE/ROOM HUB

Input signals to the Office *Zone* follow the directional arrows shown next to each cable. As the signals enter the front of the *Zone Hubs*, they will also leave the back of the Hub through the conductors contained by wire 'Bundle #1 & #2 as shown in Figure 1-10. From here the signals travel to the Office *Zone* and are received by the appropriate equipment plugged into the Office *Interactive Receptacle* or *Service Outlet*.

The Office houses the personal computer designated as the *Server* for all Ethernet and Internet activity in the home. Both the Internet and Ethernet cables required by the *Server* are connected between the *Server* and the appropriate *Interactive Receptacle* jacks as shown in Figure 1-14. To provide both Internet and other Ethernet *services* to the other computers on the network, an Ethernet cable is connected to the rear modular connector at the back of the *Interactive Receptacle*. This allows signals to travel back to the *Distribution Panel* through the conductors contained by 'Bundle #1' shown in Figure 1-10, to distribute signals to other network computers.

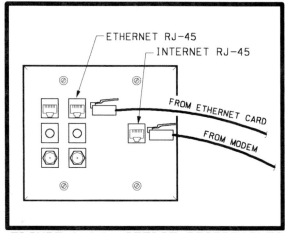

**FIGURE 1-14    OFFICE RECEPTACLES**

The Office Video Output can be used to send video signals back to the *System Hub* to share with the other *Zones*; however, there is no VCR, DVD or CCTV camera in this room at this time. A better example of a Video Output is illustrated in the 'Theater Hub Connection Diagram' shown in Figure 1-16. This figure illustrates a coax cable identified as (Video Output from Theater DVD or VCR) contained by 'Bundle #2 that is connected to the back of the Theater *Zone Hub*. On the front of this Hub shown in Figure 1-15, there is a patch cable connected from a modular jack on the left side of the *Zone Hub* to the Video Input side of the *Coax Distribution Hub*. From here the signals enter the Video Input side of the Hub to receive signal conditioning and amplification before traveling to the Video Output side of the Hub for the other *Zones* to use. This is how signals generated from a DVD, VCR or CCTV in one room are routed back through the *Structure Wiring System* to provide video to the other rooms in the home.

# THEATER HUB CONNECTIONS

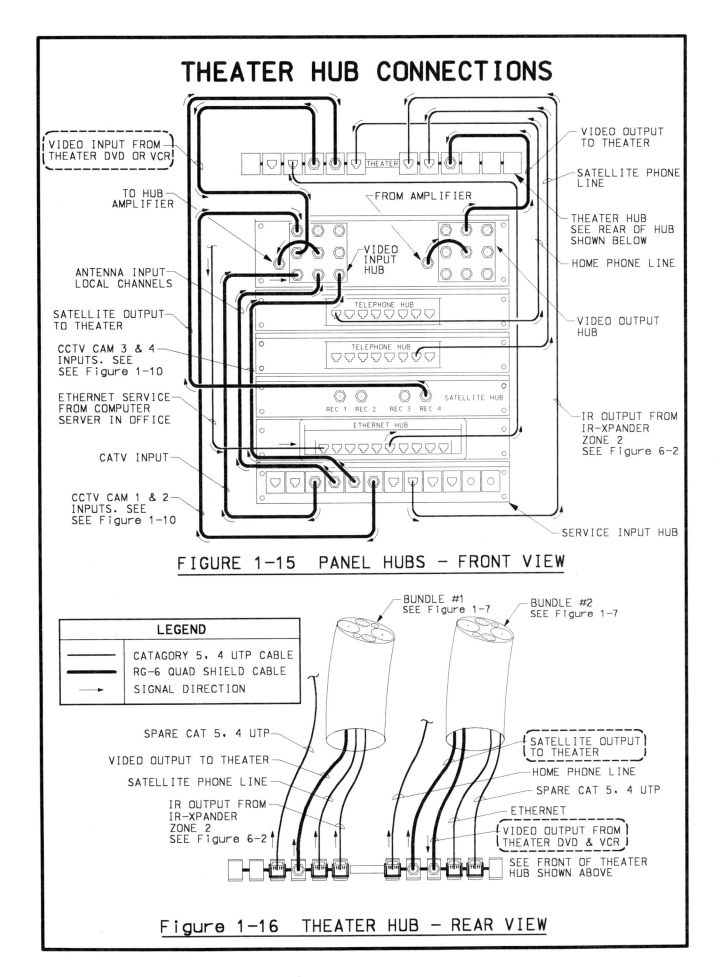

VIDEO INPUT FROM THEATER DVD OR VCR

TO HUB AMPLIFIER

ANTENNA INPUT LOCAL CHANNELS

SATELLITE OUTPUT TO THEATER

CCTV CAM 3 & 4 INPUTS. SEE SEE Figure 1-10

ETHERNET SERVICE FROM COMPUTER SERVER IN OFFICE

CATV INPUT

CCTV CAM 1 & 2 INPUTS. SEE SEE Figure 1-10

FROM AMPLIFIER

VIDEO INPUT HUB

THEATER

TELEPHONE HUB

TELEPHONE HUB

SATELLITE HUB
REC 1   REC 2   REC 3   REC 4

ETHERNET HUB

VIDEO OUTPUT TO THEATER

SATELLITE PHONE LINE

THEATER HUB SEE REAR OF HUB SHOWN BELOW

HOME PHONE LINE

VIDEO OUTPUT HUB

IR OUTPUT FROM IR-XPANDER ZONE 2 SEE Figure 6-2

SERVICE INPUT HUB

FIGURE 1-15   PANEL HUBS - FRONT VIEW

LEGEND
| | |
|---|---|
| —— | CATAGORY 5, 4 UTP CABLE |
| ▬▬ | RG-6 QUAD SHIELD CABLE |
| → | SIGNAL DIRECTION |

BUNDLE #1 SEE Figure 1-7

BUNDLE #2 SEE Figure 1-7

SPARE CAT 5, 4 UTP

VIDEO OUTPUT TO THEATER

SATELLITE PHONE LINE

IR OUTPUT FROM IR-XPANDER ZONE 2 SEE Figure 6-2

SATELLITE OUTPUT TO THEATER

HOME PHONE LINE

SPARE CAT 5, 4 UTP

ETHERNET

VIDEO OUTPUT FROM THEATER DVD & VCR

SEE FRONT OF THEATER HUB SHOWN ABOVE

Figure 1-16   THEATER HUB - REAR VIEW

17

Most of the *Zone Hubs* will have modular connector slots available for future expansion purposes as long as there are the proper type and quantity of conductors available in the 'Bundle' dedicated to a drop. For this reason, the designer in some cases may consider running more than one 'Bundle' or separate cables in addition to a 'Bundle' to rooms that have the potential of requiring additional *services* in the future.

Depending on the application, two rooms could utilize one *Zone Hub*. One room could use the right side of the Hub while the other room uses the left side of the Hub. This particular option will be utilized later on in this chapter during the 'Example Home' design process.

**1-12 Ethernet Hub:** The *Ethernet Hub* is an eight port, (10Base-T) Hub that is used to support a local area network (LAN). This is accomplished by connecting up to one *Server* and eight computers, printers, or other network devices such as a scanner, fax machine, credit card reader, etc. Figure 1-11 shows the front view of the *Distribution Panel* configured for the

ETHERNET HUB

Home Office. Notice that the *Ethernet Hub* is located in the lower portion of the *System Hub* section. As previously mentioned, the PC designated as the *Server* is located in the Office. This *Server* provides data to the *Ethernet Hub* for the other computers and network devices in the home to utilize. To provide this data to the other computers and network devices, a (CAT 5, 4 UTP) cable with RJ-45 connectors is connected from the Ethernet network interface card located inside the *Server,* to the Ethernet *Interactive Receptacle* jack located near the *Server*. A (CAT 5, 4 UTP) cable contained by a wire 'Bundle' is connected to the rear of the *Interactive Receptacle* and is routed back to the Office *Zone Hub* located in the *Distribution Panel*. From there a *patch cable* is connected from the front connector of the Office *Zone Hub* to the *Ethernet Hub* as shown in Figure 1-11.

For the other computers and network devices

to utilize the data provided by the *Server, patch cables* are connected from available RJ-45 ports on the *Ethernet Hub* to the *Zone Hubs* that serve the Master Bedroom computer, Bedroom 'B' computer and Web TV Ethernet interface units for the Family Room and Home Theater TVs. These *patch cables* can be seen in (Figure 1-17 Master Bedroom) (Figure 1-12 Family Room.), (Figure 1-15 Theater) and (Figure 1-19 Bedroom 'B'). For further information on the Ethernet System, refer to Chapter Two.

**1-13 Satellite Distribution Hub:** The *Satellite Hub* is the next section of the *Distribution Panel* we will take a look at. This Hub provides signal distribution from one dual LNB digital satellite dish to four locations in the home. The *Satellite Distribution Hub* will provide satellite program signals to the 'Example Home' Theater, Master Bedroom and Family Room through a single coaxial cable routed to each of these three *Zones*. Each TV that receives satellite program signals can be connected to a separate satellite *receiver*. Notice the coaxial cable connector in

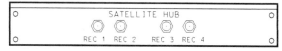

SATELLITE HUB

Figure 1-11, labeled (REC 3) on the front of the *Satellite Hub*. Satellite signals received by both (REC 3 & 4) are provided by 'LNB Input A' as shown at the rear of the *Distribution Panel* in Figure 1-10. Also notice that (REC 1 & 2) receives satellite signals from 'LNB Input B'. In Figure 1-12, an RG-6 *patch cable* is connected between the *Satellite Distribution Hub* (REC 3) connector and the corresponding satellite input connector on the front of the Family Room *Zone Hub* located at the top of the page. Satellite signals will then travel through the *patch cable* and to the modular connector located on the rear of the *Zone Hub* shown in Figure 1-13. The rear of the Hub is where 'Bundle #1' conductors are connected along side 'Bundle #2' conductors to provide satellite entertainment as well as a number of other services. A separate RG-6 cable could be pulled to the Family Room instead of routing another 'Bundle' for only one additional

# MASTER BEDROOM HUB CONNECTIONS

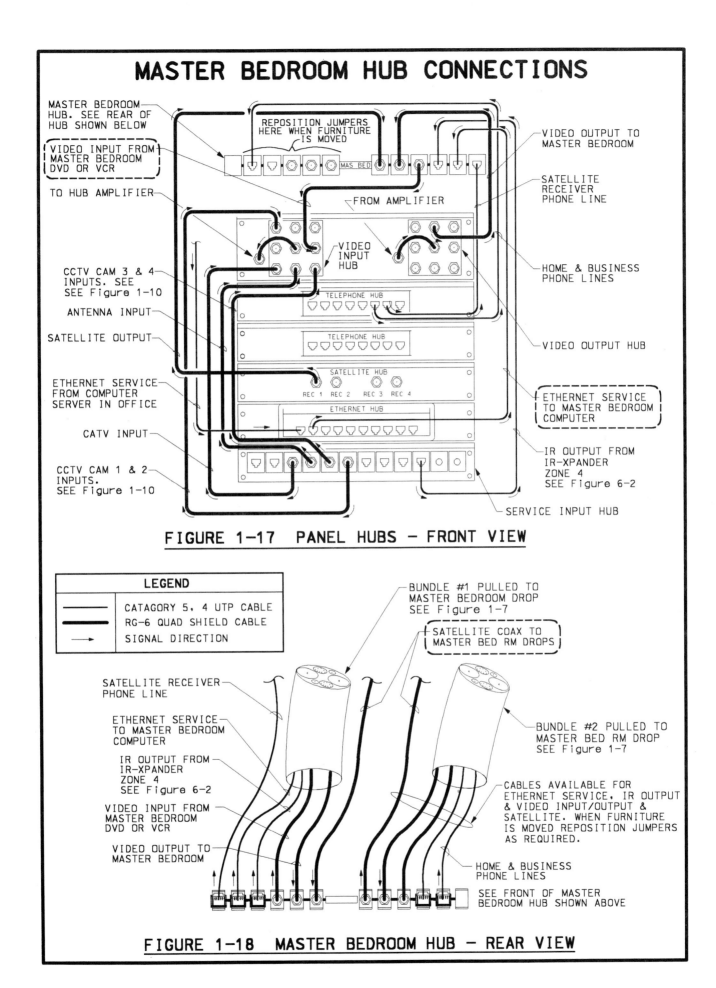

FIGURE 1-17   PANEL HUBS - FRONT VIEW

FIGURE 1-18   MASTER BEDROOM HUB - REAR VIEW

# BEDROOM 'B' HUB CONNECTIONS

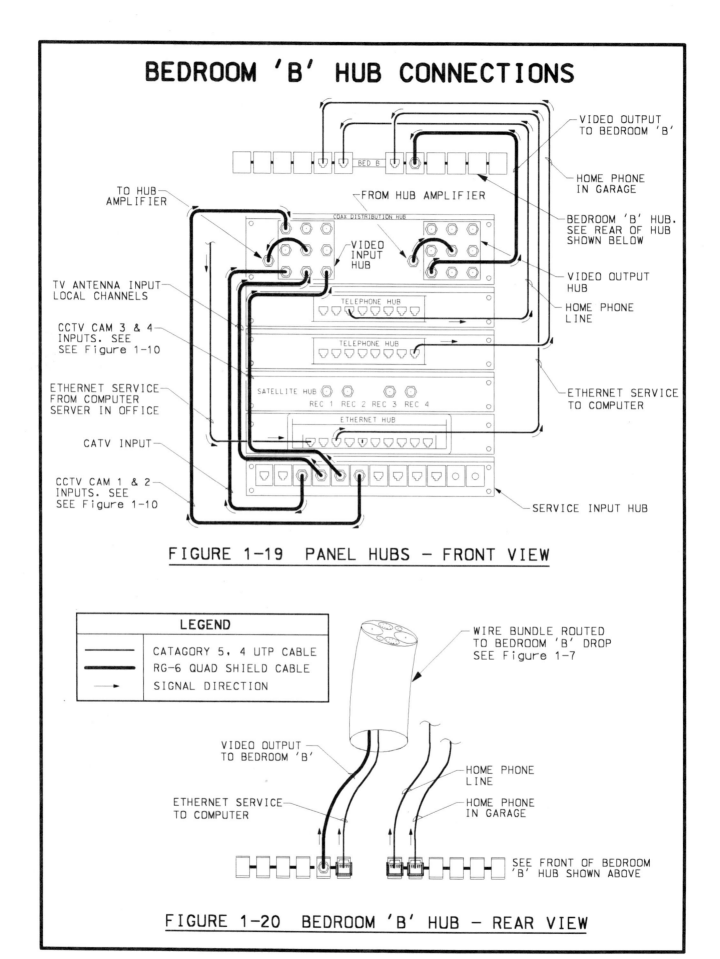

FIGURE 1-19   PANEL HUBS - FRONT VIEW

FIGURE 1-20   BEDROOM 'B' HUB - REAR VIEW

coaxial cable; however, the designer in this particular case felt that the unused conductors of 'Bundle #2' may be used in this particular room in the future. Bundle #2 will be pulled along with 'Bundle #1' in a 'Home Run' topology to the Family Room Drop shown in Figure 1-7. This means that a separate *Service Outlet* needs to be installed along side the standard *Interactive Receptacle* shown in Figure 1-21, to furnish satellite entertainment. The designer decided not to replace the standard Ethernet jack on the *Interactive Receptacle* with an F-connector to provide satellite entertainment, even though there is no computer in this location. This is because an occupant may want to surf the Internet over the Family Room TV (ie: Web TV). In Figure 1-12, notice the patch cable connected between the *Telephone Hub* and the *Zone Hub*. This provides telephone *service* for the customer to order 'Pay Preview' entertainment.

Satellite input cables are not connected to the Video Input side of the *Coax Distribution Hub* for signal distribution. This is because satellite program signals do not need signal conditioning and amplification.

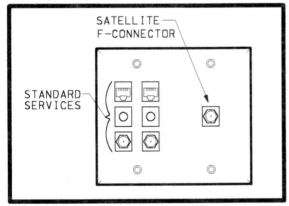

FIGURE 1-21    FAMILY RM SERVICES

Anther room furnished with satellite entertainment is the Master Bedroom. This room receives satellite program signals from (Input B) because a *patch cable* is installed from (REC 1) to the Master Bedroom *Zone Hub* as shown in Figure 1-17. In Figure 1-18, notice the separate satellite coaxial cable that is routed along with each of the two 'Bundle' drops. These cables are pulled separate from the 'Bundle' because only two coaxial cables are furnished per 'Bundle'. The Master Bedroom, Family Room and Theater

use REC 1, REC 3 & REC 4 coax connectors on the front of the *Satellite Hub*. REC 2 is left unused until satellite entertainment is desired in another room of the home. See Section 1-23 for more on the *services* provided to the Master Bedroom.

**1-14 TP Bus Distribution Hub:** This 8 port/3 line twisted pair Hub is used for connecting and distributing voice and data. The primary application for a *TP Bus Distribution Hub* is to provide telephone *service* distribution. For clarity purposes we will refer to this interface as a *Telephone Hub*. As shown in Figure 1-10, notice the Amphenol connector on the back of each *Telephone Hub*. These large connectors provide extension line inputs to both 8 Port/3 line

TP BUS DISTRIBUTION HUB

*Telephone Hubs*. These extension line Inputs to the *Telephone Hubs* are Outputs from the Panasonic KX-TD1232 Digital Hybrid telephone controller described in Chapter Eight. The top Amphenol connector provides telephone extensions (1 through 8) while the bottom Amphenol connector provides telephone extensions (9 through 16). Telephone extensions are distributed from each *Telephone Hub* to their corresponding *Zone Hubs* before being distributed to the appropriate rooms.

Refer to Figure 1-22 and notice the (CAT 5, 4 UTP) *patch cable* connected to the 'home & business' phone jack on the *Telephone Hub*. This patch cable is routed up to the RJ-45 telephone jack on the Living Room *Zone Hub* located at the top of the figure. This cable provides connections for the Living Room home & business telephone extensions assigned by the Panasonic KX-TD1232 Telephone Controller. Refer to Chapter Eight for more on the Digital Hybrid telephone system.

*TP Bus Distribution Hubs* can also be used to accommodate applications that require the distribution of *Stargate* Digital Inputs, Analog Inputs, low voltage Relay Outputs, security system sensory conductors and other low voltage circuits.

# LIVING ROOM HUB CONNECTIONS

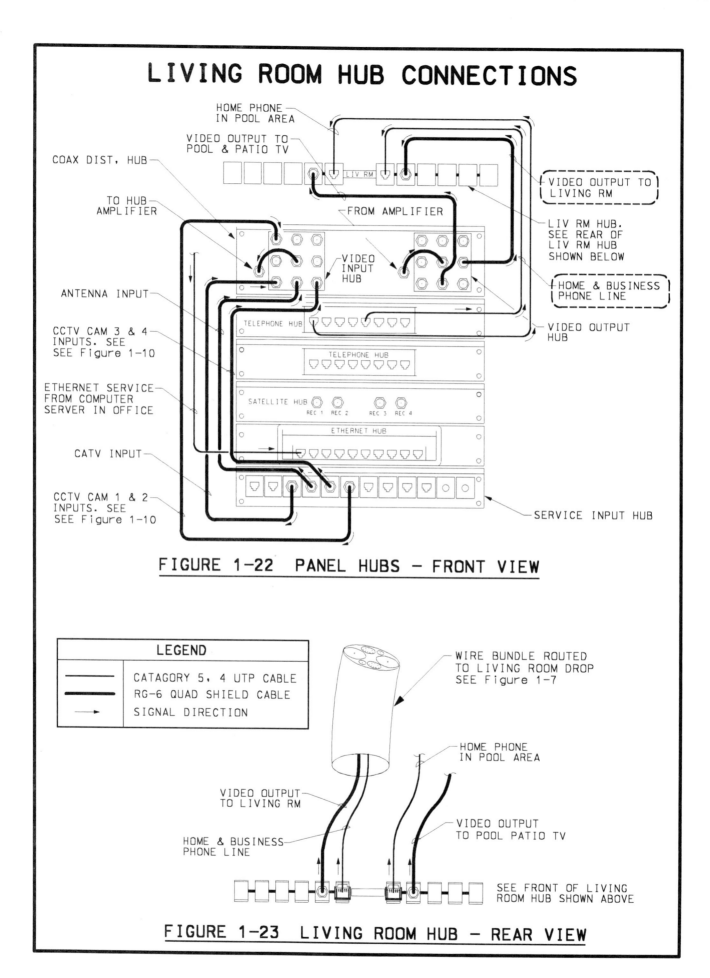

HOME PHONE IN POOL AREA

VIDEO OUTPUT TO POOL & PATIO TV

COAX DIST. HUB

TO HUB AMPLIFIER

ANTENNA INPUT

CCTV CAM 3 & 4 INPUTS. SEE SEE Figure 1-10

ETHERNET SERVICE FROM COMPUTER SERVER IN OFFICE

CATV INPUT

CCTV CAM 1 & 2 INPUTS. SEE SEE Figure 1-10

LIV RM

FROM AMPLIFIER

VIDEO INPUT HUB

TELEPHONE HUB

TELEPHONE HUB

SATELLITE HUB    REC 1  REC 2    REC 3  REC 4

ETHERNET HUB

VIDEO OUTPUT TO LIVING RM

LIV RM HUB. SEE REAR OF LIV RM HUB SHOWN BELOW

HOME & BUSINESS PHONE LINE

VIDEO OUTPUT HUB

SERVICE INPUT HUB

## FIGURE 1-22  PANEL HUBS - FRONT VIEW

### LEGEND

| | |
|---|---|
| —— | CATAGORY 5, 4 UTP CABLE |
| ▬▬ | RG-6 QUAD SHIELD CABLE |
| → | SIGNAL DIRECTION |

WIRE BUNDLE ROUTED TO LIVING ROOM DROP SEE Figure 1-7

HOME PHONE IN POOL AREA

VIDEO OUTPUT TO LIVING RM

VIDEO OUTPUT TO POOL PATIO TV

HOME & BUSINESS PHONE LINE

SEE FRONT OF LIVING ROOM HUB SHOWN ABOVE

## FIGURE 1-23  LIVING ROOM HUB - REAR VIEW

22

**1-15 Coax Distribution Hub:** This Hub distributes video to TV's and video recording devices in the home that originate from CATV *Service*, TV antenna, CCTV cameras, VCR's, DVD players, etc. This Hub is also 'cable modem ready' and permits high speed Internet access through a CATV and/or telephone communications supplier. In Figure 1-12, the front of the *Distribution Panel* shows a quantity of four (4) RG-6 coaxial *patch cables* routed from the *Service Input Hub* up to the *Video Input* side of the *Coax Distribution Hub*. These

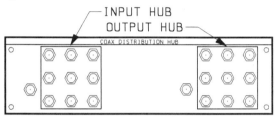

## COAX DISTRIBUTION HUB

*Service Inputs* include CATV, TV antenna, and CCTV Cameras 1, 2, 3 & 4. Notice that the signal directional arrows indicate that the video signals are traveling towards the *Video Input* side of the Hub. All signals entering the input side of the Hub are combined together and travel through the short RG-6 *jumper* cable before entering the built-in 15db bi-directional amplifier. Once these signals leave the amplifier and signal conditioner, they travel over to the Video Output side of the *Coax Distribution Hub* through the other short coaxial *jumper*. The Video Output side of the Hub provides eight (8) Video Output connectors as shown. An RG-6 *patch cable* is then connected from the Video Output Hub to the corresponding connector of the Family Room *Zone Hub* located near the top of the figure. This will allow video to be distributed to the Family Room TV or VCR for recording. This configuration is the same for all *Zones* requiring video service from the sources previously described.

The Example Home 'two cable' *Audio/Video Distribution System* supports Video Output entertainment from specific *Zones* of the home to be shared with the other *Zones* in the home. As illustrated in Figure 1-12, a *patch cable* is connected from the Family Room *Zone Hub* to the Video Input side of the *Coax Distribution Hub* identified as (Video Output from Family Room DVD or VCR). This provides a path for *Video* entertainment signals from the Family Room's DVD or VCR to be available to the other rooms in the 'Example Home'. To receive this video in the other rooms, *patch cables* are simply connected between the Video Output side of the *Coax Distribution Hub* and the appropriate *Zone Hubs*.

**1-16 Interactive Receptacles and Service Outlets:** There are basically three application options that the designer has to choose from when using *Interactive Receptacles* and *Service Outlets*. One option is to use *Interactive Receptacles* exclusively throughout the home to provide the homeowner will all the major *services* at each drop location whether the designer thinks the *services* will be used or not. This will help to 'future proof' the home because what the homeowner needs today may be different tomorrow. The use of *Service Outlets;* however, will generally provide *services* that are needed at the time of the system design and does not necessarily provide *services* that could be required in the future. This option is normally selected when the system budget will not support future proofing efforts. The third option is to use a *Service Outlet* along with an *Interactive Receptacle* to provide additional *services* when required. *Service Outlets* are also used when a fewer quantity of *services* are required than what is offered by an *Interactive Receptacle*.

All of the major system cables except speaker cables are routed from the appropriate *Zone Hubs* to one or more *Interactive Receptacles* located in each room. This device is used as a point of connection for telephones, TVs, Ethernet *Service*, Internet *Service*, Video Inputs, Video Outputs as well as other future *Services*. To get a close-up view of this component, take a look at Figure 1-24. Notice the six modular cable connectors shown in the rear view of this device. This illustrates were the three different types of conductors are terminated to the back of the modular connectors located inside the wall. As a standard configuration in most rooms, the modular RJ-45 telephone and computer Ethernet/Internet modular jacks are snapped into the top two positions of the

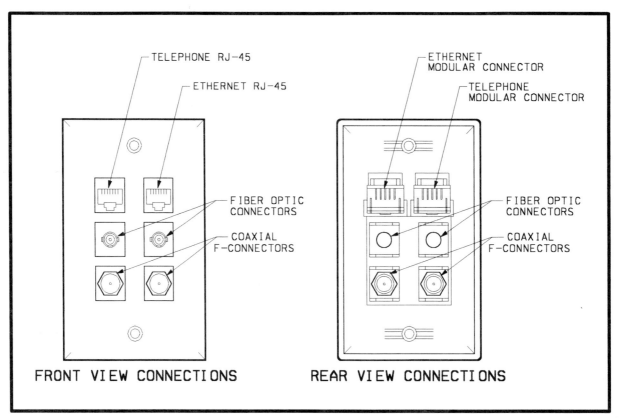

FRONT VIEW CONNECTIONS          REAR VIEW CONNECTIONS

FIGURE 1-24    FUTURE PROOF INTERACTIVE RECEPTACLE

*Interactive Receptacle.* RJ-11 modular jacks can be used for a single line (1 Pair), or an RJ-25 can be used for three lines (3 Pair). When the project budget permits, we recommend using RJ-45 modular jacks. This will allow all 4 pairs of a (CAT 5, 4 UTP) cable to be terminated to the modular jack. This will in turn allow additional services to be added in the required locations of the home while also providing the capability of changing to a completely new *service.* Fiber optic modular jacks are snapped into the middle positions and the Input & Output coaxial modular F-connectors are snapped into the bottom positions. For a better view of these modular jacks, see Figure 1-25. If one or more fiber optic modular jacks are not desired in a room, these jacks can be removed and replaced with additional data, telephone, coaxial and possibly even speaker binding post modular connectors. If this particular situation should arise, a different type of 'Bundle' (different types of conductors) or even individual cables can be pulled in place of the standard wire 'Bundle'. Although speaker wire can be connected to modular binding posts that are snapped into an

*Interactive Receptacle,* this option is generally not used unless the speakers are floor standing.

Telephones, computers, printers, scanners audio/video equipment and other devices can utilize the *Structured Wiring System* by simply plugging-in the equipment to the corresponding modular jacks located on the front of an *Interactive Receptacle* or *Service Outlet.*

*Service Outlets* are similar devices to an *Interactive Receptacle;* however, *Service Outlets* will generally offer a smaller quantity of *services.* These devices allow the designer to select *Service Outlets* that will provide only the *services* required at the time of the system design. The designer could also provide additional conductors to a *Service Outlet* for future use; however, this is what the wire 'Bundle' and *Interactive Receptacle* combination do best. An *Interactive Receptacle* along with a wire 'Bundle' is slightly more expensive to install compared to the *Service Outlets* with individual conductors. This is because the 'Bundle' offers more capability in most cases, and is designed for 'future proofing' purposes. It helps the home-owner to avoid having to pull additional cables

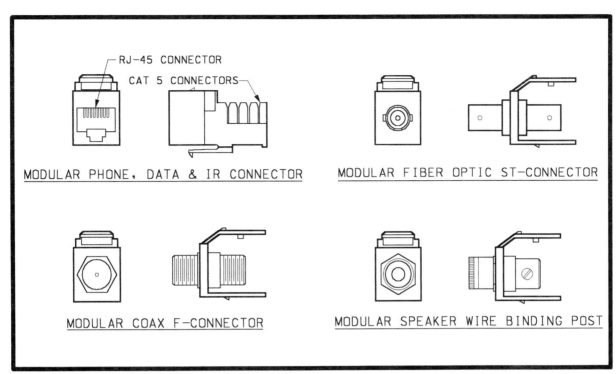

RJ-45 CONNECTOR

CAT 5 CONNECTORS

MODULAR PHONE, DATA & IR CONNECTOR

MODULAR FIBER OPTIC ST-CONNECTOR

MODULAR COAX F-CONNECTOR

MODULAR SPEAKER WIRE BINDING POST

## FIGURE 1-25   MODULAR JACK DETAILS

after the home is complete. The 'Bundle' is also easier to pull and takes less time to installing compared to an equal number of separate cables.

There are a large number of manufacturers that offer various combinations of *Service Outlet* jacks. This allows the designer to put in what is only required at the time of design to help lower the initial equipment costs and installation costs. This is sometimes necessary for 'Design/Build' contractors in order to stay competitive; however, if the system will not provide the customer with 'future proof' capabilities, it may become obsolete or at least difficult and expensive to upgrade in the future. Refer to Table A on page 30, for a list of the available *Service Outlet* jacks and the standard *Interactive Receptacle*.

**1-17 Topologies:** Cable topologies characterize how the *Interactive Receptacles* and/or *Service Outlets* are ultimately connected to the *Distribution Panel*. The Star topology (more commonly known as 'Home Run') and the 'Daisy Chain' topology are considered the two main wiring configurations used in the industry. *Structured Wiring* designers almost always use the 'Home Run' topology. The 'Home Run' topology

means that a dedicated cable is pulled from the *Distribution Panel* to each *Interactive Receptacle* and/or *Service Outlet*. Changes made to the system can be incorporated much easier with the 'Home Run' topology and trouble shooting of the system is greatly simplified because potential system problems can be isolated and repaired with less effort. If a cable gets damaged during construction, the loss of the conductor is confined to one run and will not affect any other cable drops in the system. The damaged wire is easily isolated through testing and trouble shooting procedures. If the homeowner needs to replace a damaged conductor, add a telephone line, or add a completely new system *service*, the abundance of (CAT 5, 4 UTP) conductors provided by a 'Bundle' will generally support these changes by re-configuring conductors at the appropriate *Zone Hub* and *Interactive Receptacle*. If a coax cable gets damaged, a new cable will have to be pulled except when the second coax cable in the 'Bundle' is un-used.

Since the 'Home Run' topology consists of individual wire 'Bundles' or separate cables pulled to each drop, this configuration will allow *service* changes to be made at the *Distribution Panel* by simply manipulating the arrangement of

25

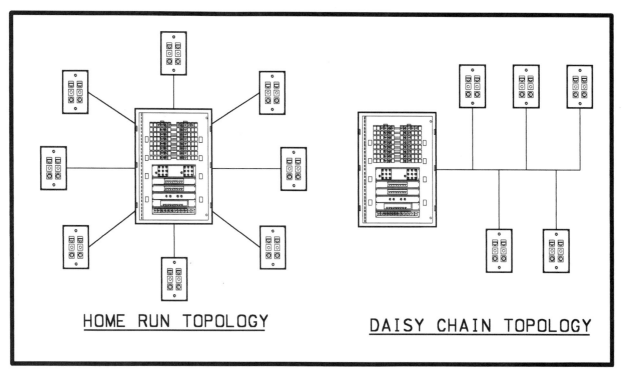

HOME RUN TOPOLOGY          DAISY CHAIN TOPOLOGY

## FIGURE 1-26   MOST COMMON WIRING TOPOLOGIES

the patch cables. This comes in handy when the homeowner wants to provide an additional *service* in a room or wants to move a piece of equipment to another room.

The 'Home Run' topology will require more wire overall compared to the 'Daisy Chain' topology; however, wire is relatively inexpensive when one considers the advantages gained by incorporating the 'Home Run' method.

The 'Daisy Chain' topology is believed by some to be an easier system to install. It does require less cable because the installer only needs one length of cable to chain all or a group of *Interactive Receptacles* and/or *Service Outlets* together. This method is generally used for **standard** residential telephone and coax cable systems. An advantage of this topology is realized when an additional telephone or TV needs to be connected to the system. This is achieved by connecting the new conductors to the nearest existing jack. The major disadvantage of this topology as previously described, is the difficulty of trouble shooting the system because individual cables cannot be easily isolated. If a break in a conductor occurs along the chain, it will bring down all system components connected down stream of the break. This topology also requires many more connection points located

inside the walls, which increases the probability of system problems in the future.

**1-18 Minimum Cable Requirements:** This section describes the minimum recommended *services* for each area of the home. *Services* may vary depending on the system requirements and budget. Please note that the plans and diagrams illustrating the 'Example Home' system incorporates a wider verity of cables and *services* compared to what is identified in this section.

In the following rooms, each telephone jack is accompanied by a (CAT 5, 4 UTP) cable and each F-connector is accompanied by an RG-6 coaxial cable.

*Master Bedroom:* A *Service Outlet* should be located on the opposite wall from the bed. This *Service Outlet* should consist of one TV coax F-connector, one satellite F-connector and one telephone jack for use by a satellite receiver. The second *Service Outlet* should consist of one telephone jack located at bedside.

*All Other Bedrooms:* Each Bedroom will generally require two *Service Outlets*. The first *Service Outlet* should be located on the opposite wall from the bed. This *Service Outlet* should consist of one TV F-connector, one satellite F-connector and one phone jack for communications to a satellite receiver. The second *Service Outlet* should be located at bedside and consist of one telephone jack. If either the CATV *service* or satellite *service* is not desired, eliminate the appropriate F-connector.

***Family Room:*** A *Service Outlet* that consists of one telephone jack, one TV F-connector and one satellite F-connector.

***Living Room:*** A *Service Outlet* that consists of one telephone jack, and one TV F-connector.

***Kitchen***: A *Service Outlet* that consists of one telephone jack, and one TV F-connector on the wall below the upper cabinet.

***Home Office***: A *Service Outlet* that consists of one home telephone jack, one business telephone jack and an Internet jack.

***Entertainment Room or Home Theater***: This room will generally require two *Service Outlets*. The first *Service Outlet* should have a telephone jack located next to the couch or easy chair. The second *Service Outlet* should consist of one TV F-connector, one satellite F-connector and one telephone jack used by a satellite receiver. If either the CATV *service* or satellite *service* is not desired, eliminate the appropriate F-connector.

**1-19 System Design Methods:** The '*Interactive Receptacle'* method of design is used when the designer incorporates all of the major *services* and upgrade capabilities into each 'Bundle' drop location of the home whether the customer intends to use the *services* at first or not. The intention behind this design method is to provide all of the main *services* that are expected to be used immediately or sometime in the future. This design logic will help to 'future proof' the home and limit system modifications that require additional cable pulling, which is often difficult and expensive. Although this design method does offer the advantage of avoiding possible obsolescence over a period of approximately 20 years or more, it will cost more initially. This is

due to the fact that additional cables, modular connectors and possibly a larger *Distribution Panel* may be required.

The '*Service Outlet'* method of design' is used when the designer concentrates on incorporating *services* that the customer needs at the time of the design without necessarily considering what may be required in the future. This method will generally not include fiber optic capabilities or *services* that help to avoid system obsolescence. Although this type of system will generally fulfill the customers needs and desires at least for a while, it will probably fall short of the customer's expectations in the future. This type of system; however, is desirable to many customers during the building stage because of the lower equipment and installation costs.

**1-20 System Design Sequence:** *Silent Servant, Inc.* recommends the following steps when approaching the design of a *Structured Wiring System* for residential applications. Taking steps to complete the design task will minimize errors and portions of the design that are often times over looked. Over a period of time, the designer will increase his or her experience level and will probably modify or even develop their own design methods that work best for them.

**Step 1**: The first and most important information to gather up front is the system requirements. Without establishing accurate requirements, the design process will most likely be prolonged. This is because changes to the design will need to be made, which can be time consuming. It is also best to spend the time required up front instead of spending even more time redesigning the system later. It is also important to avoid redesigns because this can cause the customer to lose confidence in a design/build contractor.

The designer must sit down and talk to the customer to explain system features and benefits. The designer must determine if the customer wants a whole house audio/video system, a conventional or hybrid telephone system, an Ethernet system, a lighting control system, an integrated security system, or an automated home control system. The designer must also determine what the customer's actual expectations are of each subsystem in order to establish the proper design approach. Once the customer's desires, needs and expectations are well understood and a contract is signed, the system designer will be able to accurately fulfill the requirements.

When the requirements are not properly understood or if there is miscommunication between a sales individual and the customer, it will generally cause problems between the designer and the sales individual, which could delay the design and installation process. This is the reason why design individuals should be talking to the customer and not a sales individual that may not have the knowledge base or may be interested primarily in making the sale for his or her commission.

**Step 2:** Once the requirements are established in Step 1, the designer will be able to determine the main control equipment required to fulfill the design requirements. This will help to establish how much room will be required in the *Equipment Room* to house these components. The designer can then look at the new construction floor plan with the homeowner to determine where the *Equipment Room* will be placed. The *Equipment Room'* should then be sketched on the house plans for the Architect to incorporate. Refer to Section 1-7, for more information on how to select the best location for an *Equipment Room* and what an *Equipment Room* will consist of with the level of control designed into the 'Example Home'.

**Step 3:** Once the *Equipment Room* size and location has been established, the designer must find out from the customer where they plan to position the furniture, computers, fax machine, audio/video equipment, etc., in each room. This is important because the *Interactive Receptacles* and/or *Service Outlets* must be positioned to best serve the customer's needs. A list of the rooms should be entered into Table A shown on page 30. Table A will make it easy to select the proper *Service Outlet* jacks required when using the '*Service Outlet*' design approach. If the '*Interactive Receptacle*' design approach is used, this device along with additional *Service Outlet* jacks can be selected from Table A as well. By

using Table A, the designer will ultimately be able to establish the total quantity of *Interactive Receptacles* as well as the type and quantity of *Service Outlet* jacks required for system component purchasing purposes.

**Step 4:** When using the '*Interactive Receptacle*' method of design, the designer will sketch a plan view similar to the *Structured Bundle Drop Plan* shown in Figure 1-7. The designer can also use a copy of the home's construction plans to sketch in the locations of the *Interactive Receptacles*. Figure 1-7 illustrates the drop locations, which is where each *Interactive Receptacle* will be installed. No *Service Identifiers* are required on this plan because all main *services* are provided or can easily be provided by changing the *patch cable* configuration on the *Distribution Panel*. This is because the 'Bundle' will generally provide all the conductors required to support the *services* desired in each room. In some cases, the designer may consider pulling more than one 'Bundle' to a room along with additional *Interactive Receptacles* if the furniture, computer, fax machine or other components may be relocated in the future. Also designate the total quantity of *Interface Receptacles* required for the design along with the color and Part No. in Table B shown on page 31.

Refer to each subsystem type in the following chapters for specific plan views and diagrams that provides additional cable requirements and points of termination. These subsystems include the Ethernet network, whole house audio/video system, security system, HVAC system, water systems, lighting system, telephone system as well as others. When using the '*Service Outlet*' method of design, refer to the *Service Outlet Cable Drop Plan* shown in Figure 1-27. This Plan identifies where each *Service Outlet* needs to be located and the types of *Service Outlets* required. This is accomplished by placing *Service Identifiers* right on the Plan as shown. These identifiers will also indicate where each type of *service* interfaces the home and what type of conductors to pull to each location. *Service Identifiers* are shown on page 31 along with their corresponding cable specifications used to provide each *service*.

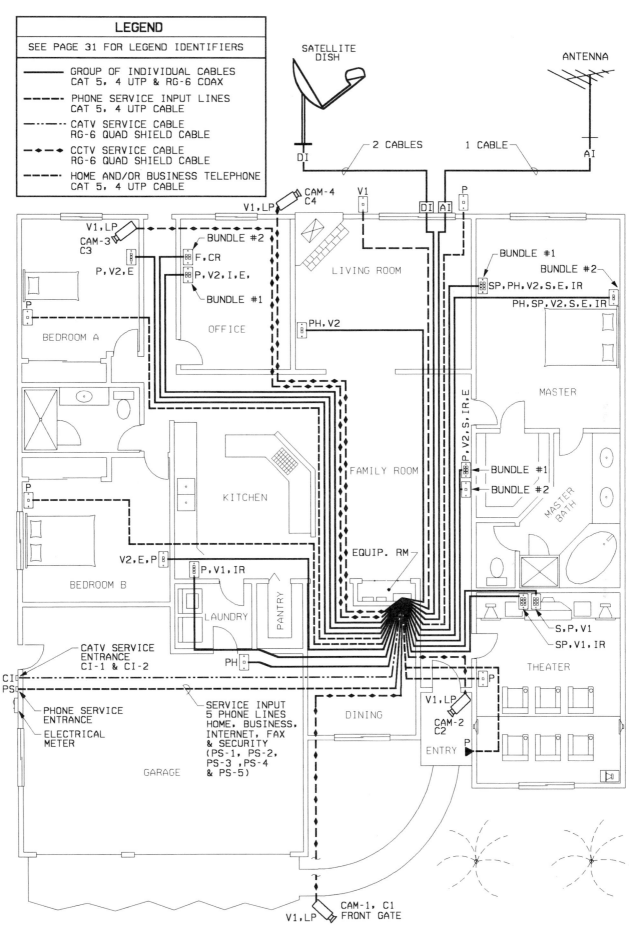

# FIGURE 1-27  SERVICE OUTPUT CABLE DROP PLAN

# TABLE A
## Services and Outlet Jacks

| Customer: Jane Doe | Project #: 4682 | Address: 5629 Berkeley Rd. Goleta CA 93017 |
|---|---|---|

| Zone | Home Phone line | Home & Business Line | Credit Card Reader Line | Satellite Phone line | Internet Line | Fast Internet Line | Fax line | Ethernet | Video Input | Video Output | Satellite | CCTV Camera | Audio Source | Speaker Pair | A/V IR Control | Interactive Receptacle | RJ-11 One Pair | RJ-25 3 Pair | RJ-45 4 Pair CAT 5 | F-Connector | RCA Speaker Jack | Speaker Binding Posts | ST Fiber Connector | Snap-in Blank |
|---|---|---|---|---|---|---|---|---|---|---|---|---|---|---|---|---|---|---|---|---|---|---|---|---|
| | | **Service Inputs** | | | | | | | | | | | | | | **Interactive Receptacle or Service Outlet Jacks** | | | | | | | | |
| Office | | 1 | 1 | | 1 | 1 | 1 | 1 | 1 | 1 | | | | 1 | 1 | 2 | | | 3 | 1 | | | | 3 |
| Living Room | | 1 | | | | | | | 1 | | | | | 1 | 1 | 1 | | | | | | | | |
| Master Bedroom | | 1 | | 2 | | | | 2 | 2 | 2 | 2 | | | 1 | 2 | 2 | | | 4 | 2 | | | | 6 |
| Family Room | | | | 1 | | | | 1 | 1 | 1 | 1 | | | 1 | 1 | 1 | | | | 1 | | | | |
| Theater | 1 | | | 1 | | | | | 1 | 1 | 1 | | | 1 | 1 | 2 | | | 2 | 1 | | 20 | | 3 |
| Kitchen | | 1 | | | | | | | 1 | | | | | 1 | 1 | | | | 2 | 1 | | | | |
| Bedroom A | 1 | | | | | | | 1 | 1 | | | 1 | | 1 | 1 | 1 | | | 1 | 1 | | | | |
| Bedroom B | 1 | | | | | | | 1 | 1 | | | | | 1 | 1 | 1 | | | 1 | | | | | |
| Pool Patio | 1 | | | | | | | | 1 | | | 1 | | 1 | | | | | 1 | 1 | | | | |
| Garage | 1 | | | | | | | | | | | | | | | | | | 1 | | | | | |
| Front Porch | | | | | | | | | | | | 1 | | | | | | | 1 | 1 | | | | |
| Access Gate | 1 | | | | | | | | | | | 1 | | | | | | | 1 | 1 | | | | |
| | | | | | | | | | | | | | | | | | | | | | | | | |
| | | | | | | | | | | | | | | | | | | | | | | | | |
| | | | | | | | | | | | | | | | | | | | | | | | | |
| | | | | | | | | | | | | | | | | | | | | | | | | |
| | | | | | | | | | | | | | | | | | | | | | | | | |
| | | | | | | | | | | | | | | | | | | | | | | | | |
| | | | | | | | | | | | | | | | | | | | | | | | | |
| | | | | | | | | | | | | | | | | | | | | | | | | |
| | | | | | | | | | | | | | | | | | | | | | | | | |
| | | | | | | | | | | | | | | | | | | | | | | | | |
| Total Services | 6 | 4 | 1 | 4 | 1 | 1 | 1 | 6 | 10 | 5 | 4 | 4 | | 9 | 9 | | | | | | | | | |
| Total Outlets | | | | | | | | | | | | | | | | 10 | | | 17 | 10 | | 20 | | 12 |

| TABLE B Interactive Receptacle and Service Outlet Selections | | | | | | | | |
|---|---|---|---|---|---|---|---|---|
| Customer: Jane Doe | | PROJECT: 4682 | | Address: 5629 Berkeley Rd Goleta CA 93107 | | | | |
| Table A Quantity | Description | Color White | | Color Almond | | Color Brown | | |
| | | Part No. | Qty. | Part No. | Qty. | Part No. | Qty. | |
| 10 | Interactive Receptacle | 14285 | 7 | 14286 | 2 | 14287 | 1 | |
| | RJ-11 One Pair | 1611 | | 1612 | | 1613 | | |
| | RJ-25 3 Pair | 1411 | | 1412 | | 1413 | | |
| 17 | RJ-45 4 Pair CAT 5 | 3601 | 15 | 3602 | 1 | 3603 | 1 | |
| 10 | F-Type Coax | 2881 | 8 | 2882 | 1 | 2883 | 1 | |
| | RCA Speaker | 2811 | | 2812 | | 2813 | | |
| 20 | Speaker Binding Posts | 1421 | 20 | 1422 | | 1423 | | |
| | ST Fiber | 1431 | | 1432 | | 1433 | | |
| 12 | Snap-in Blank | 1461 | 12 | 1462 | | 1463 | | |

### SERVICE IDENTIFIERS:

**AI** = TV Antenna Input  (RG-6 Coax)

**CI** = CATV Company Input (RG-6 Coax)

**CR** = Credit Card Reader (CAT 5, 4 UTP)

**DI** = Digital Satellite Input (RG-6 Coax)

**E** = Ethernet (CAT 5, 4 UTP)

**F1** = One Fiber Optic Cable (Multi-Media)

**F2** = Two Fiber Optic Cables (Multi-Media)

**F** = Fax (CAT 5, 4 UTP)

**I** = Internet (CAT 5, 4 UTP)

**IR** = Infrared A/V Control (CAT 5, 4 UTP)

**IS** = Internet Input (CAT 5, 4 UTP)

**LP** = Low Voltage Power (18 GA, 1 Pair)

**P** = Home & Business phone for Hybrid system (CAT 5, 4 UTP)

**PB** = Business Phone (CAT 5, 4 UTP)

**PH** = Home Phone (CAT 5, 4 UTP)

**PR** = Printer (CAT 5, 4 UTP)

**PS** = Phone Input Service (CAT 5, 4 UTP)

**S** = Satellite (RG-6 Coax)

**SC** = Ceiling Speaker (16 GA, 1 pair)

**SF** = Floor Standing Speaker (14 GA, 1 pair)

**SI** = In-wall Speaker (16 GA, 1 pair)

**SN** = Scanner (CAT 5, 4 UTP)

**SP** = Satellite Phone line (CAT 5, 4 UTP)

**V1** = One Video (RG-6 Coax)

**V2** = Two Video (RG-6 Coax)

*Note 1:* CATV, CCTV Cameras and TV antenna *services* are all available through **V1** or **V2** when using a *Distribution Panel.*

*Telephone Subsystem:* On the *Service Outlet Cable Drop Plan* shown in Figure 1-27, the designer will identify the locations where the telephone service entrance enclosure (PS) and the *Service Outlets* must be installed. *Service Identifier* (PH) is used for home telephone service without access to the business line as shown in Figure 1-27. If the system incorporates a hybrid telephone system that provides multiple lines that can be used for both the home and business, a **(P)** *Service Identifier* will be sufficient. Telephone jacks are located in the Family Room, Living Room, all Bedrooms, Office, Theater, Kitchen, Garage, Pool Patio, front door and outside the property access gate.

*Ethernet (LAN) Distribution:* Ethernet *Service Outlet* jacks should be installed in each room that could practically contain a computer or system peripheral such as a printer, scanner, fax machine, etc. This will help to 'future proof' the home if there is enough funds in the budget. All bedrooms should contain Ethernet *service* because bedrooms are always prime locations for a future computer as children come of age and are often used to establish a home business. On the *Service Outlet Cable Drop Plan,* notice the locations where an Ethernet jack will be installed. The designer uses *Service Identifier* **E** = Ethernet to identify these locations. For more on the Ethernet network, refer to Chapter Two.

*Video Distribution:* Locations in the home that require video cable drops for TVs, CCTV cameras, computers, etc., should be identified on the *Service Outlet Cable Drop Plan* using *Service Identifiers* **V1** = One Video Coax cable and **V2** = Two Video Coax cables. Also identify where the TV antenna *service* entrance and CATV *service* entrance are located.

The **V2** identifier for 'two cable' video systems use one cable to receive an assortment of program signals to each room (Video Input) and the other cable is used to share video (Video Output) with occupants in other rooms of the home. A **V2** *Service Identifier* can also be used to designate the use of an Video Input along with a Satellite Input. See Chapter Six, 'Whole House Audio and Video Systems' for more on 'two cable' audio/video systems.

*Satellite Video Distribution:* When there is a requirement for satellite *service* in a room, the designer will identify the *Service Outlet* location on the *Service Outlet Cable Drop Plan* as (S) shown in Figure 1-27. Also use *Service Identifier* **DI** for the satellite *service* entrance location on the exterior wall of the home as shown. In the 'Example Home', the *Satellite Distribution Hub* provides satellite programming to the Theater, Family Room and Master Bedroom through a single coax cable to each room that does not require modulation. This separate (RG-6 Quad Shield) coaxial cable is pulled along with the 'Bundle' to the Master Bedroom and is terminated at the *Service Outlet* located next to the *Interactive Receptacle* shown in Figure 1-29. Refer to Section 1-13 for more on satellite *service* distribution.

**Step 5:** When the designer refers to Table A, he will be able to identify the number of locations in the home that require each type of *service.* He will then know the number of connectors required on each *System Hub* to determine the proper size

and Part No. Generally only one *System Hub* is required for each subsystem; however, additional Hubs maybe needed in large homes that have a greater number of *Interactive Receptacles* and/or *Service Outlets.*

The different types of *System Hubs* to select from include the *Ethernet Hub, Satellite Hub, TP Bus Distribution Hub* and the *Coax Distribution Hub.* The designer will enter each *System Hub* Part No. and quantity into Table C shown below. The designer will then determine the number of *Zone Hubs* required by counting the number of rooms or areas of the home that will receive an *Interface Receptacle(s)* and/or *Service Outlet(s).*

| TABLE C | | |
|---|---|---|
| DISTRIBUTION PANEL & HUBS | | |
| PROJECT # 4682 | | |
| COMPONENT DESCRIPTION | PART NO. | QTY. |
| DISTRIBUTION PANEL | 6405 | 1 |
| SERVICE INPUT HUB | 7066 | 1 |
| SATELLITE HUB | 7044 | 1 |
| TELEPHONE HUB | 6122 | 2 |
| COAX HUB | 6418 | 1 |
| ETHERNET HUB | 6312 | 1 |
| ZONE HUB | 6002 | 8 |

The designer should consider combining areas of the home that do not require more than four *services,* with another *Zone* that has a sufficient quantity of available *Zone Hub* modular jack slots. In the 'Example Home'; for instance, eight *Zone Hubs* will effectively provide service to 12 *Zones* because the pool patio, garage, front door and access gate are combined with other *Zone Hubs* that have available modular connector slots. The designer must also make sure to consider the future when the project budget permits. The designer will then enter into Table C, the quantity and Part No. of the *Zone Hubs* required. He will also enter the Part No of the *Service Input Hub* as well.

**Step 6:** Based on the type of Hubs selected and the total quantity of each type of Hub determined in Step 5, the designer can then select the proper *Distribution Panel* to use. The specific manufacturer or supplier of a *Distribution Panel* can also be of help to select the proper panel. The designer will then enter the *Distribution Panel* Part No. into Table C.

**Step 7:** The designer will need to select the type of cables to be pull from the *Distribution Panel* to each *Interactive Receptacle* and/or *Service Outlet* location. He will also select the type of *Service Input* cable to pull to each *service* entrance location. The designer will then enter into Table D, the total number of cable drops and *service* input cables for each type of cable along with the total length of each cable type required.

When the *'Interactive Receptacle'* method of design is used, wire 'Bundles' will provide the primary conductors; however, in some cases there may be separate cables pulled along with the 'Bundles' to provide additional *services*. Both the 'Bundles' and separate cables are identified in the *'Structured Bundle Drop Plan'* shown in Figure 1-7.

When the *'Service Outlet'* method of design is used, cable types are not directly identified on the *'Service Outlet Cable Drop Plan'* shown in Figure 1-27. The installer must refer to this Plan and the specifications listed along with the *Service Identifiers* shown on page 31. From here he will be able to determine the type of cables to pull to each location.

**Step 8:** The designer must calculate the total length of each cable type that needs to be pulled from the *Distribution Panel* to each *Interactive Receptacle* and/or *Service Outlet*. He must also calculate the total length of each type of *Service Input* cable that will be pulled from the *Service Input Hub* to the appropriate *service* entrance locations.

There are two methods used to determine the total cable length of each type of cable required in a particular project. One method is to measure the length of each cable pull while remembering to allow for additional cable that will be pulled down inside the walls to the appropriate *Interactive Receptacle* and/or *Service Outlet*. These measurements must be conservative to assure that there will be enough cable on the job site. This method is time consuming and may not

be practical for some installation companies; however, it is the most accurate. The other method estimates an average length for each cable drop and another average length for each *Service Input* cable pull. An average length commonly used for cable drops is 75 feet and the average length for a *Service Input* cable pull is 65 feet. These average distances will vary depending on the size of the home, where the *Equipment Room* is located in the home and what the configuration of the home is. In the body of Table D, the total number of cable pulls multiplied by the average cable pull lengths will determine the grand total cable length required for each cable type to complete the project.

**Step 9:** The designer should make a bill of materials to identify all of the components required to fulfill the *Structured Wiring* project. This documentation is used to purchase the equipment and material.

**Step 10:** The designer needs to prepare a project cost estimate to determine how much the system will cost the 'design build contractor' in order to determine the cost to the customer. The costs we are referring to are the total equipment and material costs, the total installation labor cost, and the design man-hour (MH) cost. Another cost that may be included in this estimate is the mobilization cost to transport installers and equipment to the job site. The 'Example Home' cost estimate sheet shown on page 35, uses fictitious costs for example purposes.

**1-21 Design Considerations:** The following section will continue to describe the 'Example Home' *Structured Wiring System* from room to room to furnish detailed descriptions of what the system consists of. This will provide information that can be applied to any Structured Wiring and Home Control project.

Most of the rooms in the 'Example Home' use only one 'Bundle', which is generally sufficient in most homes. In some cases; however, an additional 'Bundle' or separate cables are pulled along with a wire 'Bundle' to provide additional *services*. For instance; a separate (CAT 5, 4 UTP) cable should be pulled to each room to

# TABLE D  DROP & SERVICE CABLE REQUIREMENTS

Project #: 4682  
Address: 5629 Berkeley Rd, Goleta CA 93017

| Table A Quantity | WALL OUTLETS - DROPS | Wire Bundle Total | RG-6 Coax Total | CAT 5, 4 UTP Total | 14 GA SPEAKER WIRE Total | 16 GA SPEAKER WIRE Total |
|---|---|---|---|---|---|---|
| 10 | Interactive Receptacle | 10x75' = 800' | | | | |
| | RJ-11 One Pair | | | | | |
| | RJ-25 3 Pair | | | | | |
| 17 | RJ-45 4 Pair CAT 5 | | | 17x75' = 1275' | | |
| 10 | F-Connector | | 10x75' = 750' | | | |
| | RCA Speaker | | | | | |
| 20 | Speaker Binding Posts | | | | 4x75' = 300' | 16x75' = 1200' |
| | ST Fiber | | | | | |
| | | | | | | |
| | | | | | | |
| | SERVICE INPUT CABLES | | | | | |
| | Home Phone line | | | 1x65' = 65' | | |
| | Business Phone Line | | | 1x65' = 65' | | |
| | Internet Line | | | 1x65' = 65' | | |
| | Fax line | | | 1x65' = 65' | | |
| | Security line | | | 1x65' = 65' | | |
| | Credit Card Reader line | | | 1x65' = 65' | | |
| | Catv | | 1x65' = 65' | | | |
| | Satellite | | 2x65' = 130' | 2x65' = 130' | | |
| | Antenna | | 1x65' = 65' | 4x65' = 260' | | |
| | Total Drop Cables | 10 | 10 | 23 | 4 | 12 |
| | Total Input Service Cables | | 4 | 6 | | |
| | Total Cable Length | 800' | 1010' | 2055' | 300' | 1200' |

# PROJECT COST ESTIMATE

| ** NOTE ** EXAMPLE ONLY<br>ALL COMPONENT AND LABOR COSTS ARE FICTITIOUS | SHEET __1__ OF __1__ |
|---|---|
| CUSTOMER<br>  JANE DOE | PROJECT #<br>  4682 |

ADDRESS    5629 BERKELEY RD, GOLETA CA 93017

| ESTIMATOR   JOE COST | DESIGNER   ROBERT BUCCERI |
|---|---|

| COMPONENT PART No. | QUANTITY | | LABOR | | MATERIAL | | TOTAL COST |
|---|---|---|---|---|---|---|---|
| | NO. UNITS | UNIT MEAS. | PER UNIT | TOTAL | PER UNIT | TOTAL | |
| 1) PRO 8 DIST. PANEL | 1 | EA | 60 | 60 | 76 | 76 | 136 |
| 2) SERVICE INPUT HUB | 1 | EA | 15 | 15 | 62 | 62 | 77 |
| 3) ETHERNET HUB | 1 | EA | 15 | 15 | 56 | 56 | 71 |
| 4) TELEPHONE HUB | 2 | EA | 15 | 30 | 44 | 88 | 118 |
| 5) SATELLITE HUB | 1 | EA | 15 | 15 | 48 | 48 | 63 |
| 6) COAX HUB | 1 | EA | 15 | 15 | 88 | 88 | 103 |
| 7) ZONE HUB | 8 | EA | 15 | 120 | 42 | 336 | 456 |
| 8) INTERACTIVE RECEPTACLE | 10 | EA | 30 | 300 | 25 | 250 | 550 |
| 9) MODULAR RJ-45 JACK | 17 | EA | 8 | 136 | 6 | 102 | 238 |
| 10) MODULAR COAX CONN | 10 | EA | 8 | 80 | 6 | 60 | 140 |
| 11) MODULAR FIBER CONN | 4 | EA | 14 | 56 | 16 | 64 | 120 |
| 12) MODULAR SPK CONN | 20 | EA | 8 | 160 | 6 | 120 | 280 |
| 13) BUNDLE ROLL | 2 | EA | 120 | 240 | 500 | 1000 | 1240 |
| 14) CAT 5 ROLL | 2 | EA | 90 | 180 | 44 | 88 | 268 |
| 15) RG-6 QUAD SHIELD ROLL | 2 | EA | 110 | 220 | 78 | 156 | 376 |
| 16) 16 GA SPK CABLE ROLL | 1 | EA | 100 | 100 | 77 | 77 | 177 |
| 17) 14 GA SPK CABLE ROLL | 1 | EA | 75 | 75 | 66 | 66 | 141 |
| 18) SINGE GANG MUD-RING | 22 | EA | 10 | 220 | .36 | 8 | 228 |
| 19) DOUBLE GANG MUD-RING | 6 | EA | 10 | 60 | .50 | 3 | 63 |
| 20) CAT 5 PATCH CABLE | 22 | EA | 5 | 110 | 9 | 198 | 308 |
| 21) RG-6 PATCH CABLE | 24 | EA | 5 | 120 | 12 | 288 | 408 |
| 22) RJ-45 PLUG | 32 | EA | 5 | 160 | .28 | 9 | 169 |
| 23) A/V MODULATOR | 2 | EA | 30 | 60 | 90 | 180 | 240 |
| 24) FASTENER 166 | 144 | EA | 1 | 144 | .09 | 13 | 157 |
| | | | | | | | |
| TOTAL MATERIAL | | | | | | 3,376 | |
| TOTAL LABOR | | | | 2,691 | | | |
| GRAND TOTAL | | | | | | | 6,067 |

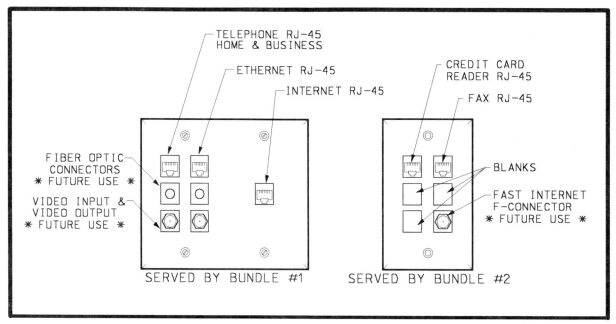

FIGURE 1-28   OFFICE RECEPTACLES

provide bedside telephone *service*. This will save money by not having to route a second 'Bundle' for just one *service*. Separate (RG-6 Quad Shield) coaxial cables are also pulled in cases where Satellite or high speed Internet *service* is required in a *Zone*.

**1-22 Home Office:** The home Office is a *Zone* that requires a quantity of two 'Bundles'. Two are needed because the Office has a fair amount of computer equipment as well as other business equipment. In the Ethernet Plan illustrated in Figure 2-4 on page 58, the PC, fax machine and 'credit card reader' are positioned in the Office as shown. 'Bundle' drop #1 located next to the PC provides Internet *service*, Ethernet *service*, home & business telephone *service*, and Video Input & Video Output *services* as well. Although the Video Input and Output *services* are not presently used in this room, they are in place in case this room is used for a bedroom in the future. One of these coax cables can be used in this room when the homeowner wishes to switch to Fast Internet *service*. 'Bundle drop #2' provides *service* for the fax machine, and credit card reader. Refer to Figure 1-28 to see what the Office *Interactive Receptacle* and *Service Outlets* look like. The cable connections required to provide all of these *services* are illustrated in the 'Office Hub Connection' diagram shown in

Figure 1-11. Notice that the *Telephone Hub* and the RG-6 jack on the far left side of the *Service Input Hub* is used to provide a telephone extension for the *Stargate* Home Controller. This controller is used in the 'Example Home' for tutorial purposes throughout this manual. The use of *Stargate* and other home control equipment is discussed in Chapter Three. Also notice that the security system telephone extension utilizes the Office *Zone Hub* for distribution purposes.

Most cable companies are now offering high speed Internet *service* through the coaxial cable system, which offers increased access and download speeds. If the customer would like to have this *service* in place of the more common telephone line *service*, this option can be provided by specifying a *Coax Distribution Hub* with enough outputs to handle the Ethernet requirements as well as the basic video entertainment requirements such as CATV. We recommend pulling an additional (RG-6 Quad Shield) coaxial cable to any room that has a computer in preparation for high speed Internet *service* from the local Cable Company.

**1-23 Master Bedroom:** As illustrated in Figure 1-27 on page 29, the bed is located on one side of the room and the TV, VCR/DVD player and PC are placed on the other side of the room. Two separate 'Bundle' drops were recommended to the homeowner in this room once the designer received an indication from the customer that the furniture may occasionally be rearrange. The Video Output and Video Input RG-6 cables plus the Ethernet and audio/video IR control (CAT 5, 4 UTP) cables are provided by **Bundle #1** as shown. The wall next to the bed is generally a good location in any bedroom for a telephone jack. This jack utilizes a (CAT 5, 4 UTP) cable provided by **Bundle #2.**. When the customer decides to change the position of the furniture, all the customer needs to do is swap the existing patch cables that correspond to **Bundle #1** with the patch cable positions that correspond to **Bundle #2**. (See Figure 1-17).

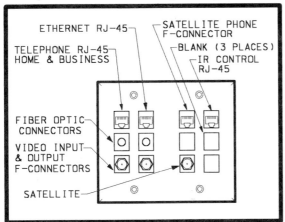

FIGURE 1-29   MASTER RECEPTACLES

This figure illustrates the patch cable connections located on the front of the *Master Bedroom Hub*. Notice the available cables at the back of this Hub that can be used when the furniture is moved to provide Ethernet, audio/video IR control, Video Inputs, Video Outputs and satellite *service*. The home and business telephone *jumper* can be repositioned over to the Ethernet modular jack connected to Bundle #1. This is only one of many advantages of a *Structured Wiring System* that is complimented when using the appropriate *Distribution Panel*.

Satellite *service* is provided to the Master Bedroom by utilizing two separate (RG-6 Quad Shield) coaxial cables routed along with 'Bundle #1' & 'Bundle #2'. These cables are illustrated in Figure 1-18.

Although there is an available (CAT 5, 4 UTP) cable provided in each 'Bundle' for

standard Ethernet and Internet *service,* we recommend pulling a separate (RG-6 Quad Shield) coaxial cable to provide the option of switching over to a high speed *Internet service* at a later date. These cables are not shown in this room due to space considerations.

Refer to Figure 1-29, to see what the Master Bedroom *Interactive Receptacle* and *Service Outlets* look like.

**1-24 Living Room:** In the Living Room there is a limited number of *services* that the customer intends to use. The designer has provided a Video Input cable to the Living Room; however, there is no Video Output cable from this room because there are no more Video Input F-connectors available on the 8 x 8 *Coax Distribution Hub* shown in Figure 1-22. In this figure, there appears to be four available F-connectors; however, they are used by other rooms in the home. The designer could have selected an 8 x 12 Coax Hub that provides additional F-connectors; however, the added cost could not be justified in this case. The homeowner felt that this room could possibly have a TV some day; however, there was no need to have a Video Output because a VCR or DVD player would not be necessary in this room. If the homeowner; for instance, would like to watch a DVD in the Living Room, he could do so by placing the DVD disk in the Family Room DVD player to watch it in any room with a TV. Sometimes issues of this type will come up in a design and should be discussed with the customer to make the proper decisions. This particular decision was based on system capability versus cost. In this case, the added benefit did not warrant the additional cost.

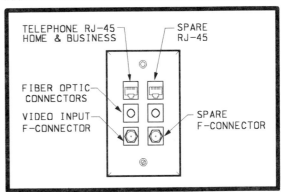

FIGURE 1-30   LIVING ROOM

Since there is no space to install a Pool *Zone Hub* in the *Distribution Panel*, the designer decides to use a portion of the Living Room *Zone Hub*. Sharing this Hub is practical in this case because the Living Room uses a small number of *Zone Hub* modular connector slots. This allows plenty of room on the Hub to add on *services* for the patio TV and telephone.

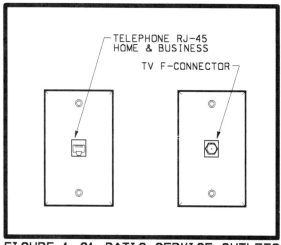

**FIGURE 1-31 PATIO SERVICE OUTLETS**

In Figure 1-22, notice the patch cables connected from the *Coax Distribution System Hub & Telephone System Hubs* to provide *services* to the Living Room *Zone Hub*. These patch cables allow signals to travel to the appropriate cables connected at the rear of the Living Room Hub shown in Figure 1-23. Notice the separate RG-6 coaxial cable and (CAT 5, 4 UTP) cable located on the right hand side. Continuations of these cables are routed to the patio TV and the telephone *Service Outlets*. The Living Room Video Output cable and Home & Business telephone cable are routed to the Living Room *Interactive Receptacle* shown in Figure 1-30. Although the Living Room *Interactive Receptacle* only has two types of *services* utilized at this time, all of the conductors from the 'Bundle' are terminated anyway. This will allow additional *services* to be provided in the future by simply connecting the appropriate conductors from the 'Bundle' to the rear of the new *Zone Hub* modular connectors. A *jumper* will also need to be connected from the appropriate *System Hub* that supplies *service* to the front of the new *Zone Hub* modular connectors.

**1-25 Family Room:** The Family Room is one area of the home that is occupied most. TV entertainment in this room is at a premium, which qualifies this area to receive all of the video *services* offered by the *Structured Wiring System*. Refer to Figure 1-7 to see where the two 'Bundle' drops are located. This particular drop offers the *services* on the Family Room *Interactive Receptacle* shown in Figure 1-32. These *services* are fed to this area of the home by configuring the appropriate cables on the rear of the Family Room *Zone Hub* shown in Figure 1-13. Notice that this drop requires an additional RG-6 coax cable to provide satellite *service*, which is supplied by 'Bundle #2'. Since this room incorporates a TV and other audio & video equipment, the designer utilizes one of the (CAT 5, 4 UTP) cables in 'Bundle #1' to carry IR control signals. This *service* was incorporated to take advantage of the power offered by the home's automated system. When the last family member is ready for bed, he or she will push a button on the *JDS* Keypad in the Family Room to initiate the 'Good Night Mode'. This mode will turn off the remaining lights and ceiling fans, turn on the appropriate lighting to create a path for the occupants to reach the bathrooms and bedrooms, *Arms* the security system, sets-back the air conditioning setpoint and turns off the remaining audio/video equipment. To ultimately provide this room with the *services* shown in Figure 1-12, patch cables need to be connected from the *Service Input Hub* to the corresponding *System Hubs* and finally to the Family Room Hub. This is how the appropriate *service* signals are linked from each *service* entrance to their final destination in the Family Room.

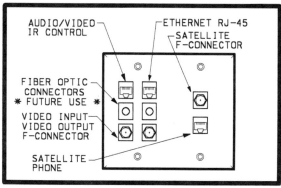

**FIGURE 1-32 FAMILY ROOM SERVICES**

**1-26 Bedroom 'A':** In this particular room the customer does not care to have a separate telephone jack next to the bed. In fact the customer does not want a phone in this room at all because this is the infant's room and the phone would just wake the child up. The lack of telephone capability in a child's bedroom would have been acceptable in the past; however, the *Structured Wiring System* needs to 'future-proof' this home. The designer must explain to the customer that telephone *service* must be provided next to the bed anyway because this child will be a teenage someday and will definitely need a telephone extension. This telephone *Service Outlet* location is shown in Figure 1-7. There is also an *Interactive Receptacle* located on the other side of the room that is connected to a 'Bundle drop'. In Figure 1-34, notice the three patch cables connected to the front of the Bedroom 'A' *Zone Hub*. These cables provide signals to the appropriate 'Bundle' conductors connected to the rear modular connectors of the *Zone Hub* as shown in Figure 1-35. From here the wire 'Bundle' is routed through the attic and down inside the wall before being terminated to the corresponding *Interactive Receptacle* modular jacks. This *Interactive Receptacle* shown in Figure 1-33, provides Ethernet, Video Input and telephone *services* along with future fiber optic *services*. Although the supporting cables are terminated to the *Interactive Receptacle,* the fiber optic cables and Video Output cable are not used or connected to the *Zone Hub* at this time.

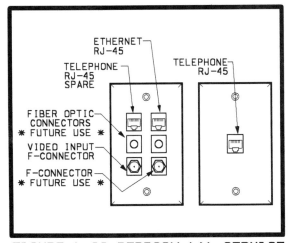

**FIGURE 1-33 BEDROOM 'A' SERVICE**

CCTV camera #3 is used to monitor the infant's room and is supported by a separate RG-6 coaxial cable. CCTV camera #4 is used to monitor the pool area and is also supported by a separate RG-6 coaxial cable. Video signals from both cameras are combined together using a device called a splitter/combiner. The single Video Input cable from the splitter/combiner is connected to the *Service Input Hub* shown at the bottom of Figure 1-10. In Figure 1-11, notice the patch cable identified as (CCTV 3 & 4) connected between the front connector of the *Service Input Hub* and the Video Input side of the *Coax Distribution Hub*. This cable supplies the home with CCTV camera video of Bedroom 'A' and the pool area as well. RG-6 cables that connect to the Output side of the *Coax Distribution Hub* provides all video signals except satellite video to most *Zone Hub*. This will ultimately provide video to *Interactive Receptacles* throughout the home. Even though this room does not have a TV at this time, it does have the capability of providing entertainment in the future.

A Video Output was not included in this *Zone* because of the additional cost associated with upgrading the 8 x 8 *Coax Distribution Hub* to an 8 x 12. Although this leaves an available RG-6 coax cable from the 'Bundle', it could not be used for the CCTV camera because the camera is installed at a different height and location from the *Interactive Receptacle.*

Refer to Figure 6-13 on page 135 for the CCTV camera cable terminations.

**1-27 Bedroom 'B':** Bedroom 'B' is similar to Bedroom 'A,' except Bedroom 'B' does not have a CCTV camera. Bedroom 'B' also has Video Output capability that is not available in Bedroom 'A'. Bedroom 'B' includes all basic *services* provided by a standard 'Bundle' drop. These *services* can be seen on the *Interactive Receptacle* shown in Figure 1-36.

In Figure 1-20, notice there are two (CAT 5, 4 UTP) cables connected to the rear of the *Zone Hub* that are not supplied by the 'Bundle'. One of these cables is routed to the opposite side of the room from the 'Bundle' drop as shown in Figure 1-7. This was added because

# BEDROOM 'A' HUB CONNECTIONS

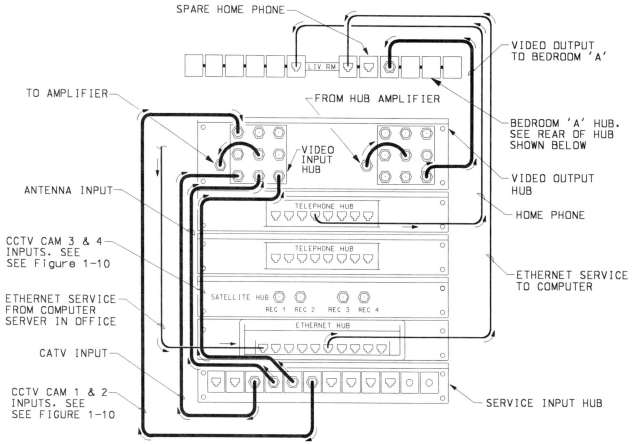

SPARE HOME PHONE

LIV RM

VIDEO OUTPUT TO BEDROOM 'A'

TO AMPLIFIER

FROM HUB AMPLIFIER

BEDROOM 'A' HUB. SEE REAR OF HUB SHOWN BELOW

VIDEO INPUT HUB

VIDEO OUTPUT HUB

ANTENNA INPUT

HOME PHONE

TELEPHONE HUB

CCTV CAM 3 & 4 INPUTS. SEE SEE Figure 1-10

TELEPHONE HUB

ETHERNET SERVICE FROM COMPUTER SERVER IN OFFICE

ETHERNET SERVICE TO COMPUTER

SATELLITE HUB     REC 1   REC 2   REC 3   REC 4

ETHERNET HUB

CATV INPUT

CCTV CAM 1 & 2 INPUTS. SEE SEE FIGURE 1-10

SERVICE INPUT HUB

## FIGURE 1-34   PANEL HUBS - FRONT VIEW

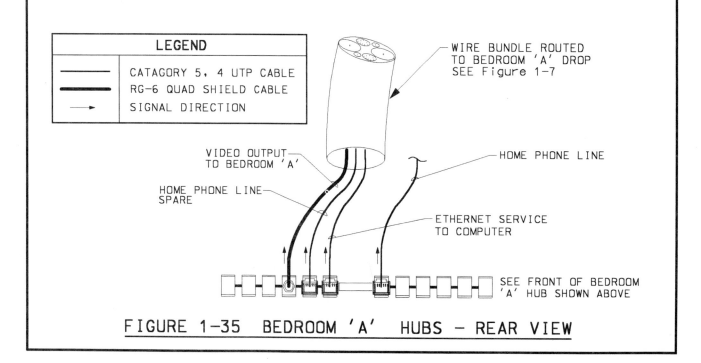

### LEGEND

| | |
|---|---|
| —— | CATAGORY 5, 4 UTP CABLE |
| —— | RG-6 QUAD SHIELD CABLE |
| → | SIGNAL DIRECTION |

WIRE BUNDLE ROUTED TO BEDROOM 'A' DROP SEE Figure 1-7

VIDEO OUTPUT TO BEDROOM 'A'

HOME PHONE LINE

HOME PHONE LINE SPARE

ETHERNET SERVICE TO COMPUTER

SEE FRONT OF BEDROOM 'A' HUB SHOWN ABOVE

## FIGURE 1-35   BEDROOM 'A'   HUBS - REAR VIEW

the designer again suggested to the homeowner that a telephone jack be installed next to the bed for the teenager.

Since there is no separate *Zone Hub* for the garage, the designer decided to use an available modular connector slot on the Bedroom 'B' *Zone Hub* to provide the garage with telephone *service*. This available slot is utilized by inserting an RJ-45 modular jack into the *Zone Hub* before connecting it to the other separate (CAT 5, 4 UTP) cable shown in Figure 1-20. A continuation of this telephone extension cable to the garage *Service Outlet* is shown in Figure 1-7.

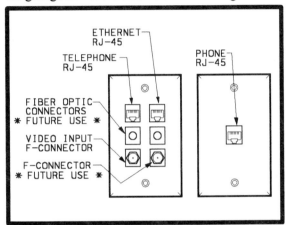

FIGURE 1-36   BEDROOM 'B'

Notice that the patch cables in Figure 1-19, are connected from the *Service Input Hub* to the appropriate *System Hubs* and finally to the *Zone Hub*. These cables provide a path for a number of *services* to ultimately be received by Bedroom 'B' as well as the garage.

**1-28 Kitchen:** The Kitchen *Zone* requires one (CAT 5, 4 UTP) cable for home and business telephone *service,* an RG-6 Video Input cable for the 'under the cabinet' TV and a (CAT 5, 4 UTP) cable that is used to control the TV remotely using audio/video IR control signals. This *Service Outlet* is shown in Figure 1-37. A Video Output is not required in the Kitchen because there will never be a VCR, DVD or CCTV camera here to provide Video Output. The Video Input cable; however, will allow the cook to view a wide selection of TV programs while the IR control conductors will support control of all 'under-the-counter' TV functions by the home's automated system.   An example of

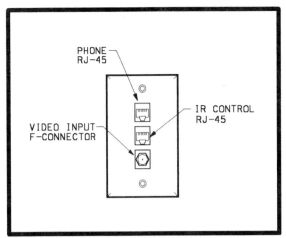

FIGURE 1-37   KITCHEN SERVICE

this type of control is as follows: When a visitor walks up to the front door, a motion detector will send a Digital Input to the *Stargate* Home Controller. This will automatically turn ON the front door CCTV camera and the Kitchen TV while selecting the TV channel assigned to the camera coverage area. The cook is then able to view these events right from the Kitchen TV after hearing a message over the whole house audio system ("*you have a visitor*").

Another example of how IR signals automatically control the Kitchen TV as well as other audio/video equipment in the home is as follows: When an occupant decides to leave the home, he or she will push a *JDS* Keypad button on the way out. This will initiate the 'Leaving Mode'. This mode turns OFF all electrical devices in the home and utilizes the IR control capabilities to turn off all the audio/video equipment as well.

The Kitchen cable terminations and patch cable arrangement on the *Distribution Panel* is shown in Figures 1-38 & 1-39.

**1-29 Theater:** The Theater is another *Zone* that will generally require two 'Bundles'. With all the advances in electronic technology and the new audio/video equipment available today and in the near future, it is a good idea to stock up on the appropriate conductors in this room. Notice in Figure 1-16, that the Satellite and the Video Output from the DVD and VCR utilize the two RG-6 coaxial cables from 'Bundle #2'. There is also a separate (CAT 5, 4 UTP) pulled to the

# KITCHEN HUB CONNECTIONS

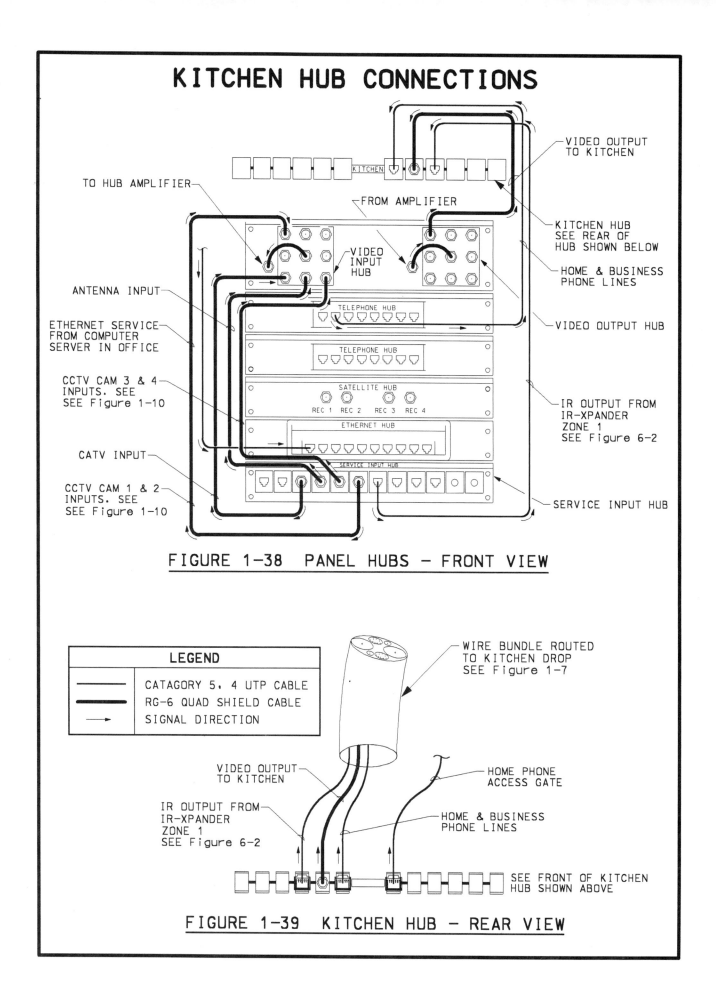

VIDEO OUTPUT
TO KITCHEN

TO HUB AMPLIFIER

FROM AMPLIFIER

KITCHEN

VIDEO
INPUT
HUB

KITCHEN HUB
SEE REAR OF
HUB SHOWN BELOW

HOME & BUSINESS
PHONE LINES

ANTENNA INPUT

TELEPHONE HUB

VIDEO OUTPUT HUB

ETHERNET SERVICE
FROM COMPUTER
SERVER IN OFFICE

TELEPHONE HUB

CCTV CAM 3 & 4
INPUTS. SEE
SEE Figure 1-10

SATELLITE HUB

REC 1   REC 2   REC 3   REC 4

IR OUTPUT FROM
IR-XPANDER
ZONE 1
SEE Figure 6-2

ETHERNET HUB

CATV INPUT

SERVICE INPUT HUB

CCTV CAM 1 & 2
INPUTS. SEE
SEE Figure 1-10

SERVICE INPUT HUB

## FIGURE 1-38   PANEL HUBS - FRONT VIEW

## LEGEND

| | |
|---|---|
| —— | CATAGORY 5, 4 UTP CABLE |
| ▬▬ | RG-6 QUAD SHIELD CABLE |
| → | SIGNAL DIRECTION |

WIRE BUNDLE ROUTED
TO KITCHEN DROP
SEE Figure 1-7

VIDEO OUTPUT
TO KITCHEN

HOME PHONE
ACCESS GATE

IR OUTPUT FROM
IR-XPANDER
ZONE 1
SEE Figure 6-2

HOME & BUSINESS
PHONE LINES

SEE FRONT OF KITCHEN
HUB SHOWN ABOVE

## FIGURE 1-39   KITCHEN HUB - REAR VIEW

42

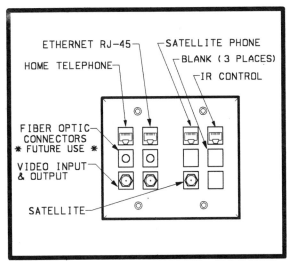

FIGURE 1-40   THEATER OUTLETS

Labels in figure: ETHERNET RJ-45, HOME TELEPHONE, SATELLITE PHONE, BLANK (3 PLACES), IR CONTROL, FIBER OPTIC CONNECTORS * FUTURE USE *, VIDEO INPUT & OUTPUT, SATELLITE

home telephone *Service Outlet* location shown in Figure 1-7. This leaves the extra RG-6 in 'Bundle #1' to be available for future use.

Wire 'Bundle #1' provides Video Input *service* to the Theater, telephone *service* to support the satellite receiver and IR control of the audio/video equipment in *Zone* 2. IR control signal outputs from the *IR-Xpander* are used to support the automated audio/video control functions throughout the home. See Sections 3-26 and 6-2 for more on the *IR-Xpander*. To see what the Theater *Interactive Receptacle* and *Service Outlets* look like, refer to Figure 1-40 shown above.

**1-30 The Rough-In Process:** The 'Rough-In' process generally refers to any work required to install a *Structured Wiring System* prior to the drywall being installed.

The first step of the 'Rough-In' process is to mount the *Distributions Panel* in the *Equipment Room*. When using a surface mounted *Panel*, this *Panel* in mounted on a 1/2" thick plywood sheet attached to the *Equipment Room* drywall and wall studs. There are also recessed *Distribution Panels* that mount between the standard 16" O.C. wall studs. This type of panel is installed by allowing the front of the panel to extend out ½" beyond the wall studs before using wood screws to hold it in place. The ½" dimension will allow the face of the panel to be flush with the drywall once the drywall is installed.

The designer must be sure to include a dedicated 20 amp receptacle in the *Equipment Room* to be used by the plug-in power supply furnished with the *Distribution Panel*. Other home control equipment will utilize this power as well. This receptacle should be installed within 3 feet of the *Distribution Panel* and other home control equipment whenever possible. The *Distribution Panel* also requires the proper grounding. This is furnished by pulling a dedicated grounding conductor from the *Distribution Panel* directly to the home's grounding rod. This grounding rod is normally located outside the home near the power meter. The grounding conductor is then connected to the grounding rod and the grounding lug located on the back of the *Distribution Panel* as shown in Figure 1-10.

The second step in the 'Rough-In' process is to install all of the mud-rings in the home. Mud-rings are used to mount the *Interactive Receptacles* and/or *Service Outlets*. Mud-ring locations are determined from the cable drop locations shown in Figure 1-7 or 1-27. This device is attached to the wall studs using screws as shown in Figure 1-41.

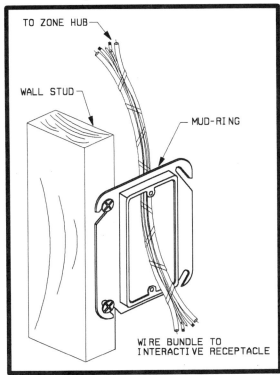

FIGURE 1-41   ROUGH-IN WIRING

Labels in figure: TO ZONE HUB, WALL STUD, MUD-RING, WIRE BUNDLE TO INTERACTIVE RECEPTACLE

When one *Interactive Receptacle* or *Service Outlet* is used per location, a single-gang mud-ring is required. When two outlets are installed side by side a two-gang mud-ring is required. Mud-rings should be installed at the same standard height above the floor as the 120V, 60 Hz power receptacles. When the home is complete, all of the outlets will be even, which makes the overall installation look much cleaner.

Above each mud-ring location a 1" diameter hole is drilled in the top plate of the wall to allow the 'Bundle' to access the space between the wall studs. This hole should be drilled at 45 degrees off the top plate whenever possible as shown in Figure 1-42. This will allow the 'Bundle' to gradually curve in a larger radius than normal as it enters the space between the wall studs. This will help keep the conductors from crimping as they enter and exit the drilled hole. This will also allow the 'Bundle' to lay down flat on the top plate to reduce tripping hazards in the attic. The 'Bundle' is then pulled through to reach the mud-ring while allowing an extra foot of 'Bundle' wire to provide enough length to work with during the trim-out process.

When using a 'flush mount' or 'recessed' *Distribution Panel*, a 1" diameter hole needs to be pre-drilled in the top plate above the *Panel* for each 'Home Run' 'Bundle'. A 1/2" diameter hole is sufficient for each separate cable 'Home Run'.

**1-31 Zone Drop Pulling Procedure:** Describing the method of pulling 'Bundles' and/or other cables assumes that the home is in the process of construction and that the drywall has not yet been installed.

All structured wiring cables should be routed after the 60 Hz electrical power has been pulled. This will allow the installer to select the proper paths for the 'Bundles' and/or other cables to avoid signal interference from the 60 Hz power conductors and other electrical noise producing devices.

Wire 'Bundles' are pulled in a 'Home Run' configuration as shown in Figure 1-7 or 1-27. These 'Bundle' paths are illustrated as straight runs from the *Equipment Room* to each *Interface Receptacle* and/or *Service Outlet* for simplicity purposes. The actual cable routing will depend

on the location of ceiling joists, roof joists, vaulted ceilings, air conditioning ductwork, 60 Hz power conductors and other construction obstructions. All 'Bundles' and separate cable pulls must be routed from the *Equipment Room* to each mud-ring. Before pulling each type of cable, the cable at hand is first placed in the *Equipment Room* on a pulling reel. This device allows the installer to pull the cable into the attic and along its path to help minimize cable binding and kinking problems.

To pull a 'Bundle' Home-Run, the end of the wire 'Bundle' off the roll is pulled through the open ceiling joists and into the attic in the direction of the drop location. Wire 'Bundles' as well as other cables are generally laid right on top of the ceiling joists and are pulled over to the top plate of the wall to each mug-ring location. A 'Bundle' or separate cable is then pulled through the pre-drilled hole in the top plate and down between the wall studs to the appropriate mud-ring. The installer should allow at least 1-foot of extra 'Bundle' or separate cable length beyond each mud-ring. When this process is finished the other end of the 'Bundle' or separate cable in the *Equipment Room* is cut off the roll. Each 'Bundle' or separate cable is then pulled through the pre-drilled hole in the top plate of the *Equipment Room* wall before being pulled through the knockout holes at the top of a recessed *Distribution Panel*. Each cable should be cut to allow the cable to reach the bottom of the *Distribution Panel*. This will provide enough cable to work with during the trim-out process.

When a surface mounted *Distribution Panel* is used like the *FutureSmart® Pro 8 Panel*, the cables will enter the back of the panel. Access to the cables is made easy because the front of the panel is designed to open like a door. The front panel contains all of the Hubs so when the door is opened, the rear of each Hub is exposed to allow cables to be terminated to the appropriate modular connectors.

As previously mentioned, each 'Bundle' or separate cable end located at the *Distribution Panel* must be labeled. It is also a good idea to label each cable end located at each mud-ring; however, this is not absolutely necessary. Cables that are not labeled in the *Equipment Room*

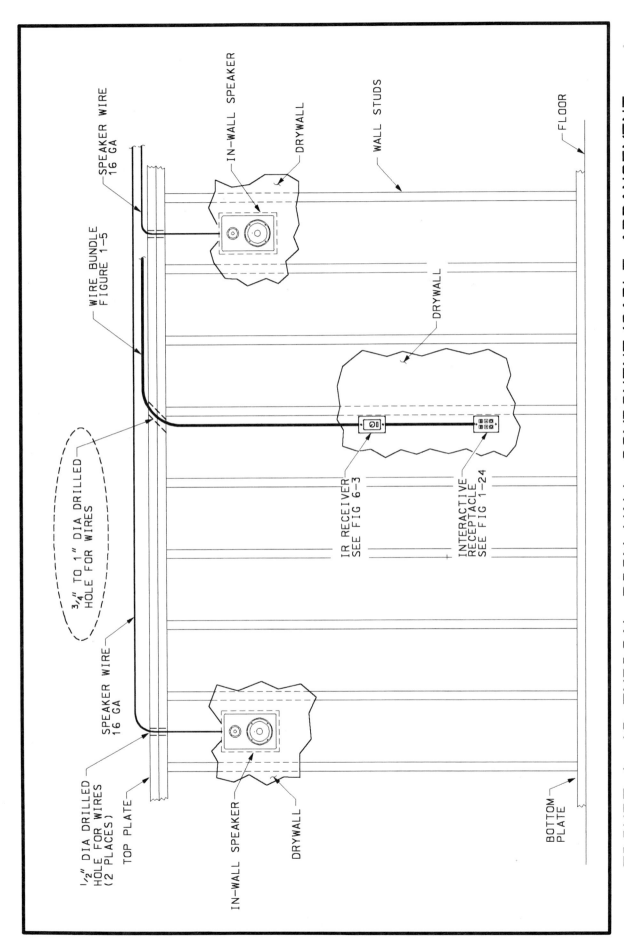

FIGURE 1-42 TYPICAL ROOM WALL COMPONENT/CABLE ARRANGEMENT

SPEAKER WIRE 16 GA

IN-WALL SPEAKER

DRYWALL

WALL STUDS

FLOOR

WIRE BUNDLE FIGURE 1-5

DRYWALL

3/4" TO 1" DIA DRILLED HOLE FOR WIRES

IR RECEIVER SEE FIG 6-3

INTERACTIVE RECEPTACLE SEE FIG 1-24

1/2" DIA DRILLED HOLE FOR WIRES (2 PLACES)

SPEAKER WIRE 16 GA

TOP PLATE

IN-WALL SPEAKER

DRYWALL

BOTTOM PLATE

45

will leave an installer frustrated during the trim-out process because he will not know what 'Bundle'/cable terminates to what Hub or other system component. Without labels he will also have to test each cable for identification purposes. Labeling will in the long run save the installer a great deal of time and anxiety.

After the cable pulling process is complete, the installer will find himself with a large number of 'Bundle' ends and separate cable ends hanging down inside the *Distribution Panel* or other home control equipment panel. This at first looks like a mess of wires and it is; however, there is no need to panic because each 'Bundle' and separate cable is labeled. Labels can consist of a sequence of numbers (1, 2, 3, etc.). Labels should be wrapped around each cable approximately 6 inches from the cable end. The designer must write down in a project notebook what location each number pertains to (1 = Living Room, 2 & 3 = Office, 4 = Family Room), etc. This will tell the installer what cable connects to what *Zone Hub* without having to walk over and look at each label number within each room. Since both ends of each cable should receive a label, obtain a packet that contains two of each number or purchase two packages containing single numbers.

Wire 'Bundle' and separate cable pulls will need to stay a minimum of six feet away from each attic access door to comply with most building codes. Never pull data or any other low voltage cable along with power conductors. Never share drilled holes in wall studs or other building members with the power cables. Cables should be pulled a minimum distance of 1'-0" away from AC power conductors and must be routed perpendicular to AC conductors if they must cross. When mounting the mud-rings, allow a minimum distance of 32 inches or two wall studs away from power receptacles. Data or low voltage wiring should not be pulled within 1'-0' of fluorescent or HID fixture ballast's, TV antenna cable, ground wires, lightning rods and associated wiring.

Cables should be routed in a manner that will avoid sharp cable bends and sharp objects that can nick the protective insulation on the conductors. Installers should also be aware of the minimum bend radius for each cable type to

avoid damage. Avoid stepping on cables or routing them in walkways in the attic space. When pulling or mounting a cable, avoid twisting of the wires because this can also damage the conductors.

Not more than 25 pounds of pulling tension should be applied to a (CAT 5, 4 UTP) cable. Specific tension limits for a verity of other cable types are provided by each cable manufacture.

Other important requirements for telephone and data wiring applications include, maintaining the correct polarity and matching the color codes of the conductors when connecting the wires. When conduit is used to protect the conductors, leave a pull cord in place for additional wire to be pulled in the future. Splicing wires is not recommended along cable lengths because these type of connections are usually where system problem will occur. If wire ties are used to manage cables, do not tighten them to the point that changes the shape of the cable. When selecting locations in a room to place an *Interactive Receptacle* and/or *Service Outlet*, avoid perimeter walls whenever possible. This is because outside walls may incorporate firewall members and/or insulation that will sometimes make the pulling process more difficult. In existing homes, avoid routing cables under the carpet because they will be subject to crushing damage. If there are no other cable routing options, conductors should be routed along the baseboards and out of high traffic areas.

**1-32 Service Input Cable Pulling Procedure:** Service Input cables provide telephone, Internet, CATV, Satellite, TV antenna and CCTV camera services. Service Input cables are routed in the configurations shown in Figures 1-7 and 1-27. The cable type recommended for each type of *service* is described in Section 1-20 page 31. Before pulling cables, the roll of each cable type is placed inside the *Equipment Room* on a pulling reel. This will allow the installer to pull the cable end into the attic and along its path with less effort. To pull a *service* input cable, the end of the cable off the roll is pulled through the open ceiling joists and into the attic in the direction of the appropriate *service* entrance location. These cables are laid right on top of the ceiling joists and pulled over to the top plate of a framed exterior wall above each service entrance. Cables are then routed through the pre-drilled hole in the top plate and down between the wall studs to a height of approximately 4'-0" above the slab. Service cables should then be extended 2'-0" beyond the outside surface of the wall stud to allow the Telephone Company or CATV installer to terminate the conductors to the appropriate terminals in each *service* entrance enclosure. If the exterior wall is block with rigid foam insulation on the inside surface, the cable should be routed down on the surface of the insulation before it is pulled through a pre-drilled hole in the block wall. The appropriate service entrance enclosure will be installed on the exterior wall next to the hole. After pulling a cable to its service entrance the other end of the cable is cut off of the roll. This cable end is then pulled through the pre-drilled hole in the top plate of the wall and between the wall studs before accessing a knockout hole in the *Distribution Panel*. Each cable should be cut to allow the end of the cable to reach the bottom of the *Distribution Panel*. This will provide enough cable to work with during the trim-out process.

The satellite, TV antenna and CCTV *Service Input* cables are also pulled from the *Equipment Room* to a location on the exterior wall where *service* will eventually enter the home. The difference between these *services* and the standard CATV and telephone *services* is that the satellite, TV antenna and CCTV *services* require exterior *source cables* that the homeowner is responsible to install. For instance; a source cable needs to be pulled from the satellite to the service entrance location where as the CATV and telephone source cables are installed by the appropriate service provider. All *service* entrance enclosures are shown on the exterior walls in Figure 1-7 or 1-27. The CCTV cameras will generally be connected to a *Service Outlet* on the exterior wall while the satellite and TV antenna cables will be terminated in their own designated enclosure.

**1-33 Service Input Cable Recommendations:**
*Silent Servant, Inc.* recommends pulling the following *Service Input Cables* from the

*Distribution Panel* to the appropriate *service* entrance locations.

**Telephone Source:** Pull two (CAT 5, 4 UTP) cables from the *Distribution Panel* to the Telephone Company *service* entrance location. These cables are terminated inside the *service* entrance enclosure supplied by the Telephone Company, which is generally located near the 60 Hz power meter. The label used to identify cables pulled to this enclosure is shown in Figure 1-7 & 1-27. Use *Service Identifier* **PS-1** = Phone Service Cable #1, **PS-2** = Phone Service Cable #2 and so on.

**Internet Source:** Pull one (CAT 5, 4 UTP) cable from the *Distribution Panel* to the telephone *service* entrance location. The Internet *service* cable should use *Service Identifier* **IS** = Internet *Service*. The (CAT 5, 4 UTP) conductors can be part of the standard telephone *service* input cable; however, the *service* shown still be identified. It is a good idea to pull an extra (RG-6 Quad Shield) coaxial cable from the *Distribution Panel* to the CATV *service* entrance. This cable may be used to provide telephone *service*, Fast Internet *service*, CATV and others in the near future. An additional 2-foot of cable length is required to work with during the trim-out process.

**Cable TV (CATV) Source:** Pull two (RG-6 Quad Shield) cables from the *Distribution Panel* to the Cable TV (CATV) *service* entrance location. These cables are labeled using *Service Identifiers* CI-1 = CATV Input #1 and CI-2 = CATV Input #2. An additional 2-foot of cable length is required to work with during the trim-out process.

**TV Antenna Source:** Pull one (RG-6 Quad Shield) cable from the *Distribution Panel* to the TV antenna *service* entrance location. Also pull one cable from the TV antenna *service* entrance location to the TV antenna itself. These cables are labeled with *Service Identifier* AI = TV antenna Input. An additional 2-foot of cable length is required to work with during the trim-out process.

**Satellite Source:** Pull two (RG-6 Quad Shield) cables from the *Distribution Panel* to the satellite service entrance location. Also pull two cables from the service entrance location to the satellite location. These cables are labeled using *Service Identifiers* DI-1 = Satellite Input #1 and DI-2 = Satellite Input #2. An additional 2-foot of cable length is required to work with during the trim-out process.

**1-34 Zone Drop Cable Recommendations:** When cable 'Bundles' are used for the majority of the drops in the home, pull one 'Bundle' from the *Distribution Panel* to each *Interactive Receptacle*. If separate cables are used entirely, consider the following recommendations. See Figure 1-27 for the appropriate *Service Identifiers*. Also reference Section 1-20 for *Service Identifier* definitions and specifications.

**Telephone Drop:** Pull a minimum of two (CAT 5, 4 UTP) cables from the *Distribution Panel* to each *Service Outlet* mud-ring. If there will be more than four telephone *service* lines used in the home, one additional (CAT 5, 4 UTP) cable should be pulled to each telephone drop.

**Ethernet/Local Area Network Drops:** Pull one (CAT 5, 4 UTP) cable from the *Distribution Panel* to each computer location. It is generally a good idea to provide this *service* to each room that could require this *service* in the future even though it may not be required at the time of the design. One (RG-6 Quad Shield) cable should also be routed to each computer location because most local CATV companies are now providing high speed Internet *service* over the coax cable.

**Television Drops:** Pull a minimum of one (RG-6 Quad Shield) cable from the *Distribution Panel* to each room where a television may be located initially or possibly in the future. For 'two cable systems' such as the system illustrated in the 'Example Home', pull two (RG-6 Quad Shield) cables for each drop instead of just one.

**Satellite/Receiver Drops:** Pull one (RG-6 Quad Shield Cable) and one (CAT 5, 4 UTP) cable from the *Distribution Panel* to each *Service Outlet* that supports a satellite receiver. This (RG-6 Quad Shield) cable will provide the video and the (CAT 5, 4 UTP) cable will provide the satellite program provider with a means of adjusting the satellite receiver and to allow the owner to order entertainment.

**CCTV Camera Drops:** Pull two (RG-6 Quad Shield) cables and one (18 GA, 2 conductor) cable from the *Distribution Panel* to each camera location. The (RG-6 Quad Shield) cables will provide both video and audio outputs from the camera while the 18 GA cable will provide the camera with DC power. If CCTV cameras provide just video, only one (RG-6 Quad Shield) cable needs to be pulled to each camera location.

**1-35 Sealing and Cable Protection:** Once all of the cables are pulled, check the requirements against the cables installed to make sure all of the cables are in place. The next step is to seal off all of the pre-drilled holes in the top plates of the walls and studs where the cables are pulled through. These holes must be sealed to block conditioned air from flowing up through the wall and into the attic. Holes are also sealed to help reduce the number of entry locations for insects. There may also be pre-drilled holes that were not used during the pulling process, which also need to be sealed up. Use an expandable foam type sealer to fill the gaps between the cables and the pre-drilled holes. This type of sealer comes in a pressurized can that will generally clog-up the applicator tube after use, so when you start sealing, don't stop until the can is empty or it will be wasted. Try and keep the foam off of your hands because it is very difficult to remove unless you are using a latex water-soluble sealer.

**1-36 Trimming-Out the System:** The 'Rough-In' process described in Section 1-30, generally prefers to any work required to install a *Structured Wiring System* prior to the drywall being installed. The Trim-Out process; therefore, refers to any work required after the drywall has been installed. This process includes the following tasks:

1) Testing the conductors.
2) Installing the *Interactive Receptacles* and/or *Service Outlets.*
3) Terminating the *Zone* conductors to each *Interactive Receptacle* and/or *Service Outlet.*
4) Installing the *Service Outlet* faceplates when applicable.
5) Terminating the *Zone* conductors to the appropriate *Zone* Hub.
6) Terminating the *Service* Input Cables to the appropriate *service* entrance enclosure.
7) Terminating the *Service Input Cables* to the *Service Input Hub.*
8) Terminating source cables to sources such as the satellite, TV antenna and CCTV cameras.
9) Terminating the source cables from the satellite, TV antenna and CCTV cameras to the appropriate service entrance enclosure.
10) Connecting the required patch cables to the appropriate Hubs.
11) Terminating all other cables associated with the home control equipment described in Chapters **Two** through **Ten.**

**1-37 Cable Terminations:** To terminate an RG-6 cable to a system component, a crimp-on type F-connector is required. There are also screw-on type F-connectors; however, they are not as secure as the crimp-on type and are generally not recommended. Crimp-on F-connectors are available in either silver or gold coated. The gold-coated connectors are better conductors and are more resistant to corrosion.

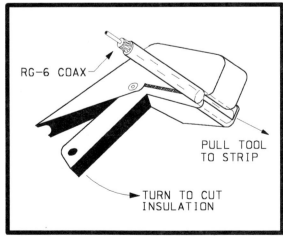

FIGURE 1-43   COAX CABLE STRIPPER

The first step to take when installing an F-connector to an RG-6 cable end is to use a tool called a RG-6 Cable Stripper shown in Figure 1-43. This device is placed over the end of the cable and rotated to allow the internal blades to cut through a layer of insulating material. The cable stripper is then pulled off the end of the cable to strip off the insulation. This process exposes the inner copper core conductor and the silver looking outer braid conductor. Once this is complete, the F-connector is pushed onto the end of the cable while twisting it until the inner copper conductor just clears the end of the F-connector. To hold the F-connector permanently in place, a device called an RG-6 crimping tool is placed over the F-connector sleeve before applying pressure to the crimping handle as shown in Figure 1-44.

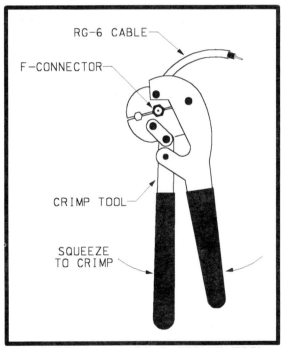

FIGURE 1-44   RG-6 CRIMP TOOL

CAT 5, 4 UTP cables that are used to support the telephone system and Ethernet network are terminated to the rear of the appropriate *Service Input Hub, System Hub, Zone Hubs* and *Interactive Receptacles* or *Service Outlets.* These conductor terminations are typically made to an 8-position snap-in RJ-45 modular connector like the one shown in Figure 1-25. A (CAT 5, 4 UTP) cable is connected to the RJ-45 modular jack by using a device called a Punch-Down Tool shown in Figure 1-45. Once each of eight conductors are positioned over their corresponding blade type connector located in the RJ-45 modular jack, the installer will use the Punch-Down Tool to push each conductor down between the blades that will first strip the insulation before grabbing hold of the conductor.

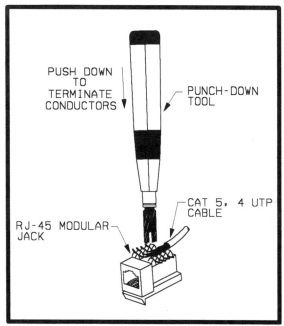

**FIGURE 1-45    PUNCH-DOWN CAT 5**

There is a number of relatively short cables used in each room that need to be fabricated to connect telephones, printers, scanners, and other equipment to the *Interactive Receptacles* or *Service Outlets*. These cables are fabricated from (CAT 5, 4 UTP) cable with an RJ-45 plug connector on each end. The plug connectors are installed using an RJ-45 crimping tool.

*Patch cables* used to direct signals from the *Service Input Hub* to the *System Hubs* and then to the appropriate *Zone Hubs* are terminated to the front RJ-45 modular Hub connectors. These cables can also be fabricated from (CAT 5, 4 UTP) cable with an RJ-45 plug connector at each end as shown in Figure 1-46. The same type of cable is used for IR audio/video control. Four IR-Outputs from the rear panel of the *IR-Xpander* are connected to the rear of the *Service Input Hub* and are identified as IR Output ZN 1, ZN 2, ZN 3 and ZN 4 as shown in Figure 1-11. The routing of these four outputs bypass the *System Hubs* and run directly to the

front modular connectors of the appropriate *Zone Hubs*. Notice in Figure 1-12, how the IR Output for *Zone 3* is patched directly to the front of the Family Room *Zone Hub*. This will allow the IR signals to travel to the *Interactive Receptacle* and out to the IR block before ultimately being received by the audio/video equipment. See Chapter Six for more on IR conductor connections for controlling the audio/video equipment.

There are many other cable terminations to be made when installing a whole house control system. Refer to the following chapters for the cable terminations required to provide specific Home Control subsystems.

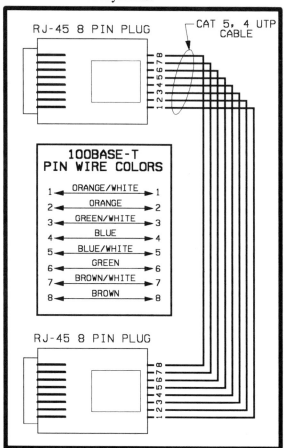

**FIGURE 1-46    PATCH CABLE**

**1-38 System Testing:** Testing the *Structured Wiring System* is always essential in order to provide the customer with a system that will fulfill their expectations and to build the customer's confidence in the dependability of the system. The installer must never install audio, video, telephone, Ethernet or other system devices until the wiring is tested for shorts, grounds, faults and opens.

After all of the cables are pulled in the home and before the system is trimmed-out, continuity checks are often performed to verify whether conductors have been damaged during the installation process. There are a number of wire testing methods used to determine the condition of a cable and whether there are shorts, ground faults or opens. One method used to determine the condition of a cable is to measure the continuity of the conductors. If for instance, the installer is checking a two conductor cable, he would take one end of the cable and twist the two conductors together to create a continuous circuit back to the other end of the cable. On the other end of the cable there will be two wire ends exposed. Using a Multi-Meter, the installer would first select the (0 to 100 Ohms) resistance range and place one test lead on each conductor at one end of the cable. For a CAT 5 cable, if a reading of more than 2.8 Ohms per 100 ft of circuit length is measured, the cable is either damaged or defective. For a RG-6 cable, if a reading of more than 3.5 Ohms per 100 ft of circuit length is measured, the cable is either damaged or defective.

The second method used to test the condition of a CAT 5 or RG-6 cable is to connect a standard 9-volt battery to one end of the cable using alligator clip wire leads as shown in Figure 1-47. Using the Multi-Meter, set the selector knob to a DC voltage = 20V. First measure the battery voltage to have a reference reading. Then place one test lead on each conductor end and read the voltage. If the voltage difference is more than .5 volts per 100 feet of cable length, the cable is either damaged or defective. This method is preferred because the cable ends do not need to be connected together as required in the first method, which avoids having to re-strip the conductors after testing. Some installers prefer the '9-volt battery method' because they can simply touch their tongue to the end of the cable to determine cable performance. We do not recommend the tongue method of testing because a low voltage conductor could possibly be touching a 120V or 240V power source in the attic, which would probably be catastrophic.

As for a ground fault condition, the installer would find a reliable ground connection and perform the following test. One of the Multi-Meter test leads must be placed against a reliable ground while the other lead touches each conductor end at the drop location. If continuity is indicated in any of the conductors, there is a ground fault condition.

To check if there are any shorts, verify that there are no continuity conditions with any other conductor at the drop. This test is performed by placing one of the Multi-Meter leads on one conductor while placing the other lead against each of the remaining conductors at the drop location. If continuity is detected, the first conductor is touching another conductor somewhere along their cable lengths.

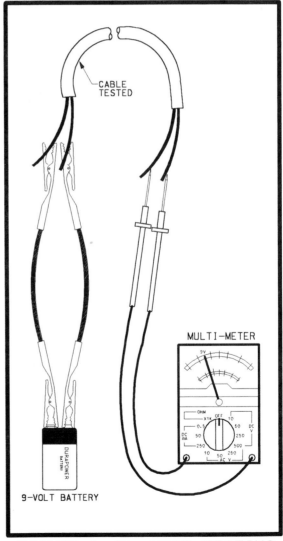

FIGURE 1-47   WIRE TESTING

51

NOTES:

# TWO

# Broadband Internet and Ethernet Networks

**2-1 Introduction:** An Ethernet system is basically a transportation method of carrying groups of data between computers, peripherals and the Internet. The ability to share system peripherals such as printers, scanners, hard drives, CD-RW drives, floppy drives, files, software and other network assets between a number of personal computers located in or outside the home will maximize system resources. The Internet is also playing a major role in our lives by providing vast quantities of information and services at ones fingertips. Stocks can be bought or sold, airline reservations can be made, the whether report can be accessed along with gathering information from the Library of Congress. By utilizing the network's ability to maximize resources, the Internet can be accessed from all computers on the network through one modem. With a network in place, there will no long be a need to transfer copied data from one computer to another using a CD or floppy disk.

An example of utilizing a shared network resource may include daily file back-ups from computer 'A' by placing a copy of files on the hard drive of computer 'B'. Another example may be computer 'A' utilizing software installed on computer 'B' to create a document and then printing the document from a printer connected directly to computer 'B'. These are only a few of the many ways that a network can maximize the home's computer resources, increase user capability and productivity.

**2-2 Ethernet Network:** An Ethernet network generally consists of five elements. The first is the media cable used to convey data between computers. The second is a set of media access codes in each Network Interface Card that allows the computers to access the common Ethernet channel. The third is an Ethernet frame, which is a group of data that consists of a set of fields used to convey data over the network. The forth element is a *Modem* and the fifth is a *Router*. The *Ethernet Hub* or *Router* are used to group computers together at a central location using (CAT 5, 4 UTP) cable. When using Dial-up Internet service an *Ethernet Hub* is used instead of a *Router*. The *Router* is used when *Broadband* Internet service is desired.

Ethernet networks are categorized by how fast information can travel between devices on the network. The speed of a network is described in megabits per second (Mbps). Todays *Ethernet Hubs, Cable Modems* and *Routers* are all capable of supporting (100Base-T) 100 Mbps Ethernet networks. The high speed is beneficial for multimedia, desktop video and other heavy graphics software.

The (CAT 5, 4 UTP) cable used to support a 100Base-T Ethernet system is shown in Figure 2-1. As in all systems used for data communication purposes, it is important that each pair of (CAT 5, 4 UTP) conductors remain twisted together along the entire length of the cable to retain its signal conveying characteristics. Cable conductor colors and RJ-45 connector pin identifiers are shown in Figure 1-46 on page 60. The data signals of a 100Base-T segment are polarized with one wire of each signal pair carrying the positive (+) signals and the other wire carrying the negative (-) signals. Wires are terminated to an eight-pin RJ-45 connector on each end of the cable and when properly configured only four pins of the eight-pin connector are actually used.

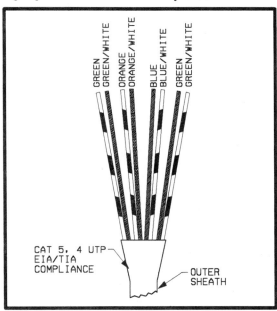

GREEN
GREEN/WHITE
ORANGE
ORANGE/WHITE
BLUE
BLUE/WHITE
GREEN
GREEN/WHITE

CAT 5, 4 UTP
EIA/TIA
COMPLIANCE

OUTER SHEATH

## FIGURE 2-1   CAT 5, 4 UTP CABLE

**2-3 Network Interface:** When using either Dial-up or *Broadband* Internet service, every computer on the network must have a Network Interface Card (NIC), or the capability to interface the network through a built-in option. The NIC is a physical connection between the network cable and the computer's internal bus. A Network Interface Card is installed in a PC by opening up the computer case and plugging the card directly into one of the computer's internal expansion slots.

**2-4 Ethernet Operation:** Each PC or Web TV equipped with a Network Interface Card is designed to operate independently of the other computers on the network. All computers are connected to a shared media system where data is broadcast to every computer on the network. Before sending an Ethernet information packet, the computer attempting to transfer data must first listen in on the network to determine if the network is idle. When it becomes idle, the computer will send the data. If there are two or more computers attempting to transfer data at the same time, these signals will collide. The computers will identify the signal collision and each computer will reschedule their transmission of data at a later time. All computers on the network will work towards avoiding data signal collisions by selecting a random time interval to transfer the data.

**2-5 Topologies:** A 'Home Run' topology is advantageous in an Ethernet network because it provides network reliability, fault detection and a configuration that is easier to troubleshoot. Another excellent feature that the 'Home Run' topology offers is the ability to relocate a network device. This is accomplished by simply disconnecting the patch cable from the *Zone Hub* that serves the device to be removed and reconnect the patch cable to the *Zone Hub* that will serve the network device in its new location within the home.

**2-6 Network Operating Systems:** Network Operating System (NOS) software must be installed on each PC to provide Ethernet network access. This software controls the flow of files, E-mail and other network data. There are two network operating systems to choose from, 'peer-to-peer' and 'client- server'. Both 'peer-to-peer' and 'client-server' network operating systems allow each PC to share hard drive space, printers, files, software and other system resources. Peer-to-peer is great for networks with 16 or less computers, which makes it well suited for some residential and small business applications. The 'client-server' NOS is used for heavy data traffic applications, which is generally experienced by larger networks. The advantages of 'peer-to-peer' over a 'client-server' network operating system are as follows: Peer-to-peer is inexpensive to set-up and maintain and it is also the easiest type of network to construct. The advantages of 'client-server' is its greater speed, greater capability of dealing with heavy traffic on the network and only one modem is required on the network for all computers to use. A significant disadvantage of 'peer-to-peer' is that each computer needs its own modem, support cabling, telephone connection and *Interactive Receptacle* or *Service Outlet* modular jack. An additional cable will also need to be pulled to each computer location from the *Telephone Hub* and an additional *Telephone Hub* may be required if the standard *Telephone Hub* does not have available jacks.

**2-7 Dial-up Supported Ethernet Network:** If the homeowner wishes to use Dial-up Internet service, an eight port Ethernet Hub shown in Figure 2-2 can be used. With this type of Ethernet network one of the computers in the system will need to be assigned as the Server. The Server will allow the other computers on the network to communicate to each other and to access the Internet. Besides being the Server, this computer acts like just another computer on the network. Each computer on the network will need to have an Interface Card. A standard telephone line that enters the home will first be connected to the modem of the Server/Computer as shown in Figure 2-2. From the Interface Card installed in the Server, a (Cat 5, 4 UTP) cable is routed to the Ethernet Hub. This will allow signals to be transmitted and received to and from up to eight other computers on the network. This complete wiring configuration is shown in Figures 1-10 & 1-11.

**2-8 Broadband Internet:** *Broadband* is described as a high capacity high speed network that can carry different services on the same conductors, such as data, voice and video. *Broadband* in regard to the Internet is referred to as bandwidth. The greater the bandwidth,

the faster one can transmit information from one location to another. When using *Broadband* technology, the Internet is 'Always On' and the data transfer speed is dramatically greater than what Dial-up Internet service can offer. Speeds range from between 50 and 900 times faster than Dial-up Internet service. To fully utilize the service offered by a *Broadband* network, all computers connected to the Ethernet network should be able to access the Internet all at the same time.

Although different services can be supported by the same conductors, we recommend in new homes to pull a dedicated (CAT 5, 4 UTP) for DSL Internet service or a separate RG-6 for Cable Internet service from outside the home to the Structured Wiring Panel.

Dial-up Internet service does not provide *Broadband* service and cannot provide the speed required to download large files and images in a reasonable period of time. Dial-up Internet service generally is used with a 56Kbps modem. With Dial-up service installed, multiple computers accessing the Internet at the same time will noticeably slow the system down. Another disadvantage of Dial-up besides the lack of speed is that it ties up the telephone line when in use.

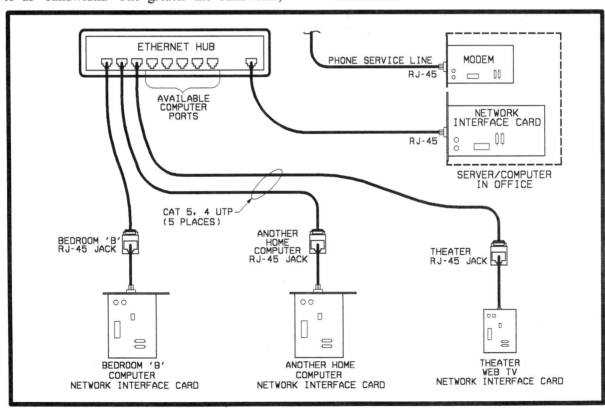

**FIGURE 2-2 OPTIONAL DIAL-UP INTERNET EHTERNET NETWORK DIAGRAM**

For the users to achieve high speed and superior capability, there are number of Internet resources that provide *Broadband* Internet service. The first type is called ISDN, which refers to 'Integrated Services Digital Network'. This service is provided by some telephone companies over (Cat 5, 4 UTP) cable. This particular Internet service transmits data up to three times faster than a Dial-up 56Kbps modem service.

To take full advantage of an Ethernet network supported by *Broadband* Internet service, the Structured Wiring System should be planned to include 'Home Run' topology from the Structured Wiring Panel to all possible locations where a computer or Web TV could practically be installed in the home. The least expensive option is to route RG-6 cable, (Cat 5, 4 UTP) cable and even fiber optic cable before the sheet rock is installed. Even when a homeowner wants *Broadband* Internet service installed in an existing home for one computer, most service providers can install the single service input cable as part of their service. Once this service is installed to serve one computer, the homeowner could develop an Ethernet network for multiple computers using wireless technology. This is accomplished by connecting one computer to a DSL or Cable Modem *Broadband* service and utilize a Wireless AP plus Cable/DSL 4-port Router. This will provide a network that all computers in the home can communicate on while having the ability to use *Broadband* Internet service on all computers at the same time if desired.

DSL refers to 'Digital Subscribed Line', which provides *Broadband* Internet service offered by most telephone or cable TV providers. This option can generally use the existing telephone line to provide data transfer speeds that are 50 to 270 times faster than a Dial-up 56Kbps modem Internet service.

The Cable Modem *Broadband* option uses the same cable that provides Digital cable TV service to the home. This *Broadband* option provides service that is 50 to 900 time faster than Dial-up 56Kbps modem Internet service. At this point in the industry, coaxial copper cable (RG-6) delivers the greatest bandwidth. This has allowed most cable TV providers an easy means of offering *Broadband* Internet access.

*Broadband* and TV cable service is generally offered by the local Cable TV provider as a packaged deal at a reduced price for both services.

Another method of receiving *Broadband* Internet service is from a Satellite company. Hughes Network DirecWay System, of instance, offers this service in 48 states except Alaska and Hawaii at the present time. Satellite *Broadband* service offers speeds up to 8 times faster than 56Kbps Dial-up modem Internet service. One of the requirements in order to receive this service is to have a clear view of the southern sky to transmit and receive signals to and from the satellite. This option is generally selected by homeowners who already have Satellite TV service or homeowners that live in rural areas that are not supported by other *Broadband* Internet service providers. Some Satellite service providers offer high speed downloads, however, they require a regular Dial-up connection for uploads. DirecWay, however, provides a high speed connection in both directions. This satellite dish is an oval shaped 24"x36" unit and is installed along with modem size receiver boxes. One receiver is connected to the USB port of each PC. Similar to other satellite services, a phone line is required to complete the initial registration for reprogramming and for trouble shooting purposes. Except for these short periods of time in use, the telephone line is otherwise free to use for other purposes. The PC should be at least a Pentium II 333mhz or better with a minimum of 64 MB of free hard drive space when using Windows 98SE and Windows ME. 128MB of RAM is required for Windows 2000 and XP. Other requirements include one available USB, a CD-ROM drive, a 28.8Kbps hardware based analog modem or better and 120 MB of free hard drive space.

Cable or DSL modem services are the two methods with the greatest *Broadband* Internet speeds. Cable modem *Broadband* can potentially offer at least one advantage over DSL *Broadband* service. A potential disadvantage of DSL is that the user must be located within 3.4 miles from the office of the service provider where as the Cable Modem *Broadband* Internet service distance is normally not a concern. The farther the user is from the DSL facility the slower the speed. With the exception of fiber optics, cable can potentially provide a faster means of sending data from one location to another.

There is the argument that DSL is not a shared Internet technology, which therefore would make it a better option. The fact is, any type of *Broadband* services is shared from some point along the line of communication. DSL does offer a dedicated connection for a short distance between the home and the service provider's facility. From this point the multiple streams are merged together into one shared network. Some also argue that the coaxial cable located in the user's neighborhood is shared and the more people on the system at one time the slower the speed. Others argue that in reality, it does not matter if a system is shared or not, it is whether the supporting cables provide enough bandwidth to satisfy all the users at any particular time. After researching these two *Broadband* options, we believe in most cases that either one will provide the user with similar speed and capability.

Cable modem *Broadband* service generally costs less than DSL because it is a shared network between the home and the cable company facility. The reason for this is that a coaxial cable running though a neighborhood connected to each home provides service to thousand of customers. A single

component at the cable company's office patches thousands of users to the Internet. As for DSL, it requires a separate pair of wires for each subscriber that already exists in the home phone cable. In addition, the telephone company needs to install a DSL modem for each house hold at the service provider's facility. When it comes right down to it, the cable company can offer their *Broadband* Internet service using much of their existing infrastructure, which is the main reason why they can potentially offer the service at a reduced cost.

Although there are a number of good *Broadband* options that a homeowner can select from, we will concentrate on Cable and DSL Modem Internet service in our 'Example Home' system that follows.

There are many service companies that offer Cable Modem *Broadband* service. One of these companies is 'Road Runner'. With this service the user is provided with a high speed Cable Modem that links a computer to the cable

fiber optic network regional data center. The user can access local news, entertainment information and other information from various computer servers throughout the local area without being on the Internet. These servers are also a gateway for connection to the Internet. Like other types of *Broadband* service, 'Road Runner' is 'Always On'. When the user clicks on an Icon or browser they will immediately be on the Internet. The user does not need to log on or off or dial a telephone number to get a connection. 'Road Runner' does not use telephone lines at all, only the same RG-6 coax cable used to provide Digital cable TV service to the home. Although the same cable can be used for both cable TV and *Broadband* service, we recommend pulling a dedicated RG-6 cable to provide Cable Modem service when a new home is being pre-wired.

This type of service is very versatile because the home occupants can watch a movie on TV, call a friend, check the movie times and locations online all at the same time using one cable. 'Road Runner' information sources include, national and local news, travel, financial, sports, educational and museum exhibits. The user can also watch movies on the computer, listen to music and play video games to mention only a few. Communication services offer E-mail, instant messenger, remote access and personal home page hosting. 'Road Runner' users can also personalize sporting news, weather, and allows the user to access their personalized account from any browser. Users can send instant messages to friends, family, business associates using 'Road Runner' Netscape, CompuServe or AOL® Instant Messenger™. Remote access also allows the user a convenient method to stay on-line and in touch when traveling.

The 'Example Home' *Broadband* plan shown in Figure 2-3, illustrates a computer data system that utilizes a 100Base-T Ethernet network supported primarily by (CAT 5, 4 UTP) cable except for the service input cables. Notice how either a (CAT 5, 4 UTP) service cable supporting DSL *Broadband*, or an RG-6 cable supporting Cable Modem *Broadband* service enters the home and connects to the Distribution Panel or Structured Wiring Panel. From the Structured Wiring Panel to each computer

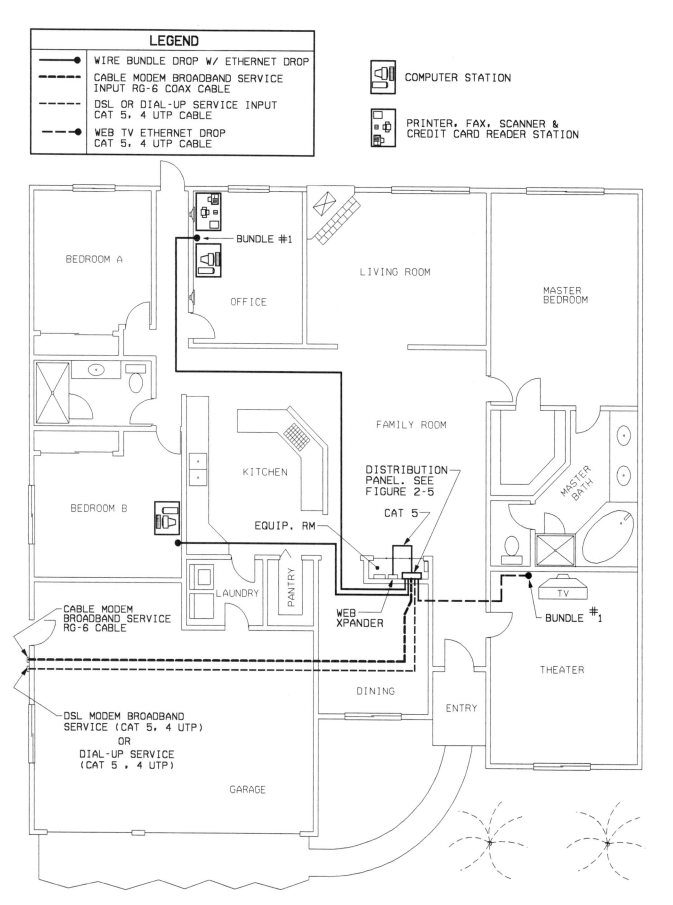

**LEGEND**

| | |
|---|---|
| ●——— | WIRE BUNDLE DROP W/ ETHERNET DROP |
| ●- - - - | CABLE MODEM BROADBAND SERVICE INPUT RG-6 COAX CABLE |
| - - - - | DSL OR DIAL-UP SERVICE INPUT CAT 5, 4 UTP CABLE |
| ●- - - | WEB TV ETHERNET DROP CAT 5, 4 UTP CABLE |

COMPUTER STATION

PRINTER, FAX, SCANNER & CREDIT CARD READER STATION

BUNDLE #1

BEDROOM A

OFFICE

LIVING ROOM

MASTER BEDROOM

FAMILY ROOM

KITCHEN

DISTRIBUTION PANEL. SEE FIGURE 2-5

CAT 5

MASTER BATH

BEDROOM B

EQUIP. RM

CABLE MODEM BROADBAND SERVICE RG-6 CABLE

LAUNDRY

PANTRY

WEB XPANDER

TV

BUNDLE #1

THEATER

DSL MODEM BROADBAND SERVICE (CAT 5, 4 UTP) OR DIAL-UP SERVICE (CAT 5 , 4 UTP)

DINING

ENTRY

GARAGE

# FIGURE 2-3 'EXAMPLE HOME' BROADBAND ETHERNET PLAN

or Web TV location, a (CAT 5, 4 UTP) for either DSL or Cable Modem *Broadband* Internet service is pulled in a 'Home Run' topology as part of the Bundles. These cables lead to each computer or Web TV location identified by black dots that represent a wall mounted *Interactive Receptacle* or *Service Outlet*.

A diagram illustrating the entire home network is shown in Figure 2-4. This layout basically shows the cabling configuration shown on the floor plan, however, in this figure it is much easier to see the required cables and network equipment required.

In this system we use a *FutureSmart* Modem and Router for example purposes as shown in Figure 2-5. Also notice the DSL Modem and Router wiring configuration shown at the bottom of Figure 2-5, which is similar to the Cable Modem installation. This panel illustrates the in-coming Modem *Broadband* RG-6 service cable or Digital TV RG-6 cable connected to the back of the Service Input Hub. An RG-6 patch cable is then connected from the front of the Service Input Hub to the front of the Cable Modem. From the Cable Modem, a (Cat 5, 4 UTP) patch cable connects to the Cable Router as shown. From the Router another (Cat 5, 4 UTP) patch cable is connected to specific Zone Hubs that ultimately connect cables to serve computers, Web TV or the *Web-Xpander*. For homes that incorporate a home automation system, the *Web-Xpander,* which is part of the *Stargate* Home Controller, allows the users to control their home from remote locations such as the users place of work, while on vacation or simply in route to the users residence. The *Web-Xpander* control capabilities will be further discussed in Section 2-9 & 2-10 that follows.

From a wiring stand point the basic difference between Cable and DSL *Broadband* is the Service Input cable type and the patch cable that jumpers signals from the Service Input Hub to the Cable Modem shown in Figure 2-5.

When using Cable or DSL *Broadband,* the patch cables used from the Router to the Zone Hubs and the cables routed to each computer, Web TV or *Web-Xpander* are (Cat 5, 4 UTP) conductors. All cables used to connect network devices to an *Interactive Receptacle* can be fabricated or purchased in the required wiring configuration shown in Figure 1-46.

When using the *FutureSmart* Router, this component safes the user's personal data by protecting the network from hacker attracts. This is accomplished by using a NAT (Network Address Transition) firewall that provides secure protection against hackers. In addition to denying hackers access to the user's network, the system will notify the user by E-mail of any unauthorized access attempts.

Most cable companies charge customers based on the number of computers in a home that will use their *Broadband* service. When a homeowner wants this service installed to ultimately be used by a computer network, he could tell the service provider that service is going to be used on one computer only. The service provider does not need to know there is a Structured Wiring Panel that will be used for distribution. He could also have the appropriate service cable from the outside hooked up to the Service Input Hub. A jumper must also be installed from Service Input Hub to the appropriate Zone Hub so when the installer shows up, the *Interactive Receptacle* or *Service Outlet* at the single computer location can provide DSL or Cable Internet service. If the homeowner originally installed a dedicated service input cable for *Broadband* service, have the service provider connect this cable in the service enclosure located outside the home.

The installer will then hook-up the company supplied external modem and interface card for the one computer. After the installer leaves, the homeowner could disconnect the service provider's supplied DSL or Cable Modem and replace it with the *FutureSmart* Modem and Router as part of the Structured Wiring Panel as shown in Figure 2-5.

When it comes to security concerns, Dial-up, ISDN, Wireless, Satellite, DSL or Cable Modem service can send an receive data to and from any other computer on the Internet. DSL, Cable Modem and Satellite *Broadband* service requires the highest level of security because these systems maintain the service 'Always On'. A Cable Modem *Broadband* service like 'Road Runner', protects their customers by using modems designed to deliver data packets only to the address that has been assigned to the users computer. This prevents the interception of data

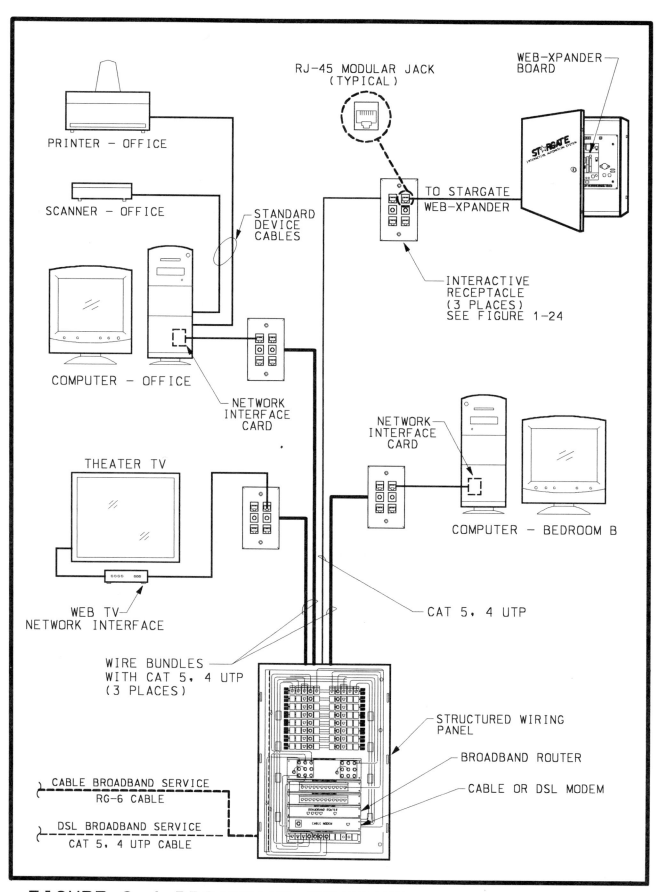

PRINTER - OFFICE

SCANNER - OFFICE

STANDARD
DEVICE
CABLES

COMPUTER - OFFICE

NETWORK
INTERFACE
CARD

THEATER TV

WEB TV
NETWORK INTERFACE

WIRE BUNDLES
WITH CAT 5, 4 UTP
(3 PLACES)

RJ-45 MODULAR JACK
(TYPICAL)

WEB-XPANDER
BOARD

TO STARGATE
WEB-XPANDER

INTERACTIVE
RECEPTACLE
(3 PLACES)
SEE FIGURE 1-24

NETWORK
INTERFACE
CARD

COMPUTER - BEDROOM B

CAT 5, 4 UTP

STRUCTURED WIRING
PANEL

BROADBAND ROUTER

CABLE OR DSL MODEM

CABLE BROADBAND SERVICE
RG-6 CABLE

DSL BROADBAND SERVICE
CAT 5, 4 UTP CABLE

# FIGURE 2-4 BROADBAND ETHERNET NETWORK DIAGRAM

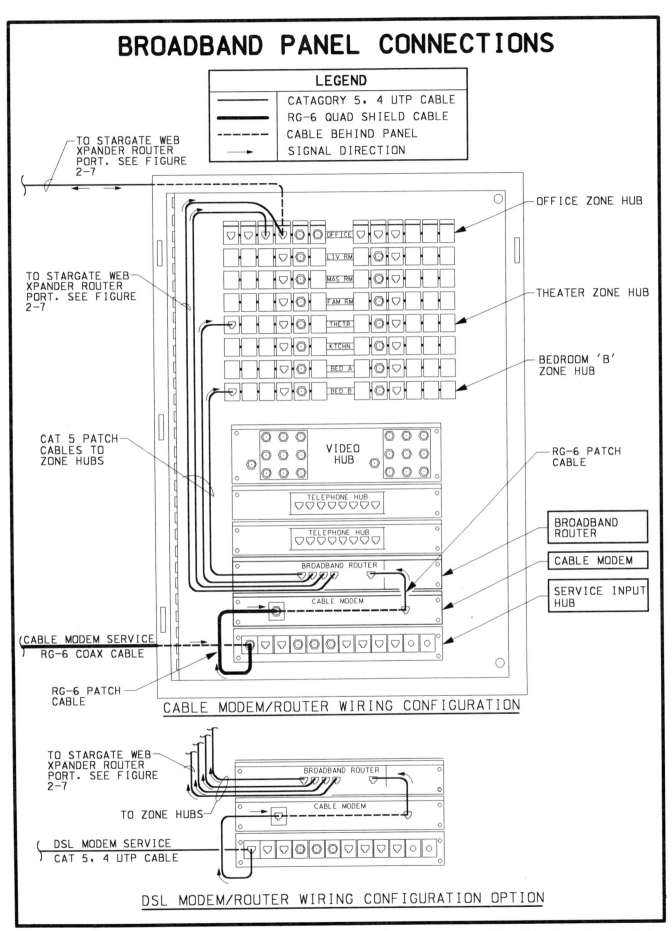

# BROADBAND PANEL CONNECTIONS

**LEGEND**

| | |
|---|---|
| ——— | CATAGORY 5, 4 UTP CABLE |
| ▬▬▬ | RG-6 QUAD SHIELD CABLE |
| - - - - - | CABLE BEHIND PANEL |
| ——➤ | SIGNAL DIRECTION |

TO STARGATE WEB XPANDER ROUTER PORT. SEE FIGURE 2-7

TO STARGATE WEB XPANDER ROUTER PORT. SEE FIGURE 2-7

OFFICE ZONE HUB

OFFICE
LIV RM
MAS RM
FAM RM
THETR
KTCHN
BED A
BED B

THEATER ZONE HUB

BEDROOM 'B' ZONE HUB

CAT 5 PATCH CABLES TO ZONE HUBS

VIDEO HUB

RG-6 PATCH CABLE

TELEPHONE HUB

TELEPHONE HUB

BROADBAND ROUTER

BROADBAND ROUTER

CABLE MODEM

CABLE MODEM

SERVICE INPUT HUB

(CABLE MODEM SERVICE) RG-6 COAX CABLE

RG-6 PATCH CABLE

CABLE MODEM/ROUTER WIRING CONFIGURATION

TO STARGATE WEB XPANDER ROUTER PORT. SEE FIGURE 2-7

BROADBAND ROUTER

TO ZONE HUBS

CABLE MODEM

DSL MODEM SERVICE CAT 5, 4 UTP CABLE

DSL MODEM/ROUTER WIRING CONFIGURATION OPTION

## FIGURE 2-5    CABLE OR DSL BROADBAND ETHERNET PANEL WIRING

packets that can be received. When the system is first installed, specialists will secure files and sharing on the user's computer. The user can also safeguard their computer by using a password. Similar features are offered by the *FutureSmart* modem.

The *FutureSmart* Router allows the user to monitor Web usage and filter out offensive Web content. Other features offer parents restriction options for children usage based on time of day, web address or keywords. These features also send E-mail reports for unauthorized Web page access attempts. This Router also allows the users to share Internet services all at the same time and lets the computers on the network share files, printers, scanners, fax machines, etc. If additional ports are needed for additional computers that need to be on the network, a second Router can be installed.

**2-9 Web-Xpander:** The *Web-Xpander* is a serial (RS-232) to Ethernet module with embedded Web pages that allow monitoring and control of *Stargate* through the Internet and/or local network. From anywhere in the world, the homeowner can adjust the home's HVAC thermostat, check the status of the security system, turn ON/OFF lights or any other control feature built into the home control system. If the home network incorporate a wireless link, the user can enjoy wireless control from their portable pocket PC, webpad or notebook computer.

We do not recommend using Dial-up Internet service at the residence where *Stargate* and the *Web-Xpander* are installed. This residence must receive some type of *Broadband* Internet service that is 'Always-On'. The users, however, can use Dial-up Internet service from a location away from the home to communicate with the *Web-Xpander* for the purpose of making adjustments to the Home Automation System or to simply check the status of the system.

The *Web-Xpander* mounts directly above the Telephone/IVR 'daughter board' using two metal standoffs and fasteners. This configuration is shown in Figure 2-7. There are a number of ways the *Web-Xpander* can be connected to a network. The *Web-Xpander* can be connected to a signal PC using a cross-over cable. The second method is to connect the *Web-Xpander* to a Network Hub, which is connected to one or more PCs. The third method is to connect the *Web-Xpander* to a Cable or DSL Router, which provides Internet access to both the *Web-Xpander* and PCs on the local network. This is the method that is ideal and the one we recommend and use in the 'Example Home'.

In the 'Example Home' wiring configuration shown in Figure 2-7, the RS-232 input port connects to the user's PC Com Port for downloading the schedule to *Stargate*. The RS-232 output port connects to COM-1 port of *Stargate* using a modular cable. The Ethernet port connects to the user's network Router using a standard Ethernet cable and the power terminals connect to *Stargate*'s on-board 12V DC power supply. The connection to the Router can be seen on the 'Example Home' panel shown in Figure 2-5.

The *Web-Xpander* can also provide E-mail support and *Stargate* can be programmed to send E-mail messages in response to any other conditions. If the user's cell phone or PDA is equipped to receive E-mail messages, the user can be automatically notified when the security system status changes (armed, disarmed, alarm, etc.). It can also let the user receive information about temperature in the home or spa, or even the simple reminder to take out the garbage or to take medication.

With the ASCII pass through feature the *Web-Xpander* can pass ASCII data strings from its Ethernet port to its RS-232 serial port to *Stargate*. This allows networked systems to communicate to *Stargate* and enable the use of a wide variety of user interface options that include both hardware and software.

The *Web-Xpander* setup software includes a utility that copies the user's *Stargate* database that consists of X-10, IR, HVAC, Security, I/O, Flags, and Variables from the user's PC and loads them into the *Web-Xpander's* memory. This allows all the user's *Stargate* system devices to be identified by their defined names (Family Room, Master Bedroom, etc.) without having to retype them.

Another feature allows the user to download *Stargate's* schedule over the Internet. This is made possible by downloading an optional software utility called 'COM/IP' from *JDS* Technologies. This software creates a virtual serial port / modem on the user's PC that when dialed actually makes a connection over the Internet. Once this feature is configured the user can use the WinEVM 'Dial PC Modem' function to connect to *Stargate* through the *Web-Xpander*. WinEVM communicates through the virtual modem port created by COM/IP and functions as if the user connected to *Stargate* over a modem connection. All features including schedule downloads are possible in this configuration.

The *Web-Xpander* can also be configured to automatically synchronize *Stargate's* internal clock daily to maintain an accurate time setting.

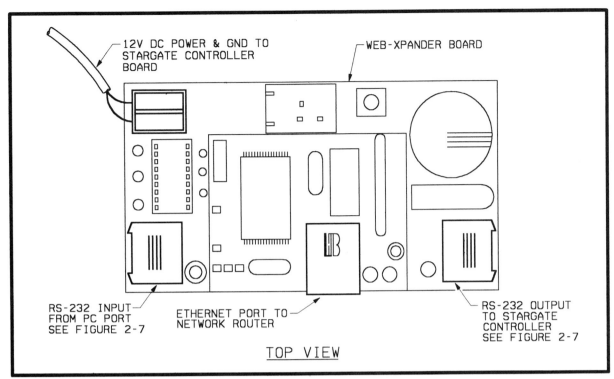

12V DC POWER & GND TO STARGATE CONTROLLER BOARD

WEB-XPANDER BOARD

RS-232 INPUT FROM PC PORT SEE FIGURE 2-7

ETHERNET PORT TO NETWORK ROUTER

RS-232 OUTPUT TO STARGATE CONTROLLER SEE FIGURE 2-7

TOP VIEW

FIGURE 2-6   TOP VIEW OF WEB-XPANDER BOARD. SEE SIDE VIEW IN FIGURE 2-7 SHOWN BELOW.

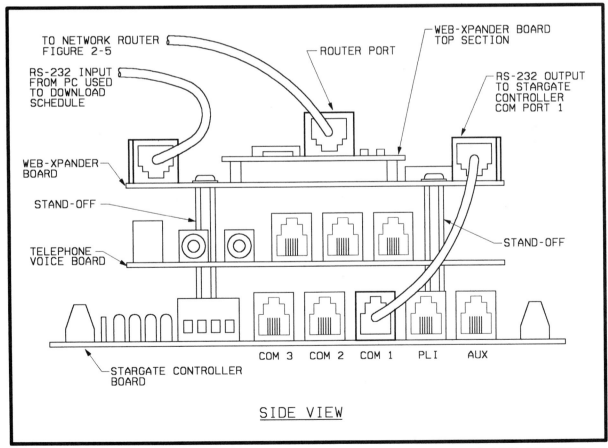

TO NETWORK ROUTER FIGURE 2-5

RS-232 INPUT FROM PC USED TO DOWNLOAD SCHEDULE

ROUTER PORT

WEB-XPANDER BOARD TOP SECTION

RS-232 OUTPUT TO STARGATE CONTROLLER COM PORT 1

WEB-XPANDER BOARD

STAND-OFF

TELEPHONE VOICE BOARD

STAND-OFF

STARGATE CONTROLLER BOARD

COM 3    COM 2    COM 1    PLI    AUX

SIDE VIEW

FIGURE 2-7   END VIEW OF STARGATE. TELEPHONE VOICE AND WEB-XPANDER BOARDS WITH THE REQUIRED CABLE CONNECTIONS.

**2-10** *Web-Xpander* **Software Windows:** The *Web-Xpander's* built-in web page provides an easy to use, point-and-click user interface shown in Figure 2-8 below, which can be viewed and operated from any browser (Internet Explorer, Netscape, etc). Direct access buttons allow the user to navigate through the control menus to control Lighting, Audio/Video equipment, Security, HVAC, X-10, Digital Inputs, Analog Inputs, Relays, Timers, Flags, Variables, ASCII, History, Message Log and Telephone Log. An example look of the lighting control software Windows and others are shown below. Each menu lists devices by their defined names with buttons that display status and provide control. The 'Lighting' menu, for example, lists the defined X-10 lights by name with the ON, OFF or Idle buttons that provide direct control and indicate status. The X-10 button takes the user to the familiar 'MegaController' menu shown on page 67, which lets the user monitor status and control all 256 X-10 addresses on a single screen.

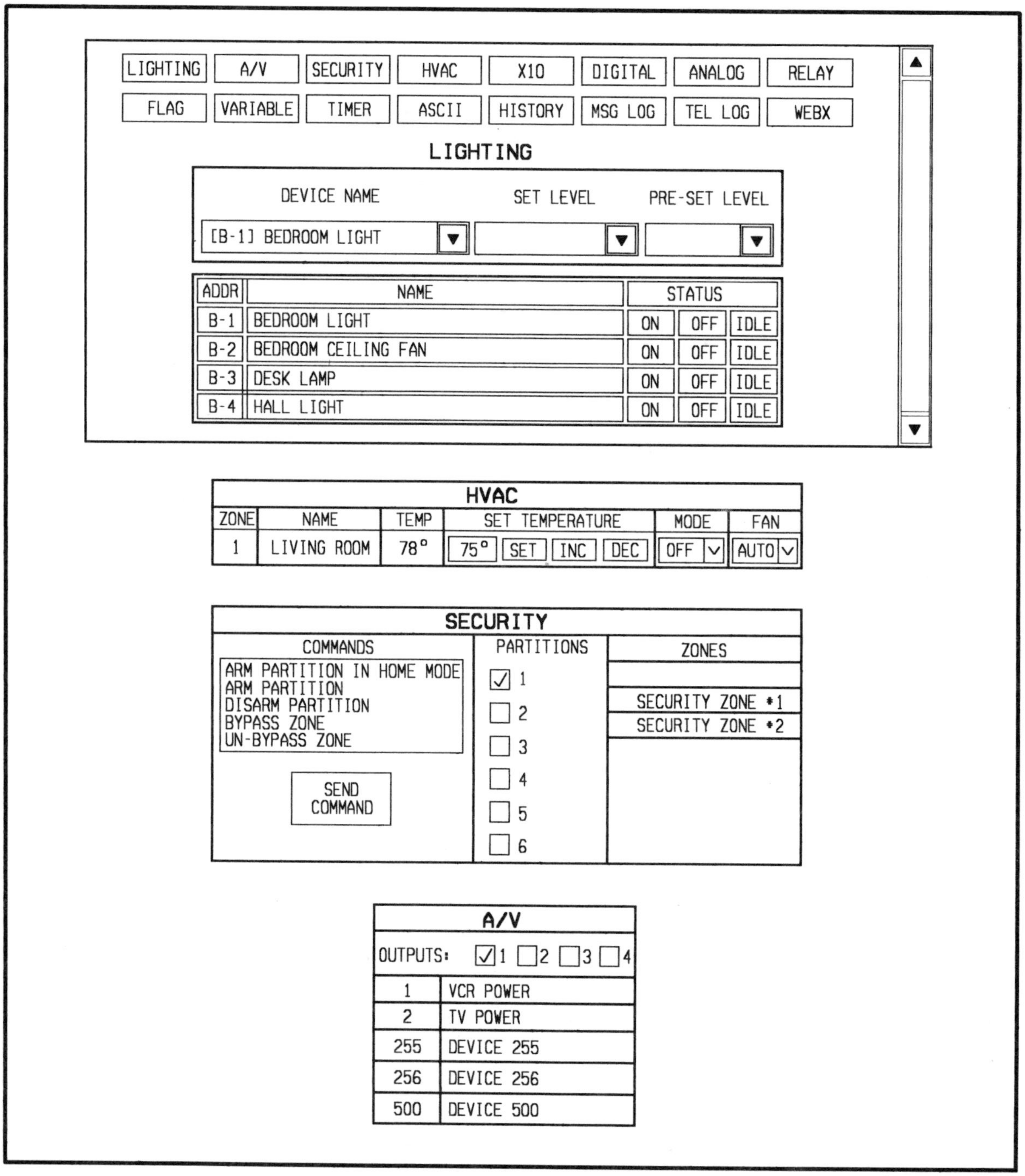

FIGURE 2-8   WEB PAGE CONTROL WINDOWS OF WEB-XPANDER MAIN MENU

## *STARGATE* Home Controller

**3-1 *Stargate:*** *Stargate* is a powerful Interactive Automation Controller that integrates control of numerous subsystems throughout the home. Subsystems controlled may include: Lighting, Security, Heating and Cooling, Entertainment (Audio & Video), Communications, Pool/Spa, Irrigation, Appliances and more as illustrated in Figure 3-1. These systems can be controlled by Home Telephones, Computers, X-10 Transmitters, IR & RF Hand-held remotes, Long range RF Transmitters, LCD Keypads, Touch Screens, Digital Inputs, Analog Inputs, ASCII text, 'Schedule Time' Events, and remotely via phone or Modem.

**3-2 Telephone Control Features:** *Stargate's* two-way telephone controller sends and receives touch-tone signals for optimum control by phone and responds to 'Ring', 'Off-Hook', 'On-Hook' and 'Caller I.D.' signals allowing unlimited communication possibilities. Any combination of telephone signals can be used to trigger Events. For example, dialing 9-1-1 can automatically flash the outside lights to help authorities locate the home. The TV or Stereo can automatically mute when the phone rings and un-mute when the phone is hung up after the call. With Caller I.D., incoming calls from friends and family can be identified and announced by name through

PA speakers or the whole house audio system ("John Doe is calling!"). When the owner is away, the caller can automatically be transferred to a cellular phone (using Telephone Company's 3-Way Calling). When using the 'hookflash' feature, the user can pick up then hang up the phone three times within 6-seconds and the *Stargate* will turn off all the lights. See example programming for 'hookflash', 'Caller ID Announced' and 'Voice Paging' on pages 77 & 78 respectively.

Three different remote access codes can be programmed (up to six digits each) and levels of access assigned. For instance; your personal remote access code can allow complete access to all *Stargate* functions while your neighbor's code may only allow control of the driveway gate and garage door when your away. Calls can be logged for later review. Calls to specific numbers (teens calling boyfriend/girlfriend) can be restricted to certain times of day and duration. *Stargate's* separate phone and intercom outputs allow control via the intercom without interfering with the outside line and vice versa. Two-line phones can be connected to both outputs for maximum flexibility.

The two-way telephone control features of *Stargate,* turns every phone at home or anywhere in the world into a powerful home automation controller. The Telephone Controller works with any touch-tone phone including cordless phones, cellular phones, auto-dialer or voice-dialer. Simple touch-tone commands control virtually any type of electrical load.

*Stargate* supports several formats of touch-tone control. The **90 Code** mode allows control of 90 addresses. * (for ON) or # (for OFF) followed by two digits. The **160 Code** mode allows control of 160 addresses using * (for ON) or # (for OFF) followed by three digits. The **256 Code** mode allows control of 256 addresses, * (for ON) or # (for OFF) followed by four digits. 'NONE Mode' disables touch-tone control. This is useful for applications that require customized touch-tone control programmed specifically for each Event. Theses addresses are normally used to control lighting and appliances using Power-line Carrier technology; however, other systems can also be controlled using these same addresses when used in the 'IF' condition section of a programmed Event.

When incorporating X-10 Power-line Carrier technology to control lighting, the controller provides ON/OFF, Dim & Brighten command codes for **letter** codes A-J & **number** codes 1-9. There are also 10 'All Lights ON' and 'All Units OFF' command codes for **letter** codes A-J.

The phone's memory can be used to activate a series of commands at the touch of a button by storing command sequences in place of phone numbers. The built-in intercom allows the occupants to communicate from room to room using existing phones with no additional wiring or modifications and allows control of the system without tying up an outside phone line. A hold command allows calls to be placed 'on hold' and transferred to other extensions.

An enable/disable code can be used as a local access code to prevent unauthorized control for on premise use. An answering machine override code is also provided. A feature called 'ring command' can be programmed to activate a light or chime when the phone rings, or to mute the TV and Stereo Receiver.

When controlling electrical loads by telephone, discrete confirmation tones acknowledge each completed command. A high tone is an ON acknowledgment. A low tone is an OFF acknowledgment and a warble is for momentary functions.

**3-3 Voice Response:** *Stargate's* built-in Interactive Voice Response feature allows voice prompts (factory presets and/or user programmed) to be issued based on any input condition(s). There are over 600 factory preset responses included with common phrases such as 'ON', 'OFF', 'UP', 'DOWN'. etc, which can be organized into sentences along with custom user-recorded responses. Up to 128 user responses can be recorded from any phone or via line-level input, and directed to any or all of 4 outputs (speaker out, line level out, phone line, or intercom line). This allows for maximum flexibility when setting up voice acknowledgments. Responses can be routed to the appropriate speakers(s) or sound system based on time of day, controller location, or any other condition(s). Custom sounds and messages can be broadcast to the appropriate room(s) for wake-up signals, system status reports, reminders, etc.

**3-4 Two-Way IR Control:** *Stargate* integrates control of TVs, stereos, DVDs, VCRs, and other infrared-operated devices with the optional *InfraRed Xpander*. Audio/video equipment can be controlled by time, X-10, IR, Telephone, Analog or Digital Input and ASCII text. Custom Macros/Modes can be programmed to turn ON power, select sources (AM/FM, TV, VCR, CD, etc.), switch channels, set volume levels, and even closes the drapes and dim the lights all at the touch of one button or at preset times of day. In addition to issuing IR commands, *Stargate* can respond to IR commands, allowing any IR remote to be used as a controller for *Stargate*. For instance; by pressing the 'power' button on the TV hand-held remote, this can initiate the 'Entertainment Mode' that turns ON the TV,

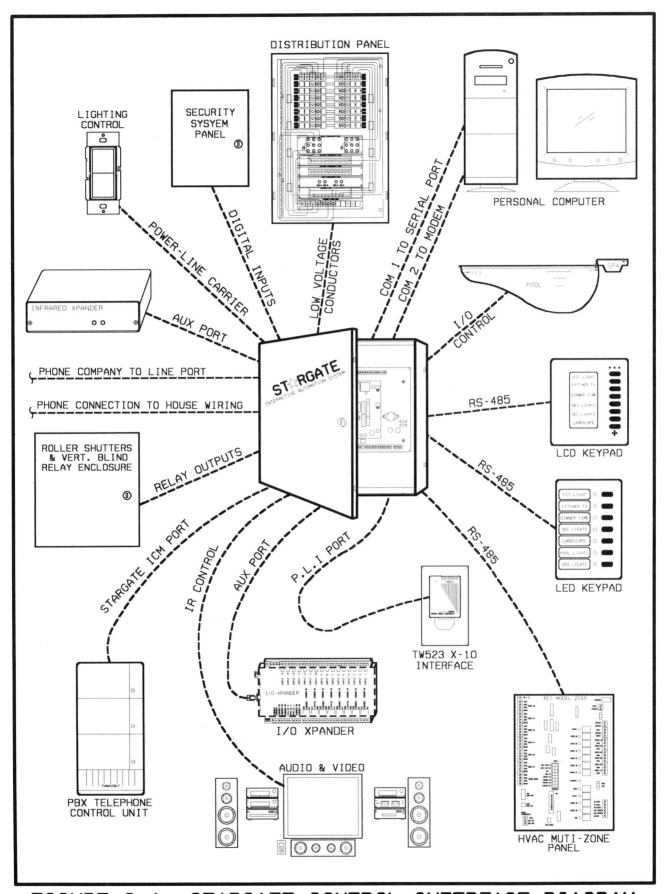

# FIGURE 3-1 STARGATE CONTROL INTERFACE DIAGRAM

turns ON the satellite receiver to channel 70, turns ON the audio receiver and adjusts the volume, dims the lights and closes the drapes. Unused hand-held remote buttons can also be assigned specific *Stargate* functions.

A unique IR sequence feature allows Events to be triggered based on a sequence of IR commands received. For example, pressing the TV mute button 3 times within 5 seconds can dim the lights or perform any other available functions.

*Stargate* stores up to 500 IR commands, which can be issued to any of its *Four-Zoned* emitter outputs. It can also 'repeat' or redirect IR commands to any or all of the *Four Zones*. Optional 'power sensors' can be connected to monitor the ON/OFF status of components (TV, VCR, etc.) regardless of how they are controlled (manually, via hand-held remote, or *Stargate*).

**3-5 *Stargate* Connections:** Wire connections to *Stargate* are shown in Figure 3-2. Communication port 1 (Com 1) connects to a computer (PC) serial port (RS232) to allow the

PC to remotely control the Home Automation System and to Download a Schedule that has been programmed to fit the users requirements. Com 2 & 3 can be connected to a modem (optional) or other serial device.

When incorporating Power-line Carrier technology into a home control system, a device called a Power-line Interface Module (TW523) connects to the (PLI) port of the *Stargate*. This connection allows X-10 communications to be transmitted and received by *Stargate*.

The *Infrared Xpander* and *I/O-Xpander* are connected to the (AUX) port. An *I/O-Xpander* can be added to the control the system when additional Analog and Digital Inputs or Relay Outputs are required. See pages 76 & 77 for more on the *InfraRed Xpander & I/O-Xpander* respectively.

When using *Stargate* with a standard telephone system, the Line Port connects to the phone line from the Telephone Company and the PHONE port connects to one line that serves the phones in the home. The ICM jack can be used with standard single-line phones.

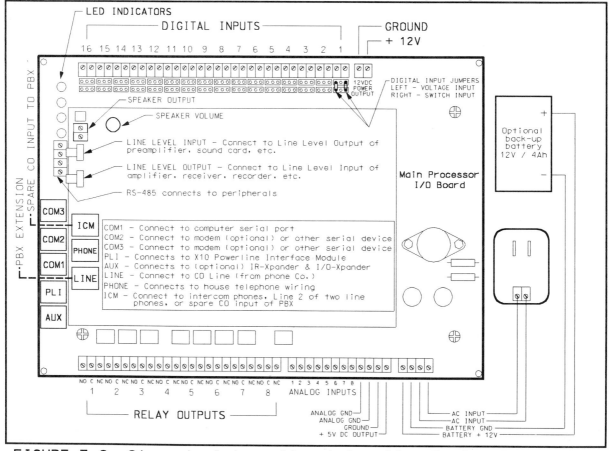

FIGURE 3-2 Stargate Interactive Automation System Controller

Voice responses can be sent directly to the whole house audio system to be broadcast throughout the home. The Line Level Output can be connected to the Line Input of an amplifier, receiver, etc., using a standard RCA-type phono cable. Also notice the speaker output that can directly drive several speakers at normal listening volume. The volume can be manually adjusted by using the volume knob on *Stargate* as shown.

The Line Level input can be connected to a Line Level Output of a sound card, mixer, pre-amp, etc., when the user wants to record their voice response for future broadcasts over the whole house audio system or other speakers.

When *Stargate* is used along with a PBX phone system such as the one used in the 'Example Home', the ICM port connects to a spare CO input to the PBX Telephone Controller. The LINE port connects to a spare station port or extension of the PBX telephone system controller. These phone connections will accommodate several advanced capabilities listed as follows:

**Advanced Telephone Features provided by *Stargate* when used with PBX Phone System:**

1) Any phone station or extension with access to a spare CO line can operate *Stargate* locally.
2) Any CO line programmed to ring at the spare station port can be used for remote access to *Stargate*.
3) *Stargate* can answer and transfer calls to other extensions for automatic call distribution (ACD) and Caller I.D. applications.
4) Voice Responses can be broadcast over the phone system's intercom and paging system.

**3-6 Digital Inputs:** There are a quantity of 16 Digital Inputs available on *Stargate,* which allows expandability to a quantity of 80. There are two types of Digital Inputs that *Stargate* can receive. One is a 'Voltage Input' and the other is a 'Switch Input'. These Input types are selected by manually positioning the jumpers as required. Jumpers are located on the *Stargate's* I/O below the Digital Inputs as shown in Figure 3-2. A Digital Input can be initiated by a contact closure, for instance; from a motion detector or

any other device that provides a circuit closure. When connecting to a set of normally open or normally closed contacts where a low voltage circuit closure provides an 'input range' of 4 to 24V DC or AC (50-1,000 Hz) across a set of I/O Digital Input terminals, one would position the specific jumper to the left (voltage input) as shown in Figure 3-2. These can be alarm panel *Zone* circuits, doorbell circuits, etc.

When connecting to a normally open (N.O.) or normally closed (N.C.) circuit and no voltage is available to the circuit, one would position the jumpers to the right (Switch Input) as shown in Figure 3-2. In this position the *Stargate* senses continuity in the circuit when the circuit is closed and also has the ability to sense that there is no continuity when the circuit is open. If a voltage source is needed, *Stargate's* 12V DC power source may be used. Caution: This power source is rated for 12V DC @ 0.5A. An external power supply must be used when more current is required.

A Digital Input is considered ON when there is sufficient voltage (4 to 24V DC) applied across the two input terminal screws. When there is no voltage differential sensed or if it is below 4V DC, the Digital Input is considered OFF. These inputs can be used in an Event's 'IF' conditions to initiate control of single electrical loads or to activate Macros or Modes of operation when the 'IF' condition(s) is true. For instance; 'IF' Digital Input 3 is ON (DI-3 ON), 'THEN' activate the 'Arriving Mode', which controls many electric loads essentially at the same time. Using Digital Inputs to make control decisions will be shown in various 'IF' condition portions of the example Events beginning on page 70.

**3-7 Analog Inputs:** There are a quantity of 8 Analog Inputs available on the *Stargate* as shown in Figure 3-2. If more Analog Inputs are required, the *Stargate* is expandable to a quantity of 40. An Analog Input from a temperature sensor, for instance; sends a varying 0 to 5 volts to the I/O Analog Input terminals of *Stargate*. This voltage variance communicates to *Stargate* the changing temperature conditions. When the outside air temperature reaches 37°F, for instance; *Stargate* may **Set** a programming 'Flag' that will not allow the sprinkler system to operate during it's normal Scheduled Time Event periods until the temperature is a minimum of 55°F. Analog Inputs connect internally to an 'Analog to Digital Converter', converts analog voltages into a digital representation compatible with *Stargate*. The 'Analog to Digital Converters' are 8 bit (range: 0-255) with an input voltage range of 0-5 volts DC. When *Stargate* reads an Analog Input, it will read a value in the range of 0-255, which represents a voltage from 0-5 applied to the input. For example, an input of 2.5V read by *Stargate* will translate to a value of 128, which is essentially 1/2 of 255. A 1-volt input would translate to a value of 51, which is 1/5 of 255.

**3-8 Relay Outputs:** There are a quantity of 8 Relay Outputs available on the *Stargate* as shown in Figure 3-2. If more Relay Outputs are required, the *Stargate* is expandable to a quantity of 40. The contact arrangement of a typical Relay Output is a single pole double throw (SPDT). Each Relay Output on *Stargate* has three terminals: Normally open (N.O.), normally closed (N.C.), and a common (C). When the relay is ON, the (N.O.) contacts located inside *Stargate* will close and complete the circuit to the common (C). This low voltage circuit closure of less than 24V DC @ 2 amps can be used to

energize a starter relay coil to start a Pool/Spa pump, turn electric water heater ON & OFF or control any other 'high voltage' electrical loads, (ie: 120-240V AC). Even air conditioning air volume dampers can be controlled opened and closed without a slave relay as long as the electrical requirements are not above 24V DC @ 2 amps. A (N.O.) relay is generally selected when there is an application where the system designer prefers the circuit to fail open. On the other hand, a (N.C.) circuit is selected when the designer prefers the circuit to fail closed. For example, in a sprinkler system were the Relay Output opens and closes a solenoid valve for watering purposes, the designer would want the circuit to fail open, which closes the valve to avoid water from running uncontrolled.

**3-9 HVAC RS-485 Connections:** *Stargate* connects to the RCS model ZC6R Multi-Zone HVAC Controller as shown below in Figure 3-3. Notice the (CAT 5, 4 UTP) cable connecting the HVAC panel to the RS-485 interface terminals of *Stargate*. With the compatible version of *Stargate's* Firmware/Software, *Stargate* has the ability to directly access HVAC control functions as well as receive status requests of the HVAC mode of operation (Cooling, Heating, Fan) and temperature within each HVAC *Zone*.

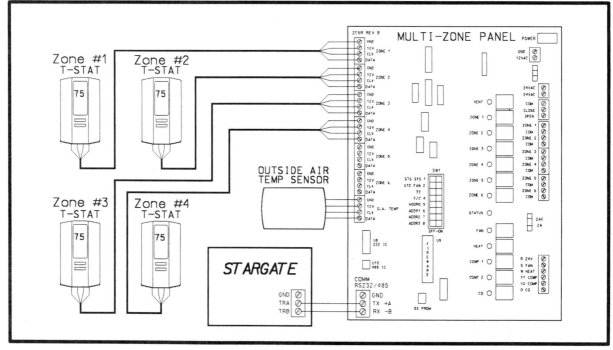

FIGURE 3-3   STARGATE TO RCS HVAC PANEL CONNECTIONS

**3-10 Mega Controller:** The Mega Controller allows total system monitoring and manual control in a single, on screen interactive workspace as shown below in Figure 3-4. The Mega Controller features include the following.

- An Interactive Status Display that displays ON/OFF status of all 256 X-10 addresses and allows manual control of the entire system.
- Control of all 256 X-10 devices if applicable.
- Send Preset Dim and Micro-Dim/Bright commands.
- An activity log that logs and displays date, time, origin, and letter/number/function codes of all X-10, IR and I/O commands as they occur.
- A History Button that recalls system activity of the previous 200 commands for review, file or print out that is an invaluable tool for monitoring or troubleshooting.
- I/O Access that displays status of Digital Inputs and Relay Output and allows direct control of relays.
- Analog Access that reads and displays status of Analog Inputs.
- IR Access that allows manual control of all learned IR commands.
- Telephone Access that allows direct access to telephone dialing functions.
- Access to read Flag status, Clear or Set. Also reads and sets Variable values and also reads Timers.
- Sends ASCII text and plays wavefiles.
- Reads Timers.
- Set or Clear Relays.
- Controls HVAC system.

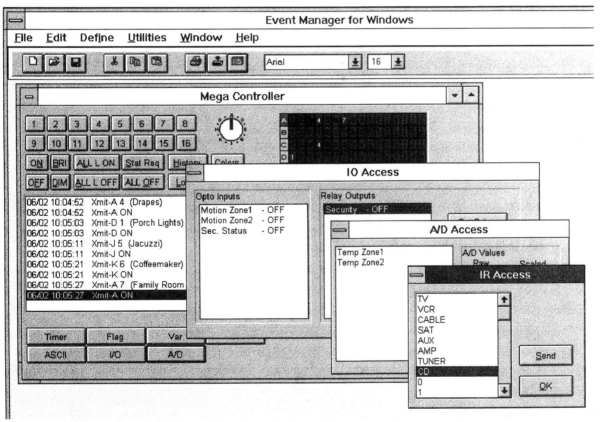

**Figure 3-4  Mega Controller**

67

**3-11 Power Failure:** *Stargate* has a built-in battery backup that allows it to retain its memory in case the house has a power failure, or if *Stargate* is moved to a new location in the home. *Stargate* can also detect when there has been a power failure and can also respond to it. When the power goes out in the home, most of the X-10 type equipment and others will go OFF. When the power comes back ON, *Stargate* may think these devices are still ON, creating an out of sync problem. Another scenario is if during the time that the power was out and the Schedule was supposed to turn a device ON, the *Stargate* will know when the power goes OFF and will perform the following: Play catch-up to the current time and force any X-10 device that has it's Play Catch-up Flag Set, to change to the state it would have been in had the power not gone OFF. *Stargate* will also Set the 'Power-Fail' Variable for use in the Schedule.

**3-12 Programming:** Before programming or creating a Schedule for *Stargate* to use, there are some requirements. The first requirement is to have an IBM PC or compatible computer capable of running Microsoft Windows, with an asynchronous serial port. This computer must also have a 3.5" high-density floppy disk drive for software installation and a hard drive with at least 1.6 mega-bytes available or a high capacity floppy diskette drive. The operating system must also be Microsoft Windows 3.1 or higher, or Windows 95, 98 or 2000.

Once the *Stargate's* software is installed, the user would proceed to the *Event Manager*, which is the user interface that runs on the PC and lets the user create Schedules for use with the *Stargate*. The following flowchart shown in Figure 3-5, illustrates the steps for creating a working Schedule and demonstrates how *Event Manager* works with *Stargate*.

Before beginning the process of writing a Schedule that will be used to control the home, it is recommended that a device database be created. This database will tell the *'Event Manager'* what devices are in the home to control. Devices may be added, changed or deleted from the database at any time. The different types of attributes that the *'Event Manager'* can use are shown below.

---

### *STARGATE ATTRIBUTES:*

- X10 Devices (up to 256)
- Timers
- Time Labels (quantity of 32 )
- Flags  (quantity of 64 )
- Variables  (quantity of 32 )
- IF Macros

- THEN Macros
- IR Commands
- Voice Responses
- Digital Inputs
- Analog Inputs
- Relay Outputs

---

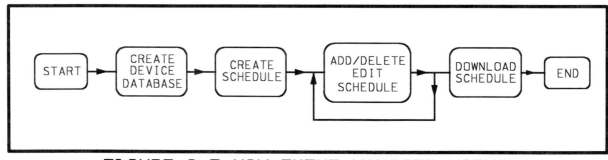

## FIGURE 3-5 HOW EVENT MANAGER WORKS

**3-13 Event Manager Windows:** *Event Manager* is the user interface that runs on a PC and lets the user create Schedules for use with *Stargate*. With *Event Manger*, you can create and edit Schedules that once downloaded to *Stargate* allow total control of the home or office. There are several types of *Event Manager* Windows that the user can choose from based on the type of control being developed. The *Event Manager* environment consists of a Window where Events are developed to produce Schedules that are used to control the home. Only one Window can be active at any time. This will be the Window that the user/programmer is currently working in. *Event Manager* makes it easy to identify the active Window by highlighting the Window title. All Windows will have a title bar, a close box and a status line as shown in Figure 3-6. The 'Title Bar' is the top horizontal bar of the Window that contains the name of the Window. The 'Close Box' of a Window is located in the upper left corner and is used to close the Window. The 'Status Line' appears at the bottom of the Event Manger screen. This area of the screen reminds the user of basic key-strokes and shortcuts applicable at the moment and tells the user what the program is doing. The second line down from the top of a Window consists of the File, Edit, Define, Utilities, Window and Help selections. There are also quick action buttons located on the third line used to begin a new file, open a file, save a file, cut and paste existing text in the Schedule and print a Schedule to describe a few. On the right side of

the Window the user will find buttons labeled [New], [Add], [Edit] and [Delete]. Selecting the [New] button will bring up the New Event box. The user will be able to customize the Event to be an IF/THEN, IF/THEN/ELSE or FAST EVENT type, define the Event's logic type as AND-OR, and insert the new Event before or after the current highlighted Event. To add programming lines to an Event, the user will selected the [Add] button and the type of control function desired. To modify an Event, the user will select the 'EDIT' button in the ToolBox. To Delete an IF Condition or THEN/ELSE action, the user will move the highlight bar to the item that is to be deleted and select the Toolbox 'Delete' button.

**3-14 Creating Events:** An Event consists of an **'IF'** section, which are **conditions**, followed by a **'THEN'** section that are **actions**. When the **'IF'** section is true, the **'THEN'** section is executed. If not, the **'THEN'** section is ignored and skipped over to read the next Event. An Event is created in the *Event Manager* Windows by selecting the (New) button that will bring up the new Event box. The Event Name, Event type (**IF-THEN, IF-THEN-ELSE**, or Always) are entered along with the Logic Type (**AND, OR**). Most of the Schedule building will be in the Window shown in Figure 3-6. There are generally many individual Events that make up a Schedule that ultimately controls the home. See the 'Event Types' and 'Event Logic Type' examples that follow.

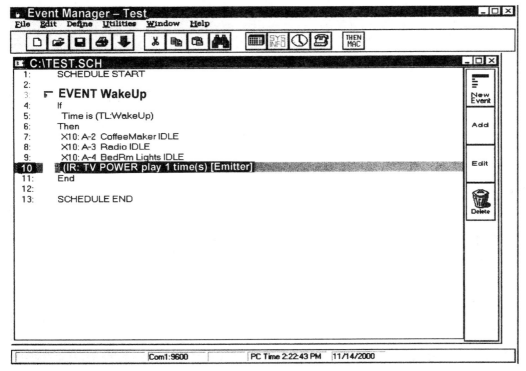

**Figure 3-6 Event Manager Window**

**Event Type:** There are two types of Events, the **IF-THEN** and **IF-THEN-ELSE**

**IF-THEN** *EVENT TYPE:*

> **IF:**
>> condition is true
> **THEN:**
>> do action
**End**

- - - - - - - - - - - - - - - - - - - - - - - - - - - - - - - - - - - - - - - - - - - - - - -

| *Event Example:* | *Description:* |
|---|---|
| **IF:** | **IF** |
| Time = 8:00 AM .MWF. | The time is 8:00 AM Monday, Wednesday & Friday |
| **THEN:** | **THEN:** |
| (RELAY: WELL PUMP) ON | Relay Output will turn ON the sprinkler pump |
| **End** | **End** |

**IF-THEN-ELSE** *EVENT TYPE:*
> **IF:**
>> condition is true
> **THEN:**
>> do action 1
> **ELSE:**
>> do action 2
**End**

- - - - - - - - - - - - - - - - - - - - - - - - - - - - - - - - - - - - - - - - - - - - - - -

| *Event Example:* | *Description:* |
|---|---|
| **IF:** | **IF** |
| Time = 8:00 AM .MWF. | the time is 8:00 AM Monday, Wednesday & Friday |
| **THEN** | **THEN** |
| (RELAY: WELL PUMP ) ON | Relay Output will turn ON the sprinkler pump |
| **ELSE** | **ELSE** |
| (RELAY: POOL PUMP ) ON | Relay Output will turn ON the pool pump |
| **End** | **End** |

- - - - - - - - - - - - - - - - - - - - - - - - - - - - - - - - - - - - - - - - - - - - - - -

*EVENT **LOGIC** TYPE:*
**IF 'AND'** logic type will look like this.....

| *Event Example:* | *Description:* |
|---|---|
| **IF:** | **IF:** |
| Time = 8:00 AM .MWF. | The time is 8:00 AM Monday, Wednesday & Friday |
| and (DI: RAIN SENSOR) is OFF | and the rain sensor does not detect moisture |
| **THEN:** | **THEN:** |
| (RELAY: WELL PUMP ) ON | Relay Output will turn ON the sprinkler pump |
| **End** | **End** |

**IF 'OR'** logic type will look like this.....

*Event Example:*
    **IF:**
        Time = 8:00 AM .MWF.
        or Time = 7:00 AM .SS.
    **THEN:**
        (RELAY: WELL PUMP ) ON
**End**

*Description:*
    **IF:**
        The time is 8:00 AM Monday, Wednesday & Friday
        or the time is 7:00 AM on Saturday or Sunday
    **THEN:**
        Relay Output will turn ON the sprinkler pump
**End**

---

**'AND' 'OR'** logic types can also be used together and looks like the following.....

*Event Example:*
    **IF:**
        Time = 8:00 AM .MWF
        and (DI: RAIN SENSOR) is OFF
    **-OR-**
        Time = 7:00 AM .SS.
        and (DI: RAIN SENSOR) is OFF
    **THEN:**
        (RELAY: WELL PUMP ) ON
**End**

*Description:*
    **IF:**
        The time is 8:00 AM Monday, Wednesday & Friday
        and there is no rain present
    **-OR-**
        The time is 7:00 AM on Saturday or Sunday
        and there is no rain present
    **THEN:**
        Relay Output will turn ON the sprinkler pump
**End**

**3-15 IF Always:** The Event in *Example #1* shown below is an 'IF Always' type of Event. When light 'A1' is turned ON, *Stargate* will send the 'B1' command followed by a 2-second delay, and keep repeating this command as long as 'A1' is ON. This type of Event will keep executing the actions as long as the IF condition(s) stay true. When using 'IF Always' it is recommended that a delay be inserted to allow time for other commands to be processed. In *Example 2*, when 'A1' is turned ON, *Stargate* will send the 'B1' command once, until 'A1' is turned OFF and ON again. This type of Event must see the conditions change before the actions are executed.

*Example #1*
EVENT:
    **IF ALWAYS:**
        (X: Light Foyer  A-1) is ON
    **THEN:**
        (X: Light Hall B-1) ON
        DELAY  0:00:02
**End**

                *if*
        *the Foyer light is ON*
              *then*
        *turn the Hall light ON*
        *Delay for 2 seconds*
        *End of Event*

*Example #2*
EVENT:
    **IF:**
        (X: Light Foyer  A-1) is ON
    **THEN:**
        (X: Light Hall  B-1) ON
**End**

                *if*
        *the Foyer light is ON*
               *then*
        *turn the Hall light ON*
        *End of Event*

**3-16  Nested IF/THEN Events:**  A Nested IF/THEN is an Event within an Event. It can be an 'AND' or 'OR' as well as IF/THEN or IF/THEN/ELSE. The maximum level of nesting is 3. Nesting can be used to simplify a complex set of criteria for doing some action.

In the example shown below, the *Stargate* checks to see if the Living Room light is (ON). If it is, the *Stargate* will then turn the light OFF. If *Stargate* also sees that the TV is OFF, then the *Stargate* will turn the TV ON.

| | |
|---|---|
| EVENT:  Nested Control | *Description* |
| **IF:** | *if* |
| (X: LIGHT LIVING A10)  is ON | *Living Room light is ON* |
| **THEN:** | *then* |
| (X: LIGHT LIVING A10)  is OFF | *Turn Living Room light OFF* |
| **End** | *End* |
| **IF:** | *if* |
| (DI: TV 1) is OFF | *TV is OFF* |
| **THEN:** | *then* |
| (DI: TV 1) is ON | *Turn TV ON* |
| **End** | |

**3-17  X-10 Devices:**  In the 'Example Home' we concentrate on Structured Wiring of a typical residential home, which includes a variety of subsystems for control of the home's lighting and appliances. The *Stargate* does provide the capability of supporting an X-10 Power-Line Carrier system. This will allow the Home Control System to incorporate this technology into the home in full or in part.

**3-18  Date and Time Conditions:**  A Time Condition is a time used to make something happen. When used in a Schedule, *Stargate* will compare the current time of day to the time that is chosen. One can select from a number of menu choices such as: **Equal** to, **Before**, or **After** a particular time and on particular days of the year.

| | |
|---|---|
| *Event Example:* | *Description:* |
| EVENT:  Christmas Lights | *Name of Event* |
| **IF:** | *if* |
| Date is After Dec 11 | *date is after December 11* |
| and Time is After 8:00 PM .SMTWTFS. | *and the Time is after 8:00 PM Sunday - Saturday* |
| **THEN:** | *then* |
| (X: LIGHTS CHRISTMAS J-5)  ON | *Turn Christmas lights ON* |
| End | |

**3-19  Timers:**  Timers are countdown timers, meaning if a time period is loaded, it will count down to zero. A Timer can be loaded with a value and started and stopped from within a Schedule. Each Timer counts down in 1-second intervals and can be loaded with a maximum time of 18 hour, 12 minutes and 16 seconds. There are 4 states that a Timer can be in: **Expiring**, **Running**, **Stopped**, and **Cleared**. A Timer is Expiring when it changes from 00:00:01 to 00:00:00. A Timer is **Running** while it is counting down. A Timer can be **Stopped** by using the Timer Stop Action in an Event or after the Timer reaches the Expiring state. A Timer is **Cleared** after every Schedule download.

All Timers need to be added to the database by opening the 'Timer Define Window' and defining each Timer. Timers are generally added to the database during the building process of an Event.

## *Timer Programming Example:*

This Event called 'ALL LIGHTS OFF', loads 'Timer 2' to turn OFF all lights 15-minutes from the moment a button is press on a *JDS* Keypad. The example programming looks like this:.....

| *Event Example:* | *Description:* |
|---|---|
| EVENT:  ALL LIGHTS OFF | *Name of Event* |
| **IF:** | *if* |
| (ALL LIGHTS 1)  OFF | *all lights '1' OFF is selected* |
| **THEN:** | *then* |
| (T: TIME 2 )  LOAD with 0: 15:00 | *Timer 2 is started and appears below* |
| End | |

**Note**: The next programming EVENT would look like this.....

| *Event Example:* | *Description:* |
|---|---|
| EVENT:  TIME 2 | *Name of Event* |
| **IF:** | *if* |
| (T: TIME  2 )  is Expiring | *Timer 2 has no time left* |
| **THEN:** | *then* |
| (X: ALL LIGHT)  OFF | *Turn all lights OFF* |
| End | *End of Event* |

**3-20 Time Labels:** A Time Label is a time with a descriptive name assigned to it. An example would be assigning the time 6:00 AM to the name 'Wakeup'. The Schedule can then refer to 'Wakeup' anywhere that a 6:00 AM time would be used in the Schedule. If the time needs to be changed and the time is used often in the Schedule, it would be useful to use a Time Label. This way, when the time is changed in the Time Label, all references to that label will also change. All Time Labels need to be added to the database by opening the 'Time Label Define Window' and proceed by defining each Time Label. Time Labels are generally added to the database during the building process of an Event.

| EVENT: | *Name of Event* |
|---|---|
| **IF:** | *if* |
| ( WAKE UP ) | *Time is equal to 6:00 AM* |
| **THEN:** | *then* |
| (X: LIGHT BEDROOM D-5 )  Pre-set Level 25% | *Turn the Bedroom light ON to 25% bright* |
| End | *End of Event* |

**3-21 Time/Delay:** Time Delays are used to delay the *Stargate* from reading the next programming line in the THEN statement. In the following example, the Hallway light is turned ON and then turned OFF after 5-minutes.

| EVENT:  Hall Light ON/OFF | *Name of Event* |
|---|---|
| **IF:** | *if* |
| (DI: HALL ) goes ON | *Motion is detected in the Hallway* |
| **THEN:** | *then* |
| (X: LIGHT HALL C-5 )  ON | *Turn the Hall light ON* |
| DELAY  0:05:00 | *Delay for 5 minutes* |
| (X: LIGHT HALL C-5 )  OFF | *Turn the Hall light OFF* |
| End | *End of Event* |

73

**3-22 Flags:** A Flag is a variable that has two states: **Set** and **Clear**. Any Event can **Set** or **Clear** a Flag as well as check the state of the Flag. Flags are very useful for communication between Events or assigning a global variable throughout the Schedule such as 'Away'. This means that during the period of time the homeowner is 'Away', certain Events such as the 'Deterrent Mode' have the potential to run. All Flags need to be added to the database by opening the 'Flags Window' and proceeding to define each Flag. Flags are generally added to the database during the building process of an Event. In the Example programming shown below, the 'Away' Flag is **Set** as part of the 'Leaving Mode'. This **Set** state is recognizes by the '**IF**' condition of the 'Deterrent Mode' shown below.

| | |
|---|---|
| *Event Example:* | *Description:* |
| EVENT: **LEAVING MODE** | *Name of Event* |
| **IF:** | *if* |
| (LEAVING) | *Initiate 'Leaving Mode' from Foyer JDS keypad* |
| **THEN:** | *then* |
| (F: AWAY) SET | *Sets the 'Away' Flag* |
| All the rest of the lines of programming in this Event | |
| "          "          "          " | |
| End | *End of Event* |

| | |
|---|---|
| EVENT: **DETERRENT MODE** | *Name of Event* |
| **IF** | *if* |
| (DI: 7 MOTION 4) is ON | *Motion sensor 4 (Digital Input) detects motion* |
| and (F: AWAY ) is Set | *and the 'Away' Flag is Set* |
| **THEN** | *then* |
| (X: LIGHT KITCHEN B-5 ) ON | *Turn Kitchen light ON* |
| All the rest of the lines of programming in the Event | |
| End | *End of Event* |

**Note:** The 'Deterrent Mode' is designed to turn ON lights, TVs, Stereos, etc., when the homeowner is away to make the house look like someone is there. This Mode is initiated when motion sensor #4 detects someone on the property only when the 'Away' Flag is **Set**. This means that both conditions have to be true before the Mode will run. Notice the 'Leaving Mode' **THEN** statement shown above. This **Sets** the 'Away' Flag and only when this Flag is **Set**, will the 'Deterrent Mode' have the potential to Run.

**3-23 Variables:** A Variable can have a value that ranges from 0 to 255. Variables can be incremented, decrement, loaded with a value and cleared. Variables are useful when you need to base decisions on reoccurring conditions and can be used to trigger other Events. An example would be to count the number of times the doorbell was activated. After 12 people or more have come to the front door the *Stargate* will notify the homeowner on arrival with a Voice Response broadcast over the Whole House Audio System. This is accomplish by opening the Variable Window, naming the Variable (doorbell), typing in the compare value (12), selecting 'value' and then selecting 'Greater Than or Equal to' ( > = ) options.

| | |
|---|---|
| *Example Event:* | *Description:* |
| EVENT: **DETERRENT MODE** | *Name of Event* |
| **IF:** | *if* |
| (DOORBELL) > = 12 | *Variable is more than or equal to 12* |
| **THEN:** | *then* |
| (VOICE: "12 Visitors today" ) | *Voice response over Audio system* |
| End | *End of Event* |

**3-24 IF Macros:** An 'IF Macro' is a series of 'IF' conditions, and the logic type associated (AND/OR). The 'IF' conditions are entered into the Macro the same way as Events. Each 'IF Macro' can be used in a Schedule any number of times. 'IF Macros' are useful when the same set of 'IF' conditions are used in more than one Event. By defining a set of 'IF' conditions as an 'IF Macro' and replacing those repeated conditions, the size of the Schedule can be reduced and can make it more readable. See the example 'IF Macro' called 'Dark Weekdays' shown below.

| | |
|---|---|
| *Example Event:* | *Description:* |
| IF MACRO (*Dark Weekdays*) | *IF Macro 'Name'* |
| MACRO BEGIN | *Beginning of Macro* |
| **IF:** | *if* |
| After SunSet .MTWTF. | *After Sunset Monday - Friday* |
| or Before SunRise .MTWTF. | *or before Sunrise Monday - Friday* |
| **MACRO END** | *End of Macro* |

| | |
|---|---|
| *Example Event:* | *Description:* |
| EVENT: (Evening) | *Name of Event* |
| **IF:** | *if* |
| IF MACRO (*Dark Weekdays*) | *Short for IF Macro shown above* |
| **THEN:** | *then* |
| (X: LIGHT PORCH G-5) ON | *Turn porch light ON* |
| (X: LIGHT LANDSCAPE G-6) ON | *Turn landscape lighting ON* |
| End | *End of Event* |

**Note:** Notice how the 'IF Macro' (Dark Weekdays) is used in short to represent the long version.

**3-25 Then Macros:** A **THEN** Macro is a series of **THEN** actions. The **THEN** actions are entered into the Macro the same way THEN and ELSE actions are in the Event Editor. Each **THEN** Macro can be used in a Schedule any number of times. **THEN** Macros are similar to IF Macros, except they use action statements instead of condition statements. **THEN** Macros are useful when the same set of actions are used over and over again in different Events within a Schedule.

| | |
|---|---|
| *Example Event:* | *Description:* |
| THEN MACRO (*All Lights OFF*) | *Name of Event* |
| MACRO BEGIN | *Beginning of Macro* |
| (X: LIGHT BEDROOM E-5) OFF | *Turn Bedroom light OFF* |
| (X: LIGHT KITCHEN B-5) OFF | *Turn Kitchen light OFF* |
| (X: LIGHT DINING C-5) OFF | *Turn Dining Room light OFF* |
| **MACRO END** | *End of Macro* |

| | |
|---|---|
| *Example Event:* | *Description:* |
| EVENT: Good Night | *Name of Event* |
| **IF:** | *if* |
| 10:00 PM .SMTWTF. | *10:00 PM Sunday through Friday* |
| **THEN:** | *then* |
| (THEN MACRO ALL LIGHT OFF) | *Short for All Lights ON Macro shown above* |
| End | *End of Event* |

**3-26 IR-Xpander:** The *IR-Xpander* is an optional 2-Way learning IR controller that provides centralized control of audio/video, home theater and other infrared controlled equipment throughout the home. In the 'Xpander Mode', which is how this controller is used in the 'Example Home', the *IR-Xpander* connects to the AUX port of the *Stargate* shown in Figures 3-1 & 3-2. The *IR-Xpander* has a capacity of 250 commands and is expandable to 500 commands when attaching the 250 command module. The *IR-Xpander* has four separate *Zone* emitter outputs to distribute IR commands to multiple rooms. This allows individual control of multiple TVs, VCRs, etc. including audio/video components that respond to the same IR command codes. This is a powerful feature because many homeowners are prone to purchase the same brands of audio/video components that use the same IR codes throughout the home. Each port has the ability to drive up to a maximum of 4 standard IR emitters. More emitters can be used in each *Zone* when using an amplified connecting block. IR emitters are plugged into 1/8" diameter output jacks located on the rear panel. The system can be programmed to issue any combination of IR commands in response to any input conditions such as time, X-10 commands, IR, Analog or Digital Inputs, as well as ASCII text communications.

In the 'Serial Mode', the *IR-Xpander* connects directly to a serial port. It can be operated from any computer capable of sending/receiving ASCII commands via RS-232. The *IR-Xpander* can also respond to IR commands received from any IR hand-held remote. For example, pressing the TV power button on an IR remote can initiate a MACRO that closes the drapes, dims the lights, turns ON select audio/video equipment or perform any other home control function.

Optional power status sensors can be connected to the *IR-Xpander* to report ON/OFF status of up to 4 components regardless of how the equipment is turned ON (via hand-held remote or manually).

The *Event Manager* software includes an IR setup menu that simplifies the learning and programming of IR commands into the Schedule. Once IR commands are defined in the IR setup menu, the 'learn' button is clicked and the *Event Manager* prompts when the hand-held remote needs to be aimed while the appropriate buttons are pressed.

The *IR-Xpander* is defined by clicking on the desired device, which will open a Window. By selecting 'IR-Xpander' and checking the enable box, *Stargate* will know which device to read and write to.

IR commands instruct the *IR-Xpander* to issue an IR command defined in the Define IR menu. IR commands are defined by selecting 'IR Commands', which will open up this Window. The emitter outputs are then given a name such as Living Room, Family Room, Master Bedroom & Guest Room for addressing purposes.

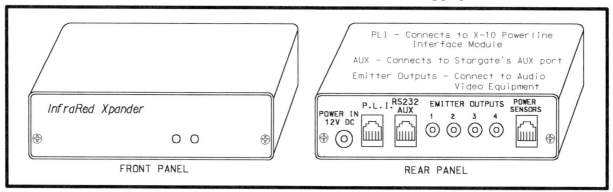

FIGURE 3-7 InfraRed IR-Xpander Controller

*Example Event:*
EVENT: **MASTER BED A/V**
  **IF:**
    (IR: TV ) play 1 time(s) [ Master Bed ]
  **THEN:**
    (IR: TV ) play 1 time(s) [ Master Bed ]
    (IR: REC # 2 ) play 1 time(s) [ Theater ]
    (IR: TV-AUDIO ) play 1 time(s) [ Theater ]
End

*Description:*
*Name of Event*
*if*
*TV button on IR remote is pushed*
*then*
*Turn Master Bedroom TV ON*
*Turn Rec #2 ON*
*Select **tv-audio** mode on Rec #2*
*End of Event*

**3-27 IO-Xpander:** The *IO-Xpander* is an optional control device that is used when additional Analog and/or Digital Inputs are required as well as Relay Outputs. This device provides 8 Analog Inputs, 16 Digital Inputs and 8 Relay Outputs. The *IO-Xpander* connects to the AUX port of the *Stargate* shown in Figure 3-8.

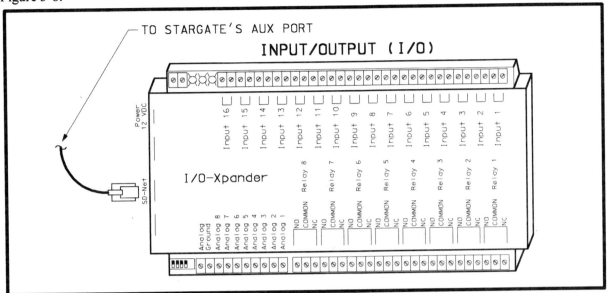

## FIGURE 3-8 I/O-XPANDER

| *Example Event #1:* | *Description:* |
|---|---|
| EVENT: **WATER ZONE 1** | *Name of Event* |
| **IF:** | *if* |
| (DI: RAIN SENSOR) is OFF | *the rain sensor (Digital Input) does not detect moisture* |
| **THEN:** | *then* |
| (RELAY: WELL PUMP ) ON | *Relay Output will turn ON the sprinkler pump* |
| End | *End of Schedule* |

| *Example Event #2:* | *Description:* |
|---|---|
| EVENT: CLOSE VERTICALS | *Name of Event* |
| **IF:** | *if* |
| (A/D: TEMP VRT 1 ) > 95 | *If Analog temp is more than 95°F* |
| **THEN:** | *then* |
| (RELAY: VERTICAL 1 ) ON | *Relay Output will close Verticals* |
| End | *End of Schedule* |

**3-28 Telephone Control:** *Hookflash Mania:* With this Event, if the user picks up then hangs up the phone 3-times within 6 seconds, the *Stargate* will turn all the lights OFF. ( ^ ) = Pick up, ( + ) = Hang up

*Example Event:*
EVENT: HOOKFLASH MANIA
  **IF:**
    Telephone Seq: ' ^ + ^ + ^ + ' is received within 6 seconds
  **THEN:**
    (THEN MACRO:) All Lights Off
**End**

**3-29 Caller ID Announce:**  In the following example, *Stargate's* Caller ID identifies an incoming call and announces the caller through a speaker. It then answers the call and plays a message to the caller. An On-Hook signal is issued after 3 minutes to prevent *Stargate* from tying up the CO line.

*Example Event:*
EVENT:  CALLER ID PAUL
  **IF:**
    Caller ID:  805-555-1212
  **THEN:**
    Voice: "It's PAUL, Pick Up" [SPEAKER ]
    Telephone: OFF-HOOK
    Voice: "Hi PAUL, hold on, I'll be right there" [ CO Line ]
    Delay 0:03:00
    Telephone: ON-HOOK
**End**

---

**3-30 Voice Paging:**  In this example, picking up the phone (^), then pressing *72 will connect the Intercom to the Speaker Output to allow live voice paging until the phone is hung up (+)

*Example Event:*
EVENT:  ACTIVATE PAGING
  **IF:**
    Telephone Seq:  ' ^ *72 ' is received within 3 seconds
  **THEN:**
    (AUDIO PATH: Connect Intercom to Speaker Output)
**End**

EVENT:  DE-ACTIVATE PAGING
  **IF:**
    Telephone Seq:  ' + ' is received within 1 seconds
  **THEN:**
    (AUDIO PATH: Disconnect Intercom to Speaker Output)
**End**

---

**3-31 Long Distance Call Alert:**  With this Event, picking up the phone ( ^ ), then pressing '1' followed by any ten touch-tone digits (9468175987) within 15 seconds will turn designated lights ON for 5 seconds to indicate that a long distance call is being made. This may be useful to monitor, for instance; teenagers who make to many long distance phone calls.

EVENT:  LONG DISTANCE CALL ALERT
  **IF:**
    Telephone Seq:  ' ^ 19468175987' is received within 15 seconds
  **THEN**
    (X: LAMP LIVING A-5) ON
    Delay 0:00:05
    (X: LAMP LIVING A-5) OFF
**End**

**3-32 Reporting Temperature to a Pocket Pager:** In the following example, if the inside temperature exceeds 80°F, *Stargate* dials a pager (goes off-hook and dials 123-4566), waits 6 seconds for the paging service to answer (3 commas), then dials the temperature (< TEMP >) followed by the pound sign (#) to complete the page and then hangs up (+). The temperature will then appear on the pocket pager display!

EVENT:   CALL PAUL'S PAGER
   **IF:**
      (Analog In: TEMP) > 80
   **THEN:**
      Telephone Out: ' ^ 123-4567,,, < TEMP > # +'
**End**

---

**3-33 Remote Voice Paging:** In the following example, the *Stargate* Line Level Output is connected to the PA amplifier with speakers throughout the premises. User 1 calls home remotely, then enters the Remote Access Code followed by **\*72** to allow live voice paging through the home's PA system or whole house audio system. The voice prompt "Paging Access ON" is sent to the CO Line to signal 'User 1' that his/her voice is about to be broadcast throughout the home. The Audio Path between the CO Line and Line-Level Output is then connected for 15 seconds during which 'User 1' speaks his/her announcement. The Audio Path between the CO Line and Line-Level Output is then disconnected and the voice prompt "Paging Access OFF" is then sent to the CO Line to signal 'User 1'.

EVENT:   REMOTE VOICE PAGING
   **IF:**
      (Remote Access – User 1 )
      and ( Telephone: \*72 ) is received within 3 seconds
   **THEN:**
      (Voice: "Paging Access ON")  [CO Line]
      (AUDIO PATH: Connect CO Line to Line Level Output)
     Delay 0:00:15
      (AUDIO PATH: Disconnect CO Line to Line Level Output)
      (Voice: "Paging Access OFF")  [CO Line]
**End**

---

**3-34 Remote Audio Monitoring (Listen In):** In the following example, a hidden microphone is connected to a pre-amplifier, the output of which is connected to *Stargate's* Line-Level Input. User 1 calls home, then enters a Remote Access Code followed by \*54 to remotely monitor sound in the home for 30 seconds.

EVENT:   REMOTE LISTEN IN
   **IF:**
      Telephone – Remote User 1
      and ( Telephone: \*54 ) is received within 3 seconds
   **THEN:**
      (AUDIO PATH: Connect Line Level Input to CO Line)
     Delay 0:00:30 (Retriggerable)
      (AUDIO PATH: Disconnect Line Level Input to CO Line)
**End**

**3-35 Recording Messages From Identified Caller**: In the following example, *Stargate* answers calls from a specific caller (identified by Caller ID) and prompts them to press '1' to leave a message.

EVENT:  RECORD PAUL
    **IF:**
        Caller ID  805-555-1212
    **THEN:**
        Voice: "Hi Paul, press 1 to leave a message" [CO Line]
    **IF:**
    Telephone Seq: '1' received within 15 seconds
    **THEN:**
    Record: 'Paul's Message' from CO Line for 20 seconds
    **End**
**End**


**3-36 Recording (Or Changing) Message Remotely by Phone:**  With the following Events, 'User 1' can call home, enter his/her Remote Access Code, then press **R-E-C (\*732)** to record or change a message that will playback through speakers at home as soon as someone arrives such as "Call me at the office as soon as you get home."

EVENT:  ARRIVE MESSAGE RECORD
    **IF:**
        Telephone – Remote User 1
        and ( Telephone Seq: '\*732' received within 10 seconds
    **THEN:**
        Record: Arrived Message from CO Line for 20 seconds
**End**

EVENT:  ARRIVE MESSAGE PLAYBACK
    **IF:**
        (DI: Armed) Goes OFF
    **THEN:**
        Voice: Arrived Message [SPEAKER]
**End**
        **Note:** *Stargate* can also be used as an answering machine.


**3-37 ASCII Input:** Programs other than the Event Manager can send ASCII text to the serial port of *Stargate* to trigger Events. The ASCII text can be up to 32 characters in length and must be terminated with a carriage return. The ASCII text sent to *Stargate* must match exactly (upper/lower case, spaces, etc.) as the ASCII-In statement used in the Event.

In the example shown below, the ASCII text 'Open Gate' is sent to *Stargate,* which will trigger the Event to open the driveway gate.

EVENT:  ASCII IN GATE
    **IF:**
        ASCII-In:  'Open Gate'
    **THEN:**
        (RELAY: GATE)  ON
**End**

**3-38 ASCII Output:** Up to 32 characters of ASCII text can be sent out the serial port to be used by other computer programs or products. Analog Inputs and Variable values can be embedded into the text as well. ASCII Out can also trigger Wavefiles (.wav.) and execute other Windows programs (.exe).

In the first example shown below, every time the front door motion detector is triggered the 'Front Door' Variable is incremented to 12, the ASCII Out string would be: **'12 people approached door'.** Variable values can be placed into the text string by placing the name of the Variable value between < > characters similar to this example: < name >.

In the second example, the Analog Input "Outside Temp" is connected to a temperature sensor and the current temperature is 77 degrees. When the ASCII-In "Temp" is received, the ASCII-Out string is sent out the serial port as: **'Temperature is 77 degrees'.**

EVENT:  ASCII OUT TEMP1
   **IF:**
      (DI: Front Door PIR 2) is ON
   **THEN:**
      (V: Front Door ) Increment
      ASCII-Out" '< Front Door > people approach door' [COM 2]
**End**

EVENT:  ASCII OUT TEMP2
   **IF:**
      ASCII-In: 'Temp'
   **THEN:**
      ASCII-Out: 'Temperature is < Outside Temp >
      ASCII-Out" 'degrees'
**End**

**3-39 Message Logging:** Messages of up to 32 characters of text each can be saved to the log. Analog Inputs and Variable values can be embedded into the text as well. The text in the Log statement will be saved in the Log and can be read out using the 'Read Log Utility' that is accessed by the Mega Controller. Analog Inputs or Variable values can be placed into the text string by placing the name of the Analog Input or Variable value between < > characters similar to this example: < name >. When the text is printed, the < name > will be replaced with the value of the Analog Input or Variable. See the example Event of Message Logging shown below.

EVENT:  Log Output
   **IF – ALWAYS:**
      (F: Log Temp) is ON
   **THEN:**
      Log: 'Temp is < Outside Temp > Degrees'
      Delay  1:00:00
**End**

**3-40 When a Schedule is Complete:** After the programming is complete, the 'Rules Check' is run to see if there are any errors in the current Schedule. The type of errors that are checked include the following: Use of a device that is not in the database and empty Events or illegal combination of Conditions and Actions. After running the 'Rules Check' a Window will open up and list the errors if there are any.

After the 'Rules Check' is complete and there are no errors, it is time to Download the Schedule as well as initial Device settings. New Schedules or changes to a Schedule must be Downloaded to the *Stargate* before it can be used. A Schedule can also be printed out to check programming logic for further modifications.

**3-41 Event Processing:** After the Schedule is Downloaded to *Stargate*, *Stargate* will start with the first Event, check 'IF' conditions and do any action, go on to the next Event, do the appropriate actions, and so on until the end of the Schedule is reached. *Stargate* then starts over at the beginning of the Schedule evaluating the first Event. See the flow chart shown below.

# Event Process

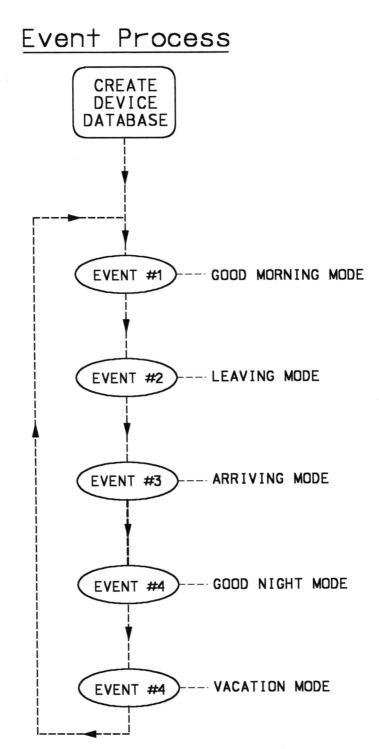

CREATE
DEVICE
DATABASE

EVENT #1 ---- GOOD MORNING MODE

EVENT #2 ---- LEAVING MODE

EVENT #3 ---- ARRIVING MODE

EVENT #4 ---- GOOD NIGHT MODE

EVENT #4 ---- VACATION MODE

# *JDS* LCD MULTI-MENU KEYPAD

**3-42 LCD-96D Keypad:** The LCD-96D is a menu-driven *JDS* Keypad that allows control of the air conditioning system, home security, audio and video systems, pool and spa, sprinkler system, voice mail and other systems that are connected to *Stargate*. This home control Keypad can be programmed to hold a maximum of 96 interactive menu screens that are created and downloaded to the LCD-96D by the installer or user using the included *Event Manager Software*. There are 8 menus that can contain up to 10 text letters across or bitmapped graphics (.bmp) format similar to what is shown in Figure 3-9. There are 8 dual-position rocker buttons shown to the right of the menu display that can be individually programmed to perform a variety of functions. The left and right side of each button can be programmed independently. The left side can turn OFF the controlled device and the right side can turn it ON. Programmable functions include: Navigational functions such as 'Go to Main Menu', 'Go to previous Menu', **'THEN'** actions such as Relay Outputs, IR command signals, Macros, VoiceMail, Voice Response, Flag, Variable, X-10, Audio Path and predefined menus such as 'Thermostat', TimeLabel, Caller ID, and Time Display. A special Two Way X-10 feature provided by this *JDS* Keypad allows any X-10 address to be assigned to a rocker button. The device can be turned ON by pressing the right side of the button and turned OFF by pressing the left side. Holding down the

right or left side of the button will brighten or Dim the light(s) respectively. ON/OFF status is indicated on the associated menu line for easy viewing. Individual menu screens or complete setups can be downloaded to *JDS* Keypads via the shared RS-485 connections or stored on a disk as templates and later loaded to *JDS* Keypads as needed. Menu line items can be cut, copied, and pasted from any menu to another for easy editing. *JDS* Keypads can also be programmed and edited remotely via the modem.

Three LEDs (red, green and yellow), are located above the rocker buttons, can be individually programmed to turn OFF, turn ON steady, blink fast or blink slow based on any condition(s). For example, the red LED could display the status of a connected security system (ON = System *Armed*, OFF = System *Disarmed*, blink = violated). The green LED could indicated VoiceMail status (ON = Old Messages, OFF = No messages, blink = New Messages). The yellow LED can indicate the status of the telephone line (ON = line in use, OFF = line is clear, blink = ringing or on hold).

The LCD-96M has a built-in high-contrast green backlight that can be programmed to stay on continuously or turn ON with any button press, then 'time out' after a specified delay time. The backlight and menu selections can also be accessed via the *Event Manager* Schedule to allow dynamic interaction with other system functions. For example, an incoming phone call

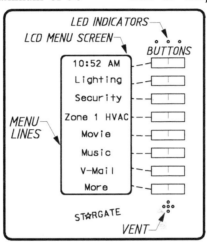

**FIGURE 3-9   JDS LCD KEYPAD**

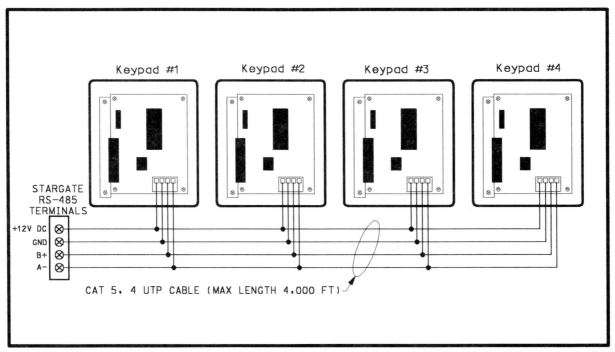

## FIGURE 3-10 LCD-96M KEYPAD DAISY-CHAIN TO STARGATE'S RS-485 PORT

can trigger any LCD-96M to turn ON its backlight and go to the Caller ID menu. A 'Good Night' Event can be programmed to turn OFF the backlight on the bedroom *JDS* Keypad during sleeping hours and back ON by the 'Morning Mode'. Even reminder messages such as "Take Out The Trash" or "Doctors Appointment at 4 PM" shown in Figure 3-16, can also be triggered by the Schedule and displayed on the appropriate *JDS* Keypad(s).

Keypads are connected in a Daisy Chain to the *Stargate* as shown in Figure 3-10. Up to 16 LCD-96M can be connected to *Stargate's* RS-485 port using two twisted pairs of (CAT 5, 4 UTP) cable. One pair is used for communication purposes and the other pair is for 12V DC power. Up to 4 LCD-96M Keypads can be powered by *Stargate's* on-board 12V DC power supply. Additional Keypads require an external 12V DC power supply. The LCD-96M faceplate measures 4" wide x 4 3/4" high and snaps into a wall-mounted enclosure.

During the construction stage of the home (CAT 5, 4 UTP) cable should be pulled to all locations in the home where *JDS* Keypad will be installed. Keypads are generally installed in the Foyer, near the interior door that enters the Garage, the Master Bedroom and any other location that the customer will best utilized the

control features of this device. Figure 3-11 illustrates how each *JDS* Keypad is installed. A hole cut-out template and utility knife is used to make the correct size opening in the drywall. The (CAT 5, 4 UTP) cable is pulled through the enclosure before it is inserted into the hole. While pushing the enclosure into the wall opening, the lock wings on the enclosure are opened to hold it securely in place. Once secured four conductors of the (CAT 5, 4 UTP) cable are terminated to the terminal screws as shown. The top of the *JDS* Keypad is then placed over the top lip of the enclosure and snapped into place.

In the following section we will discuss some of the features of the LCD-96M Keypads and illustrate what the LCD display may look like. When the VoiceMail button is pressed, the display switches to the associated VoiceMail menu, with pre-defined buttons for Play/Skip, Repeat/Stop, Back 5 seconds, Forward 5 seconds, Play all new and old messages or new messages only and delete messages. The top menu line of the VoiceMail menu displays the Box Number and the number of new and old messages in the mailbox as shown in Figure 3-14.

When the Caller ID button is pressed, the display switches to the Caller ID menu, which stores and displays Caller ID data (time, date, number and name) for the last 50 calls. The most

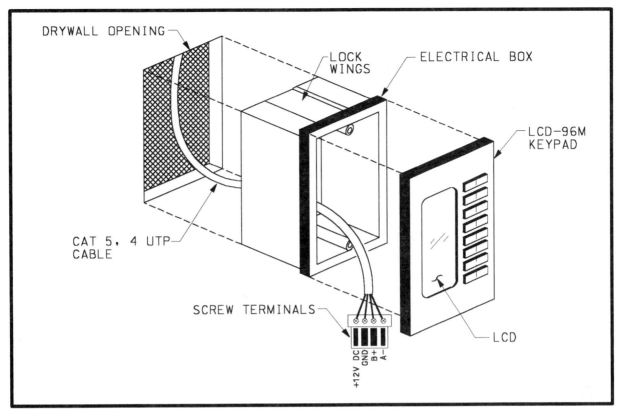

**FIGURE 3-11   LCD-96M KEYPAD IN-WALL INSTALLATION DIAGRAM**

recent call is listed first. Pressing the left or right arrow button allows the user to scroll through and review the previous calls. The caller ID display will look something like Figure 3-12.

Selecting DigitalPad as a menu item will bring up the DigitalPad field. The DigitalPad menu contains pre-labeled buttons similar to a telephone keypad. The press of a single button or a sequence of buttons can perform any home control function. The DigitalPad can serve as a 'security keypad' with multiple access codes to *Arm* or *Disarm* the security system. This requires an *'Armed'* output from the security system panel connected to one of *Stargate's* Digital Inputs and one (N.O.) Relay Output that is connected to a security *Zone* programmed for 'Keyswitch' operation. The telephone like keypad can also be used to control devices through X-10 commands similar to how a regular telephone can. Pushing *11 will turn ON any X-10 Receiver coded A1. (* = an ON command) and (11 = X-10 code A1). The LCD display just described will look like Figure 3-17.

A verity of Modes can be listed on the display to select from. A Mode is initiated by

simply pressing the desired Mode button shown to the right in Figure 3-18.

The Keypad can be used as a means of displaying information about the air conditioning system. When the 'Thermostat' button on the *JDS* Keypad is pressed, the display switches to the Thermostat menu. The Thermostat menu displays the air conditioning *Zone* name, temperature, setpoint, mode (heating, cooling, auto & off) and allows control of the setpoint, mode and fan. Up to 16 thermostat *Zones* can be defined and accessed from the Thermostat menu. By using a *JDS* Keypad and an analog temperature sensor in each air conditioned *Zone* in the home along with the use of the *Stargate*, standard thermostats and a control panel are not necessary. The *JDS* Keypads can be used as an interface to adjust temperature setpoints and select modes similar to any other thermostat. *Stargate* can also be programmed to display all the rooms in the home on any *JDS* Keypad. The user will first select the room where a particular electrical load resides. Another screen will be displayed with all the loads in the room to select from with commands (ON, OFF, Dim, Bright).

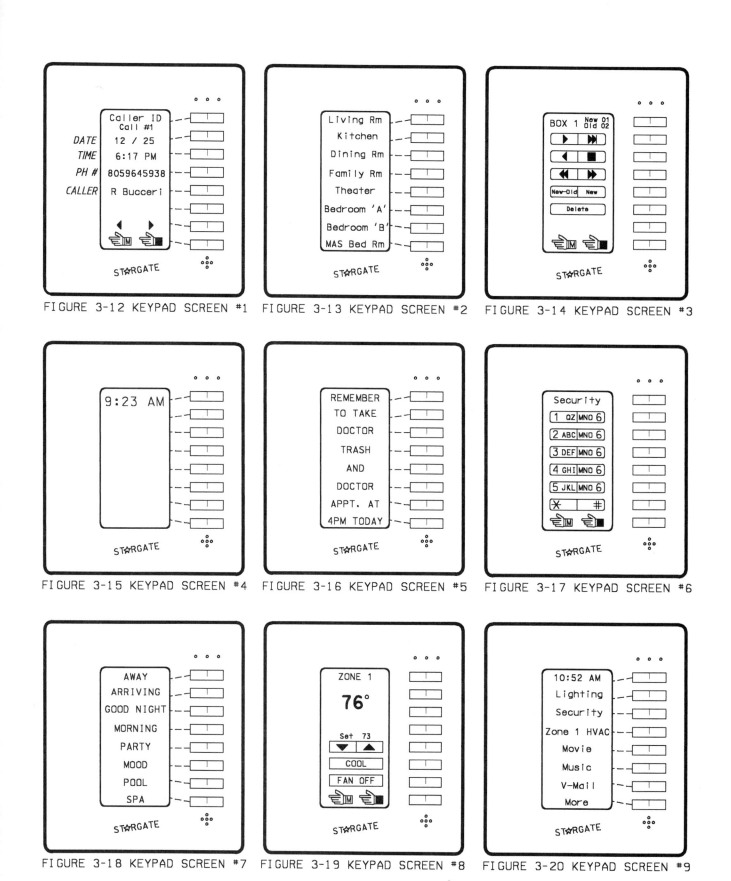

FIGURE 3-12 KEYPAD SCREEN #1

FIGURE 3-13 KEYPAD SCREEN #2

FIGURE 3-14 KEYPAD SCREEN #3

FIGURE 3-15 KEYPAD SCREEN #4

FIGURE 3-16 KEYPAD SCREEN #5

FIGURE 3-17 KEYPAD SCREEN #6

FIGURE 3-18 KEYPAD SCREEN #7

FIGURE 3-19 KEYPAD SCREEN #8

FIGURE 3-20 KEYPAD SCREEN #9

Specifications and descriptions of *Stargate, I/O Xpander, IR Xpander*, LCD Keypad
and programming examples displayed in this chapter are courtesy of *JDS Technologies*.

# CHAPTER
# FOUR

## Lighting Control Systems

**4-1 Hardwired Lighting Control Systems:** Hardwired lighting control systems provide user friendly wall interfaces and convenient control capabilities for more than just a home's lighting system. Most systems will also offer control of other types of sub-systems that may include: Audio & video, air conditioning, motorized window shades, storm shutters, sprinklers and pool/spa motors to name a few. Hardwired lighting systems are generally able to

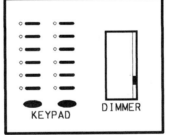

interface and control other types of electrical equipment with the use of low voltage contact closures and/or slave relays, infrared control functions and by RS-232/485 serial control protocols. Hardwired lighting systems do provide some advantages over Power-line Carrier systems; however, the equipment as well as the installation of hardwired lighting systems is more expensive. A Power-line Carrier system transmits and receives commands over the home's 120/240V power wiring to control electrical loads. Power-line Carrier systems do allow the do-it-yourselfer an easier method of automating their new or existing home. For information on how to design, install and program Power-line Carrier control systems, refer to the 'Automated

Home Control, Design Installation and Programming Manual' shown at the back of this book.

There are of course customers that prefer to own a hardwired system over the Power-line Carrier option simply because hardwired systems in most cases will offer an all in one fully integrated control system. Because hardwired systems use dedicated data wiring to control the system, they are able to avoid the power lines as a control media and the electrical noise that could possibly cause control interference. Another reason may include the fact that the home is easily accessible during the time of construction, which is a good time to incorporate a well-planned pre-wired infrastructure. Some systems can even be installed by do-it-yourselfers that have an understanding of basic wiring techniques, have a design and installation manual and experience operating a PC.

If we begin to look at the features of a typical hardwired system, we will find that the homeowner has the ability to control any number of lights or other equipment from a push button wall mounted 'control keypad'. Pushing a specific button on a keypad can be programmed to instantly turn ON or OFF every light in the

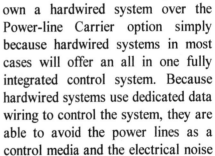

KEYPAD    DIMMER

home if desired. This feature comes in handy if a noise is heard during the night and the homeowner wants to potentially scare off intruders. By pushing another button, specific groups of lights can be dimmed to any brightness level to create what we call scenes.

When the owner leaves the home, the push of a keypad button located in the Foyer or Garage will activate the 'Leaving Mode'. This mode is normally programmed to turn OFF all lighting, ceiling fans, audio/video equipment and any other electrical load the homeowner desires. Select electrical loads can also be turned ON with this mode as well. In other words, the homeowner can choose what state each and every electrical load will be in when away from the home. This type of scenario includes control of many different electrical devices at the same time, which is referred to as a Macro or Mode. In fact any control sequence can be incorporated into the system programming to fulfill any lifestyle as well as to improve the home's energy management requirements. For instance, when entering the home after sunset, additional safety and security features are provided when one or more lights in each room are automatically turned ON. Microprocessors are used to make control decisions based on their conditional logic capabilities. This allows the system to turn lights ON only after Sunset or turn them OFF after Sunrise. Music can also be turned ON when first arriving home only on the weekends if desired, and the window shades can be adjusted open or closed based on the outside temperature. The air conditioning (cooling & heating) temperature setpoints can also be changed automatically based on the time of year. Another conditional example may allow the 'Deterrent Mode' to potentially run only if the 'Vacation Mode' is already running. The 'Deterrent Mode' is triggered by an exterior motion detector that detects unauthorized individuals approaching the home. Upon detection, the 'Deterrent Mode' will automatically turn ON specific exterior and interior lighting, audio/video equipment and any other electrical load in the general area of detection to provide a localized appearance that the home is occupied.

The 'Vacation Mode' is similar to the 'Deterrent Mode'. The 'Vacation Mode' is generally controlled by a microprocessor that has the ability to monitor and maintain a recorded history of the state of all system devices in the home for future use. When the 'Vacation Mode' is initiated by the homeowner before leaving the home, the microprocessor will play back these Events. This will provide a very realistic lived-in appearance of activity within the home that may help to discourage burglars.

Another feature of the system may provide a lighted path to the Kitchen or Bathroom that can be initiated by pushing a button on a 'control keypad' or touch-screen located at bedside. This is a convenient option because the homeowner will never have to find light switches in the dark and stub their toe on the furniture again. On most systems the status or state of specific electrical loads can also be monitored by simply looking at the status LEDs located next to the associated 'control keypad' buttons. Events can also occur automatically at specific times of the day or night with the use of 'Time Events'.

A number of schedules can be created by programming the microprocessor to allow different 'Time Events' to operate on weekdays, weekends and even on holidays. Time Events can be disabled and enabled through a programmed Event that either Sets or Clears a Flag as part of the 'Time Event's' IF condition. The disabled or enabled functions can be initiated by simply pushing a specific keypad button. Other conditional logic of a 'Time Event' may include specific days of the week, whether the owner is home or away, or whether a specific mode is operating at the time.

Most hardwired lighting systems can be interfaced with the home's security system. In an alarm condition, the lighting system can be initiated to flash the exterior lights to attract attention and to provide a lighted path for the occupants to exit safely. Another security feature is the 'Panic Mode'. This mode can be initiated from any push button keypad, which will activate the security alarm, control exit lighting and notify the authorities by phone.

A lighting system's primary function is to create custom lighting scenes that enhance the beauty of the home. By pushing one button on a 'control keypad', specific lights can be dimmed for a romantic dinner or another button can be programmed to turn ON and dim specific lighting to create a party atmosphere.

There is generally an available telephone interface that is used with this type of system to allow users to both access and control Events from any touch-tone phone located at home or anywhere in the world. The numeric buttons on a touch-tone phone provides the same response as a button on a 'control keypad'. Similar to other keypads, each button can be individually programmed to initiate control commands. Example control functions may include: Turning on the spa shortly before arriving home so it is hot and ready, initiate the 'Vacation Mode' from a remote location, open the garage door from the Office when a family member forgets their house keys, and check the status of the security system if the homeowner can not remember if the system was *Armed*. While using some telephone control systems, the homeowner may receive help from 'voice messages' along with 'verbal responses' when a function or Event has actually been activated. Voice messages provide an easy way for the homeowner to activate control functions, check the status of the lighting systems while receiving a voice conformation when the control changes have been made.

**4-2 'Control Keypad':** Push button keypads are user interface devices that provide the occupants with the ability to control and monitor lighting, audio & video, pool/spa pump, property access gate, garage door, modes, etc. Keypad buttons can be programmed to control an individual light, any group of lights, or a lighting scene for a room or the entire home. Keypads are designed to take the place of several switches and to minimize the wall space required while maximizing the number of available control functions. There are normally a wide variety of keypad types available with varying quantities of control buttons and features.

'CONTROL KEYPAD'

Push button keypads require control wiring (hardwiring) from the microprocessor to each keypad. Keypads do not directly switch 120V

AC electrical loads ON & OFF or perform dimming. Keypads transmit command signals to the microprocessor to allow the microprocessor to initiate 'local' or 'remote switches' to control the electrical loads. A cross sectional view showing the wiring arrangement of a typical in-wall 'control keypad' is shown in Figure 4-1.

Keypads are generally placed in entryways such as the Foyer, in the exit way to the garage on the way to the car, exiting the home to the pool/spa area and in the Master Bedroom as well as the Home Theater.

There are hardwired lighting systems that provide both design and programming software that can be used by a system designer for any home control project. Laying out the system, programming system features and assigning keypad buttons to specific control functions are generally accomplished using Windows 95®, 98® or 2000® operating systems. System information is normally stored in a database, which allows global changes to be made throughout all design documentation.

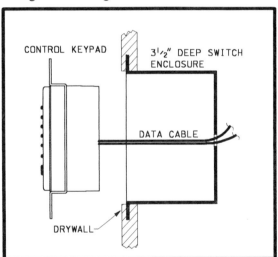

Figure 4-1   KEYPAD INSTALLATION

**4-3 'Local Control Switch':**
Hardwired control switches are designed to take the place of standard mechanical dimmer switches and ON/OFF lighting switches. These 'local control switches' are used in areas of the home that require local switching or dimming control without a need to control lighting and other electrical loads located in other

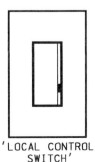
'LOCAL CONTROL SWITCH'

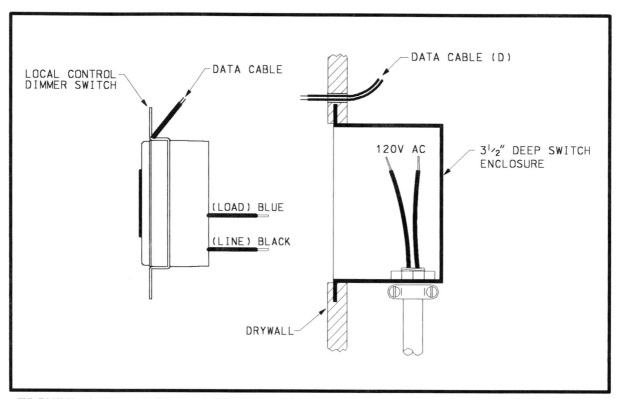

FIGURE 4-2 'LOCAL CONTROL DIMMER SWITCH' & ENCLOSURE DETAIL

areas of the home. The difference between the hardwired 'local control switch' and a standard mechanical switch is that the 'local control switch' will in most cases have an integral microprocessor that allows it to be incorporated into a centralized lighting control system. The internal microprocessor's intelligence allows each 'local control switch' to be controlled from any 'control keypad', touch-screen, universal remote or touch-tone telephone.

There are two types of 'local control switches'. One is designed to switch lighting loads ON & OFF only, while the 'dimmer control switch' provides full range dimming control as well as ON & OFF control. There is generally a separate slide lever located on the 'dimmer control switch' next to the ON & OFF button that will allow one light or a whole group of lights to be dimmed or brighten.

'Local control switches', 'dimming control switches' and 'push button keypads' are mounted in-wall similar to a standard manual mechanical switch. While 'local control switches' are wired to both the 120V AC wiring and the data control wiring, keypads are only connected to the data control wiring. A cross sectional view of the wire arrangement for a typical 'dimming control switch' is shown in Figure 4-2.

**4-4 Remote Control Switches:** 'Remote control switches' are normally mounted in the main control panel along with the main microprocessor. These devices are controlled from 'control keypads' or by other means. These 'Remote Control Switches' are designed to perform the switching function of an electrical load from the main control panel. This means that 120V AC wiring must be 'Home Run' configured from each 'Remote Control Switch' to the corresponding electrical load(s).

**4-5 Contact Closure Inputs:** Contact closure inputs provide the system designer with a means of initiating a control response by providing a low voltage contact closure. The input board will generally have a quantity of eight to sixteen contact closure inputs that can be connected to devices that produce a low voltage circuit closure. These devices may include motion detectors, vehicle detectors, rain sensors, temperature sensors, water detectors, magnetic switches, as well as other devices. An input received from a low voltage circuit closure internal to a detection device can automatically control lighting, provide indication that a vehicle is entering the driveway, provide automatic closure of window shades when the temperature reaches a high limit condition, provide indication that there is a water leak in the home, and to provide automatic initiation of Macros or Modes when the front door or garage door is opened. See Chapter Five for more on system sensors.

Inputs are normally programmed in the same manner as a keypad would be and each input can be configured for a momentary or maintained contact closure. Some systems even have LED input indicators that display the state of the connected input device. Wiring required to connect these types of detection devices to an input board is generally 22 GA, 2 or 4 conductor unshielded wire; however, a (CAT 5, 4 UTP) cable may provide additional advantages. Some contact closure devices such as magnetic switches require only 2-conductors while a motion detector requires 4-conductors. Eight conductors provided by a (CAT 5, 4 UTP) cable may seem to offer more conductors than required; however, conductors can get damaged during the installation phase of the project or many years later. It is much easier to disconnect damaged conductors and reconnect extra conductors instead of having to run new cable.

**4-6 Contact Closure Outputs:** Contact closure output boards allow the designer to control window shades, hurricane shutters, pool/spa pumps, sprinkler pumps, sprinkler solenoid valves, fireplaces, garage doors, motorized gates, IR transmitters and just about any other electrical device. Each output board will generally provide a quantity of eight to sixteen low voltage controlled relay output closures. Some lighting systems even have push buttons located right on the output boards that are used to manually turn electrical devices ON or OFF for function testing purposes. Output boards will generally offer low voltage normally open (N.O.) and normally closed (N.C.) relay outputs to select from for a variety of control requirements. Each relay output can normally be programmed to provide momentary or maintained contact closure.

**4-7 Design Options:** There are normally three basic design options available to the system designer when laying out a hardwired lighting control system. The designer is provided with the choice of using wall mounted 'local control switches' only, 'remote control switches' only, or a design that maximizes the control system by combining both types of control switches. Each method of design has its benefits and disadvantages compared to one another. The designer should first determine the design requirements of the project based on the homeowner's needs, desires and budget and select the system attributes that will best achieve these requirements. This will help to choose the proper design method described in the following Sections.

**4-8 Local Control Design Method:** The 'local control design' method uses wall mounted 'local control switches' that directly switch and dim lighting loads in a room locally. This arrangement is most familiar to occupants and is easy to understand because the electrical loads are controlled in a similar manner as they would be if standard mechanical wall switches were used. These 'local control switches'; however, can also be controlled remotely by the microprocessor when initiated from a wall keypad pushed button or by other means. Keypads are also a part of this design method. They are used to provide control of a number of lights on separate 'local control switches' within a room. They can also control lighting and other electrical loads in other areas of the home. Control of a single light or a group of lights is accomplished by creating Modes using the programming software that comes with the microprocessor. Modes generally consist of a number of lights or other types of electrical loads that are controlled all at the same time. For instance; pushing a button called 'Party' will instantly turn ON several lights or several groups of lights to any desired brightness level as well as turn ON background music. If an assigned keypad button is pushed to initiate a specific Mode, the microprocessor will receive this command and send control signals to the appropriate 'local control switches' to perform the final switching and dimming functions.

'Local control switches' and dimmers allow the occupants to control lighting manually at the wall switch when entering or exiting the room.

These switches are normally required as a basic means of control if power to the microprocessor is temporarily interrupted or if a system failure should occur.

**4-9 Central Control Design Method:** The central control design method uses 'remote control switches' to control all lighting and other electrical loads. This eliminates the need for local dimmers and ON/OFF control switches that were used in the 'local control design' method. 'Remote control switches' are generally mounted inside the main control panel located in an electrical equipment closet, or equipment room. In this particular design, all lighting and other electrical loads are controlled from keypads only, which provides maximum control flexibility while minimizing the number of control interfaces on the walls throughout the home. This method maximizes control flexibility since the programming that assigns the keypad buttons to control functions can be changed or modified. In other words, what a specific keypad button controls today can be changed to control entirely different electrical loads tomorrow.

Keypads can be programmed to control lighting in the same room as the keypad, as well as control lights located across the other side of the home. Keypads can also be programmed to initiate Macros/Modes that will control any number of electrical loads at the same time by the push of one button. To stress this point, keypads will allow an infinite amount of flexibility in programming and control possibilities. Since this design method does not include 'local control switches' that provide manual push button control of electrical loads, a failure of the microprocessor itself may bring down the whole control system. This means that 'local control switches' will not be available to perform basic manual control.

**4-10 Maximized Control Design Method:** This design method combines the benefits of both the 'Local Control' and 'Central Control' design methods. With this design approach, 'local control switches' are used in bathrooms, guestrooms and any other area where familiar control methods are desired. Lighting loads located in the Foyer and other entry/exit ways, Living Room, Dining Room, Master Bedroom and the Home Theater are often wired to 'remote control switches'. This method will also reduce the number wall mounted control devices for a cleaner looking installation. Keypads

are located in strategic locations of the home to provide the occupants with whole house control capabilities and system control flexibility as well. This design method also allows changes to be made during the installation stage as well as after the system is installed. This is because lighting can be added or removed without having to make changes to the line voltage wiring.

**4-11 'Example Home':** To illustrate how a typical hardwired lighting control system may look, we have incorporated this type of system into the 'Example Home' lighting plan shown in Figure 4-3. In the 'Example Home', the 'Maximized Design Method' was selected. Figure 4-3 shows lighting loads, 'control keypads', 'local control switches', 120V AC power wiring and low voltage data/control wiring. Lighting loads include: Incandescent, fluorescent, halogen and low voltage lighting. Lighting loads are either wired through 'local control switches' located on the wall of each room or through 'remote control switches' located in the main control panel. 120V AC wiring connected directly to a 'local control switch' will provide control of the lighting manually at the switch or from a keypad located anywhere in the home. The 120V AC conductors that power specific lighting loads without the use of 'local control switches' are routed back to the appropriate 'remote control switches' located in the main panel shown in Figure 4-4. These 120V AC wires are identified in Figure 4-3 as (RS) for remote switch.

Data communication wiring identified as (D) in Figure 4-4, are connected to both the 'local control switches' and the Keypads. Data wiring is routed back to the microprocessor to allow both types of user interfaces to communicate control commands to the microprocessor as shown in Figure 4-4. This Figure illustrates the 'Example Home' system in a schematic representation that identifies system components and shows how the system is typically wired. The data wiring allows the microprocessor to communicate command signals to the 'local control switches' that will in turn switch or dim the appropriate lights. Data wiring is also connected from the microprocessor to 'remote control switches', which are short runs of wire since they are both located in the main control panel.

In Figure 4-2, notice how the control wiring is connected to the 'local control switch' outside of the 120V AC enclosure. This is required per the National Electrical Code for safety purposes to

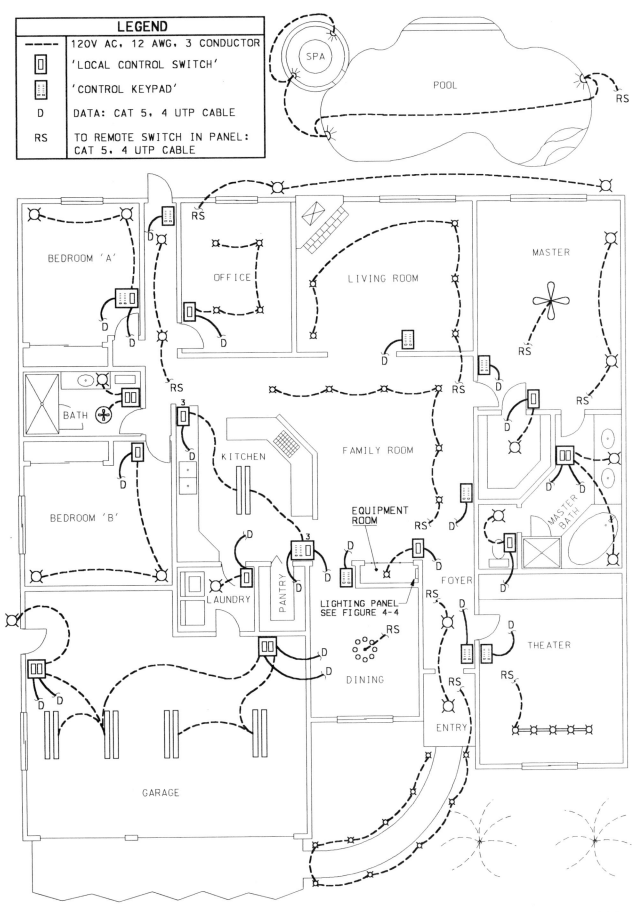

# Figure 4-3  AUTOMATED LIGHTING & APPLIANCE PLAN

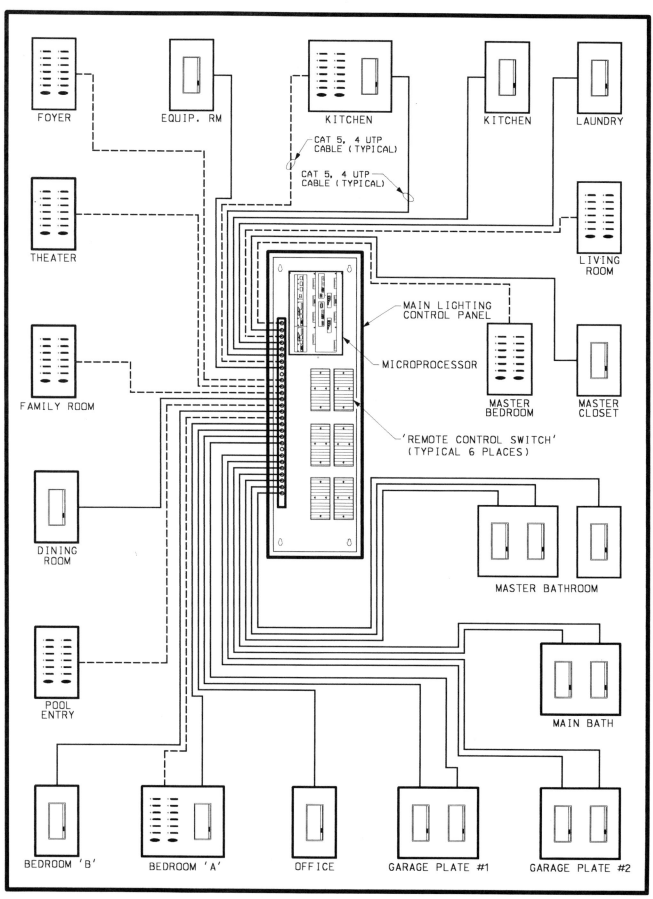

FIGURE 4-4   HARDWIRED LIGHTING CONTROL WIRING DIAGRAM

94

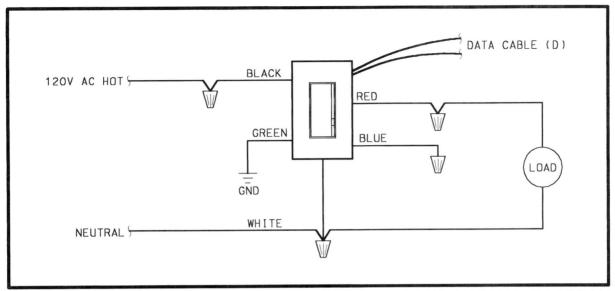

Figure 4-5  LOCAL CONTROL DIMMER SWITCH WIRING DIAGRAM

eliminate the possibility of shorting 120V AC wiring with data wiring. Also notice in Figure 4-1, how the data wiring connects to a keypad installed in an electrical enclosure. 120V AC wiring is not required when installing the keypad because it does not directly switch electrical loads. Keypads only send control commands to the microprocessor for the microprocessor to send command signals to 'local' or 'remote' control switches. Typical wiring of a 'local control switch' is illustrated in Figure 4-5.

As previously mentioned, 'local control switches' are used in locations of the home where simplicity and familiarity are important for both occupants and guests. A 'local control switch' works similar in some respects to a standard mechanical switch when it comes to manual control of lighting. Although they may work similar to a standard switch when operated by hand, these 'local control switches' are programmed to be controlled remotely from any push button keypad in the home.

In the 'Example Home' plan shown in Figure 4-3, notice that the 'local control switches' are located in most of the Bedrooms, Bathrooms and Kitchen area where familiarity is important. Keypads on the other hand are located in the Foyer, Laundry Room area and at the back door that leads the occupants out to the Pool/Spa area. These push button keypads allow occupants to control entry/exit lighting and to initiate an abundance of Macros/Modes. They can also be used to change the air conditioning modes and

temperature setpoints, *Arm* the security system and close the window roller shades. When the occupants arrive home, one push of a keypad button labeled (Arriving) will create a lighted path for entry purposes when it is before sunset. When the 'Arriving Mode is initiated after sunset, one light will be turned ON in each room for safety and security purposes. Other 'Arriving Mode' functions may include: Turning on shelf lighting, playing the homeowner's favorite music, resetting the air conditioning temperature setpoints, and *Disarmed* the security system for a convenient entry.

The Kitchen push button keypad allows the user to control the Kitchen lights, ceiling fan, music and provides a view of the children in the 'pool area' on the 'under-the-cabinet' TV from CCTV camera video. It can also initiate the 'Panic Mode', 'Dinner Mode', open/close the property access gate or any other control function from this location.

In the Home Theater, keypad push buttons control room lighting, open and close window shades, initiate the 'Entertainment Mode', 'Good Night Mode', 'Party Mode' and any other mode or feature that provides convenience, safety, security and energy management benefits.

The 'Entertainment Mode' is programmed to turn ON the amplifier and adjust the volume level, turn ON the TV, select the cable TV base channel 3 or 4, turn ON the satellite receiver, select ESPN, adjust the room lighting to a 30% brightness level and close the window shades all by the push of one button that is labeled 'Entertainment' on the keypad. The 'Good Night Mode' is activated when the entertainment is over and when the occupants want to retire for the evening. By pushing one button, all lighting in the home will turn off except a number of lights selected to create paths for the occupants to walk to the bathrooms and bedrooms. Window shades will close, the water heater will be turned OFF to save energy, the air conditioning and heating temperature setpoints will be set-back, the security system will be *Armed* and all audio/video equipment throughout the home will be turned OFF as well.

Control capability is also provided to the homeowner from the Master Bedroom. From this location the homeowner may use the keypad to initiate the 'Morning Mode'. This mode will gradually brighten the lights over a period of 1/2 hour to simulate a sunrise. It will also create a lighted path to the Kitchen and Master Bathroom to get ready for work. Select window shades will open, the 'under-the-cabinet' TV will turn ON in the Kitchen for the morning news and the security system is *Disarmed*, all by the push of one button. This Mode could also be initiated at a specific time of day by placing the following programming line in the 'IF' condition section of the Event: ('IF' 6:00 AM Monday through Friday). This means that every time this statement becomes true, the Mode will 'THEN' be initiated. Each home will have its unique group of modes and other programming features to compliment the family's lifestyle.

**4-12 Expanding Control Capabilities:** To expand the control capabilities of a lighting system that will provide control of other types of electrical loads, the designer must utilize input and output boards as a means of communication and system integration. In other words, an input board can utilize sensory devices to communicate to the microprocessor, so it can control both resistive loads (lighting and heating elements) and inductive loads (motors) with the use of a relay output board. For instance; in Figure 4-6, notice that the input board is wired to a number of input devices that will close a low voltage circuit sensed by the microprocessor. The motion detector illustrated, closes the low voltage

digital input circuit when it detects the presents of someone in a room. This closure is detected by the microprocessor through the assigned terminals of the input board so it can identify what device is the source of the input. A circuit closure will prove a programming 'IF' condition true, which could tells the microprocessor to turn ON a specific CCTV camera.

The vehicle detector shown in Figure 4-6, also closes a digital input circuit that is wired to a specific port of the input board. This input is used to turn on select TVs so the homeowner can view individuals approaching. The rain sensor is another sensory device that will send a digital input when sufficient moisture is detected to avoid watering the lawn when it is raining.

Water sensors located in the Kitchen and Laundry Room provide a digital input upon a leak detection that notifies the microprocessor to turn OFF the main water supply or sound a local alarm. The microprocessor can even make a phone call to a pre-assigned telephone number for notification purposes. It can also play a 'voice response' message over the whole house audio system that states "Kitchen Water Leak".

Magnetic contacts that are typically used in security systems can be used on a door to trigger automatic lighting control in the entryway and hallways. This type of sensor can also trigger the 'Arriving Mode' when the front door is opened the first time after the 'Away Mode' is initiated. Any detection device that provides normally open (N.O.) or normally closed (N.C) contacts has the ability to communicate to the microprocessor so it can act upon a specific request.

Without the use of a relay output board, the lighting system will only be able to control lighting loads. With the use of a relay output board, the microprocessor can open and close low voltage circuits to control equipment such as pumps, valves, garage doors, fireplaces and electric door locks as shown in Figure 4-7, or virtually any other electrical load. Since the control circuit is low voltage, it can only control devices that utilize 24V DC power or less. For instance; the relay output board can handle the power to control the sprinkler valves open or closed because they generally require 12V to 24V DC power to operate. If a 120V AC or a 240V AC motor needs to be controlled, this will require

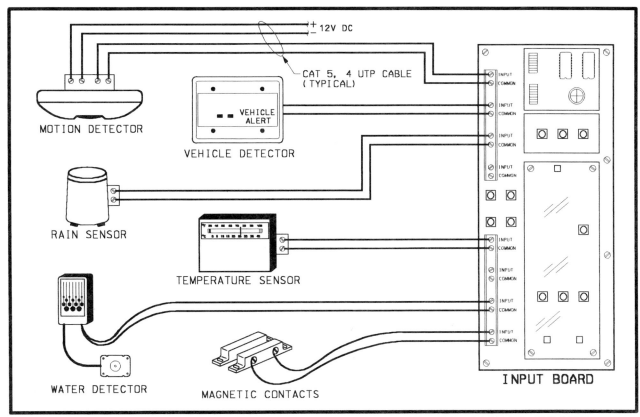

FIGURE 4-6    CONTROL SENSORS WIRED TO INPUT BOARD

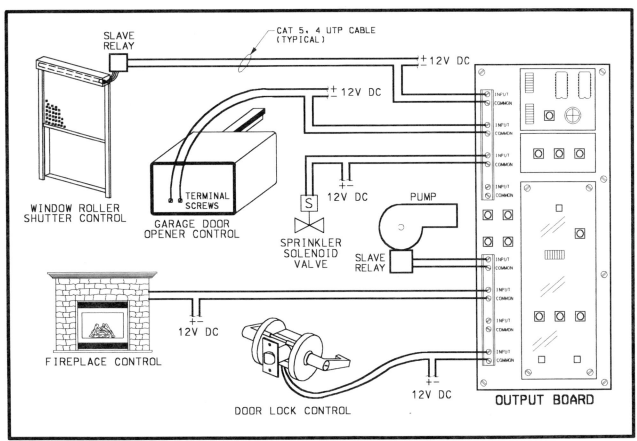

FIGURE 4-7    ELECTRICAL LOADS SWITCHED BY RELAY OUTPUT BOARD

the use of a slave relay that has a separate set of contacts to handle the higher power requirements. This is generally the case when controlling the sprinkler pump, pool/spa pump, window shades, property access gate, etc.

The last control scenario involves devices that only require a low voltage relay closure (dry contact closure) like the garage door or gate operator to provide open and close control functions. These devices have internal reversing relays that will open or close the door when it senses continuity in the circuit created each time the circuit is momentarily closed. To simulate a momentary contact closure the relay output contacts must be closed and then opened after a one second delay in the 'THEN' statement.

**4-13 Automatic Lighting Control:** Automatic lighting control can also be integrated into the 'Example Home' system to control lighting ON and OFF automatically. When an individual enters a specific room in the home, the lighting serving the room will immediately be turned ON. As the individual moves about the room or is present in the room, the lights will continue to stay ON. If the person stays motionless for an extended period of time, the lights may turn OFF. Lights will normally not turn OFF because even small motions like writing, typing, lifting the hand-held remote and turning ones head will be sensed by an Ultrasonic type motion detector, which will maintain the lights ON. The period of time that a detection of motion will maintain the lights ON can be adjusted as a timer function in the programming used by the microprocessor. When an individual leaves the room, the motion sensor will not sense motion over a pre-determined period of time. When the timer reaches 0 seconds, a programming 'IF' condition will become true and the microprocessor will turn the lights OFF.

There are a variety of occupancy sensors available on the market that include: Passive Infrared (PIR) occupancy sensors, Ultrasonic occupancy sensors and Dual Technology occupancy sensors. Dual Technology sensors combined Infrared and Ultrasonic technologies. The specific type of occupancy sensor selected depends on where automatic lighting control is

required. If lighting control is desired in the Hallway, Foyer, Kitchen, Closet or Garage where individuals are either pasting through or are present for a short period of time, a ceiling mounted 360 degree PIR motion sensor can be used effectively. When lighting control is desired in the Living Room, Bedrooms, Family Room or other rooms where family members spend the majority of their time relaxing, a (PIR) motion sensor may not be able to detect there presents. In these areas a ceiling mounted 360 degree Ultrasonic motion sensor is recommended.

The 'Example Home' automatic lighting system is shown in Figure 4-8. Motion detectors are mounted and positioned near the door in each room. As an occupant approaches the doorway, motion will be immediately detected when the occupant enters or moves about the area. A quick response time is important to get the lights to turn ON before the individual entering the room gets to far into a dark space. Each motion detector placed in the 'Example Home' is located near the door as shown in Figure 4-8, but is also located a short distance from the center of the room to detect motion within the space as well.

In the Kitchen and Family Room, a motion detector is placed in the center of the rooms to pickup motion equally as well if entered from either end of the room.

When a motion detector is used for automatic lighting purposes, its internal (N.C.) contacts will open when it detects motion. The input board will no longer sense continuity in the circuit and the microprocessor will read this condition at the same moment. The processor will then send signals to a 'local control switch' or 'remote control switch' to automatically turn ON specific lighting that is programmed into an Event. The wiring required to connect a motion detector to an input board is shown in Figure 4-9. Notice that the motion detector is wired to the input board and the security system panel so that each motion detector can control lighting as well as provide security system intrusion detection.

**4-14 Optional Lighting Control:** Although this is a *Structured Wiring Manual*, it would be unreasonable to over look the option of using the power lines as a control signal medium for the

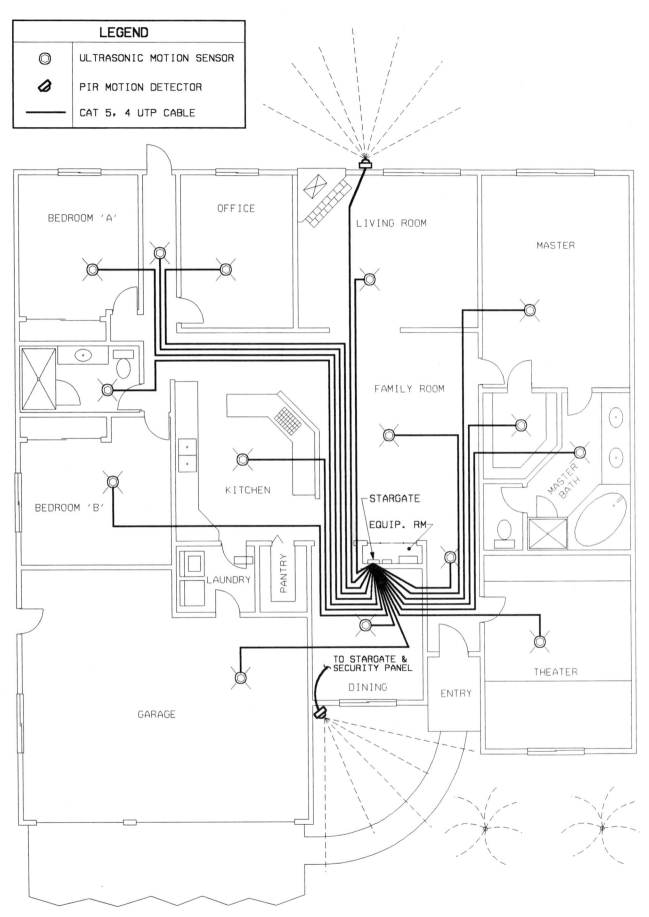

# FIGURE 4-8 AUTOMATIC LIGHTING CONTROL PLAN

purpose of controlling the lights or most other electrical loads in the home. This type of system controls electrical loads by transmitting X-10 signals over the 120V & 240V AC wiring in the home to Receiver Switches that are also connected to the home's power lines. When an addressed transmission is received by the appropriate Receiver Switch set to the same address code as the Transmitter, the Receiver Switch will turn the light(s) ON or OFF and dim or brighten the light(s) depending on what command code is transmitted. The *Stargate* Home Controller described in Chapter Three is used to control all electrical loads in the 'Example Home' except the hardwired lighting. If Power-line Carrier communications is selected by the system designer as a means of controlling the home's electrical loads, this would avoid having to purchase and install cable and another microprocessor to support the lighting system. *Stargate* has the full capability of controlling X-10 lighting as well as inductive electrical loads. A Power-line Carrier lighting system can be control by using push button Transmitters, hand-held remotes, and can also be controlled

automatically using motion detectors and other sensory devices similar to the method used in the hardwired lighting system previously discussed in Section 4-13 .

Wiring a motion detector to both the *Stargate's* I/O and Security System is also illustrated in Figure 4-9. This diagram shows the motion detector used in a dual purpose role by providing automatic lighting control while also having the ability to detect motion for security purposes. Notice that the motion detector's normally closed (N.C.) contacts are wired in series with *Stargate's* I/O Digital Input terminals and the security *Zone* terminals. If an intruder enters the area, the (N.C.) contacts located inside the motion detector will open. The security *Zone* will sense the open circuit before initiating the 'Security Alert' Mode.

If a 1000 Ohm resistor, for instance; is used in the security circuit and this type of dual purpose control is being incorporated into the design, the wiring configuration may affect controllability due to the added resistance in the circuit. To resolve this problem, the standard 1,000-Ohm resistor must be replaced with a 500

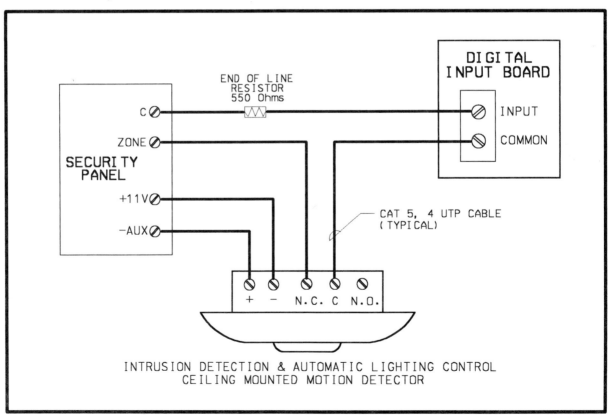

INTRUSION DETECTION & AUTOMATIC LIGHTING CONTROL
CEILING MOUNTED MOTION DETECTOR

FIGURE 4-9    MOTION DETECTOR USED FOR BOTH INTRUSION DETECTION AND AUTOMATIC LIGHTING CONTROL

Ohm device to bring the total resistance back to 1000 Ohms. If the original resistor, for instance; is 1200 Ohms, a 700 Ohm device must be used.

The full operating sequence of an automatic lighting control system is as follows: When an individual enters a room, the motion detector will sense their presents and open the internal normally closed (N.C.) contacts that will send a Digital Input OFF command to the *Stargate*. The *Stargate's* programming 'IF' statement will then be true, which will allow the 'THEN' statement functions to send signals to the appropriate Receiver Switche(s) to turn the light(s) ON. See the programming for a typical automatic lighting control sequence shown on page 102. When motion. is no longer detected, the motion detector's (N.C) contacts will close and the Digital Input will go ON. This condition will start a 2-minute timer. When Timer 1 expires after 2-minutes, the 'IF' statement will then be true and the 'THEN' statement will have the *Stargate* send the appropriate X-10 signals to the Receiver Switch to turn the lights OFF. As part of the 'Good Night Mode', a Flag called (Motion 1) will be Set so the Event's 'IF' statement will not be true. This will essentially deactivate the automatic lighting control feature in the bedrooms at night to avoid having the lights turn ON when someone rolls over in bed.

These same motion detectors are also used to automate the heating and air conditioning system. When an occupant enters the Living Room, for instance; the *Stargate* will receive notification and command the multi-zone air conditioning system controller to make sure the air conditioning system is ON. It will then begin to satisfy either the cooling or heating temperature setpoint by opening the motorized *Zone* damper to supply air to the room. When a temperature setpoint is satisfied, the damper will close. When the room becomes unoccupied, a 5 minute time delay will occur before the *Stargate* will set-back the temperature setpoint, which will close the conditioned air damper. Automatic control of the air conditioning will increase the level of energy conservation above what a typical multi-zone air conditioning will ordinarily furnish.

Motion sensors are wired to the *Stargate's* Digital Inputs using 22 GA, 4-conductor cable. Two conductors are connected to the assigned Digital Input terminals. These conductors provide the Digital Input while the other two conductors are used for 12V DC power to operate the motion detector.

Pulling of the motion detector cables used to automatically control sub-systems in the home begins in the *'Equipment Room'*. A 1,000 foot reel of cable is first positioned in the *'Equipment Room'*. One cable for each motion detector is pulled into the attic and routed over to the location where the motion detector will be mounted as shown in Figure 4-8. Each cable should be labeled in the *'Equipment Room'* to identify what cable connects to what Digital Input. Cables should be positioned in the attic on top of the ceiling joists next to the vertical members of the roof trusses. This will position the cables out of areas where people may walk to avoid possible cable damage. Motion detector cables can be organized in the attic by using long wire ties (lightly pulled) to avoid possible damage to the conductors.

An additional foot of cable length should be allowed in the *'Equipment Room'* to make sure there is sufficient length for terminating the cables during the trim-out stage. An additional foot of cable should also be allowed to hang from the ceiling joist at each motion detector location. This will provide sufficient length to terminate the cable to the sensor at a later time. The drywall crew must be made aware of these cables so they will pull the cables through.

After all of the cables are pulled, cable ends in the *'Equipment Room'* should be gathered together and neatly arranged into a bundle with the use of wire ties. Each cable end will need to penetrate *Stargate's* metal enclosure so the installer can terminate one pair of conductors to its designated Digital Input. The other pair of conductors are connected to a 12V DC terminal strip located outside of the *Stargate's* enclosure to provide low voltage power to each motion detector.

The motion detector located outside the home near the front entryway works similar to the interior sensors with some small differences. When someone approaches the home, the *Stargate* will receive a Digital Input from the motion detector and turn the entryway lights ON. It will also trigger the front door CCTV camera and turn ON the TV in the Kitchen and Master Bedroom to the channel assigned to this camera location. This will allow the homeowner to view guests or potential trouble and give the homeowner time to call 911 if needed. This system is also programmed to automatically dial a pre-assigned telephone number when the homeowner is away to provide notification that someone is on the gated property.

# Motion Detector Automatic Lighting Control Programming

*Description:*

EVENT: **MASTER BED RM MOTION LIGHT ON**                 *Feature name*
  **IF**                                                                                 *if*
    (DI: MD1 ) goes OFF                                    *If motion detector MD1 detects motion*
    and (F: NIGHT ) is CLEAR          *and the 'Good Night' Mode is not running, (Night Flag is Clear)*
  **THEN**                                                                             *then*
    (X: MASTER  LIGHT A-1) ON                        *Turn the Master Bedroom light ON*
End

---

EVENT: **MASTER BED RM MOTION LIGHT OFF**                 *Feature name*
  **IF**                                                                                 *if*
    (DI: MD1 ) goes ON                             *If motion detector MD1 stops detecting motion*
  **THEN**                                                                             *then*
    (T: TIME 1 ) LOAD with  0 : 02 : 00               *Start 2 minute 'Timer 1' shown below*
End

---

EVENT: **TIME 1**                                                                     *Feature name*
  **IF**                                                                                 *if*
    (T: TIME 1 ) is Expiring                             *When 2 minute timer has expired*
  **THEN**                                                                             *then*
    (X: MASTER LIGHT A-1) OFF                       *Turn the Master Bedroom light OFF*
End

---

EVENT: **ENTRY MOTION, LIGHT, CCTV & TV ON**                 *Feature name*
  **IF**                                                                                 *if*
    (DI: MD16 ) goes OFF                          *If entryway motion detector detects motion*
    and (F: AWAY ) is Set                                *and the 'Away Flag' is Set*
  **THEN**                                                                             *then*
    (X: ENTRY LIGHT  D-5) ON                          *Turn entryway light ON*
    (RELAY: CAMERA # 2)  ON                          *Turn CCTV Camera # 2 ON*
    (IR: TV KIT  ) play 1 time(s) [Kitchen]                *Select Kitchen TV*
    (IR: POWER ) play 1 time(s) [Kitchen]                *Turn Kitchen TV ON*
    (IR: 7 ) play 1 time(s) [Kitchen]      *Select first digit of channel 74 to view front door camera*
    (IR: 4 ) play 1 time(s) [Kitchen]     *Select second digit of channel 74 to view front door camera*
    (TIME 5 )  LOAD  with  00:15:00               *Timer 5 will count down from 15 min to 0 min*
End

---

EVENT: **TIME 5**                                                                     *Feature name*
  **IF**                                                                                 *if*
    (T: TIME 5 ) is Expiring                             *When 15 minute timer has expired*
  THEN                                                                                 *then*
    (X: ENTRY LIGHT D-5) OFF                         *Turn entryway light OFF*
    (IR: TV KIT  ) play 1 time(s) [Kitchen]                *Select Kitchen TV*
    (IR: POWER ) play 1 time(s) [Kitchen]                *Turn Kitchen TV OFF*
    (RELAY: CAMERA-2)  OFF                          *Turn CCTV Camera-2 OFF*
End

# FIVE

# Integrated Security Systems

**5-1 Example Home Security System:** Before a security system can be installed, a sketch should be made of the home to illustrate the locations of the security panel, detection devices, keypads, CCTV cameras, sirens/bells as well as other components. This sketch should look something like the 'Example Home' sketch shown in Figure 5-3. The security system used in the 'Example Home' contains a wide variety of components that provide the homeowner with an above average level of home security. This system is also integrated with the *Stargate* Home Controller to provide automation capabilities as well. Notice in Figure 5-3, the variety of system

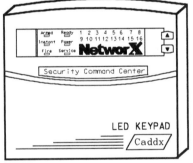

components shown throughout the plan along with the component identifiers listed in the legend. Individual security system sensors and miscellaneous components are covered in Sections 5-5 through 5-16. All cable routings and the type of cable required for each system component is also illustrated in Figure 5-3.

The security panel is installed in the *Equipment Room* where it is dry and hidden away from potential burglars. The panel uses an unswitched 120 AC power receptacle and a telephone extension line shown in Figure 1-8.

The appropriate conductors are pulled from the *Equipment Room* in a 'Home-Run' wiring topology to each magnetic switch, motion sensor, glassbreak sensor, etc. on the property.

Twenty two gauge, 4-conductor cable (2 conductors used) is pulled for all window and door magnetic switches. Twenty two gauge, 8-conductor cable (4 conductors used) is pulled for all motion sensors, infrared beam sensors, glassbreak sensors, keypads and other system components. During the rough–in process in a newly constructed home each cable 'Home Run' is pulled off of a reel from the *Equipment Room,* up into and through the attic towards the location of each system component. In a wood framed home, cable is pulled for each magnetic window switch and is passed through a 1/2" diameter pre-drilled hole in the top plate of the exterior wall. It is then pulled down to and through another pre-drilled hole in a wall stud located right next to the window opening where the switch will later be installed. Cable used for a magnetic switch installed in an exterior door opening is routed through a 1/2" diameter pre-drilled hole in the top plate of the wall and door header. This cable will later be passed through the door casing by the door installer. All cables are cut 1-foot longer than required to provide enough working cable length during the trim-out stage. These cables must be anchored to the stud so they will not be accidentally pulled out of place. When a sensor is installed to protect a door or window in an exterior block wall, the supporting cable is routed as follows: Each cable is pulled through the attic and down on the interior surface of the wall insulation between the furring strips to where the sensor will be installed. Cable will need to be supported by the rigid insulation using plastic wire clips. When a cable is routed to a motion sensor or other device that will be mounted to the drywall, the installer will pull the cable to where the device will be installed and anchor the cable to a wall stud or ceiling joist. Each 'Home-Run' cable should be identified by attaching a label 6" from the end of the cable located in the equipment room. This will allow the security system installer to know what cable supports what sensor or keypad. This will also permit the installer to wire groups of sensors in series from inside the security panel to create security *Zones*. Each *Zone* will then be terminated to a pair of *Zone* terminal screws located on the appropriate module.

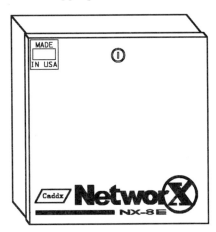

FIGURE 5-1 CADDX SECURITY PANEL

Notice the Infrared Beam sensors installed on the property perimeter in Figure 5-3. These sensors are wired by pulling burial cable to each location. The CCTV surveillance camera portion of the security system shown in Figure 5-3, is best described in Section 6-5 on page 132.

The security system panel located in the *Equipment Room* is a *Caddx NetworX*, which is used for 'Example Home' purposes. The main core component of this system is the NX8-E control module. Figure 5-4 illustrates the 'Example Home' control module, security components and support cabling. The NX8-E control module provides 8 fully programmable hardwired *Zones* and can be expanded to 192

*Zones* by adding Expansion Modules. In the 'Example Home', we added on one 16 *Zone* hardwired Expansion Module model NX216-E as shown in Figure 5-5. An optional 8 *Zone Caddx* NX-408E Wireless Module shown in Figure 5-6, could also be used in areas of the home where it is very difficult to pull hardwires.

The *Caddx* NX8-E security system has the capability of providing eight separate partitions that allow the system to function independently if desired. The *Caddx* system's microprocessor has EEPROM memory that maintains system programming if there is an AC power failure or backup battery failure. The security panel requires a 16.5-Volt, 40 VA transformer to furnish power to the overall system. This transformer connects to the AC terminals shown in Figure 5-4.

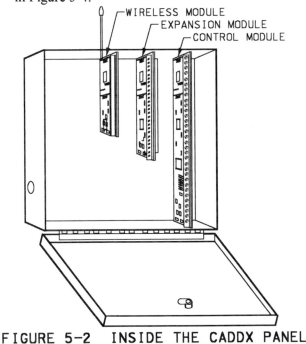

FIGURE 5-2 INSIDE THE CADDX PANEL

The battery backup provides the system with power in case the home's AC power source should fail. This battery will also provide additional current when the system's power consumption exceeds the output power of the transformer. This can occur when the panel is in an alarm condition.

The (AUX PRW) and (COM) terminals shown in Figure 5-4, provide a maximum of 1 amp to sensory components such as motion sensors, glassbreak sensors, strobe, etc.

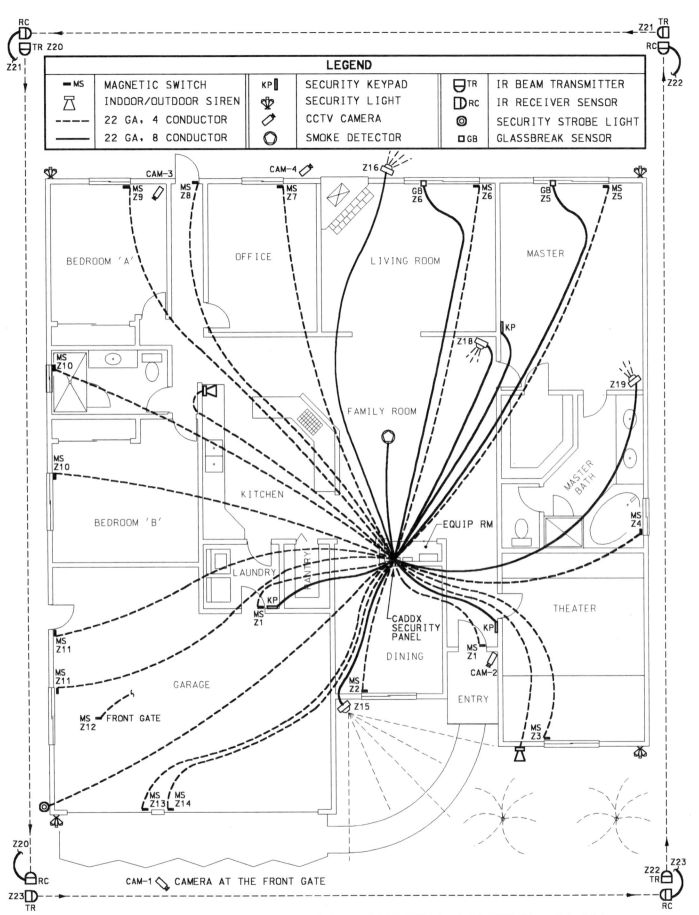

# Figure 5-3   SECURITY SYSTEM CONTROL PLAN

SEE Figures 5-4 & 5-5 FOR PANEL WIRING DIAGRAMS

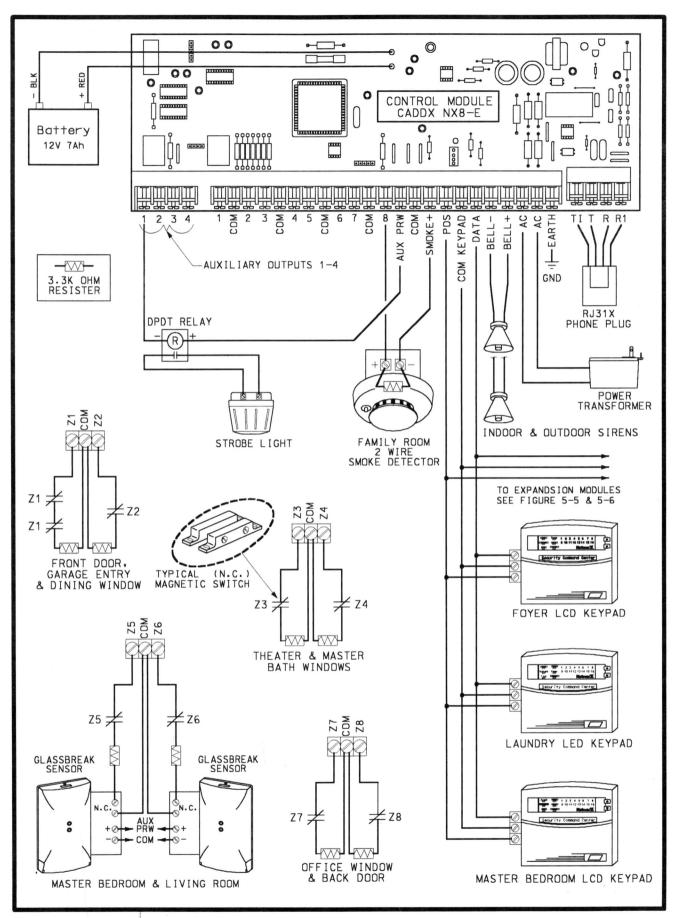

# Figure 5-4 SECURITY SYSTEM WIRING DIAGRAM

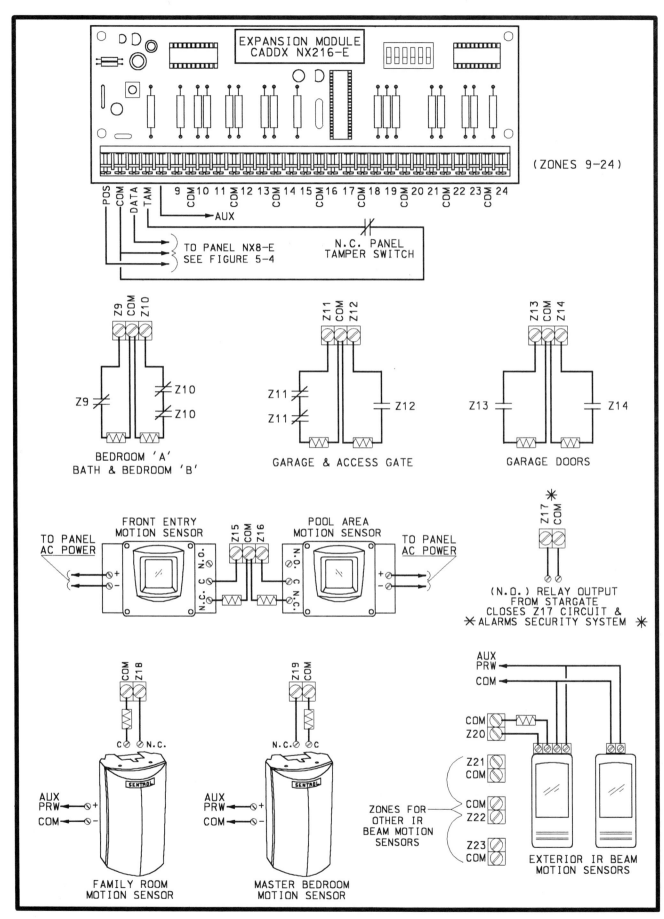

# Figure 5-5    SECURITY SYSTEM WIRING DIAGRAM

The 'Bell Output' terminals provide a maximum of 2.5 amps of current at 12V DC and are used to power alarm bells, sirens, and other alarm warning devices except a strobe light. The strobe is wired to a DPDT relay that is connected to the control module as shown in Figure 5-4. Bells and sirens provide an audible warning while a strobe provides the occupants with a visual indication that the home has been broken into while away from home. The system can be programmed to turn the strobe ON and keep it ON even after the panel automatically turns the alarm OFF after a preprogrammed period of time. When the authorities see that the coast is clear, the homeowner can manually enter a code into the keypad to turn the strobe OFF.

The Keybus terminals shown in Figure 5-4, identified as POS, COM KEYPAD and DATA are used as a communication path for Keypads, *Zone* Expansion Modules and other optional modules connected to the main control module. Some of the optional Expansion Modules will soon be introduced and described.

The next terminals to identify are the programmable auxiliary outputs 'AUXOUT 1 thru 4'. When an auxiliary output terminal is programmed to close, it will close a circuit to common or ground. Each auxiliary output is rated for 50mA and can be used to activate LEDs, relays, strobe lights and small buzzers.

*Zone* input terminals are identified on the security modules as Z1 thru Z24. Detection devices such as magnetic switches, motion sensors, glassbreak sensors etc., are wired to these terminals as shown in Figures 5-4 & 5-5. One device can be wired to each pair of terminals or several devices can be wired in series to create a *Zone*. This can be done as long as the loop resistance does not exceed 300 Ohms.

The telephone line terminal connections T, R, T-1 & R-1 are used to communicate to a central monitoring station or for downloading the security program to the panel microprocessor.

The *Caddx* system supports hardwired sensors and/or wireless sensors. Using hardwired sensors will reduce the likelihood of false alarms and do not require batteries that need replacing. Although wireless technology is considered to be more susceptible to false alarms, they are still

very dependable and only on rare occasions will they cause a premature alarm condition.

In Figure 5-5, notice that the 16 *Zone* NX216-E Expansion Module is used in the 'Example Home' to provide additional *Zones* for magnetic switches, motion sensors, etc. This device is connected to the POS, COM & DATA terminals shown on the NX8-E control module.

In Figure 5-6, notice the 8 *Zone* NX-408E Wireless Expansion Module and other wireless security components. 1 to 48 *Zones* can be wireless. If an intruder enters the home, sensors will transmit RF signals to the wireless NX-408E to trigger the alarm. Wireless sensors also transmit supervisory RF signals every 63 minutes to notify the system that the sensors are operating properly. If the wireless module hears from the transmitting sensors on a regular basis, there is no problem reported. If the panel does not receive a supervisory signal it will generate a *Zone* supervisory trouble indication.

An optional NX-540 Telephone Interface Module allows any touch-tone phone to act as a fully functional keypad. This option helps to minimize the quantity of security wall keypads in a system. Some of these functions include: *Arm*, *Disarm* and *Check Status* of the system while at home or away. This module also provides a built-in interface to control a maximum of 32 Power-line Carrier Receiver Switches. These units receive signals over the home's powerlines to control electrical loads and are primarily used in existing homes that do not incorporate a hardwired control system. These devices control lighting, ceiling fans, HVAC, etc. For example, a security sensor like the magnetic switch serving the front door can be used to trigger electrical loads OFF when leaving the home and ON when arriving home.

There is also an optional NX-320 Power Supply Output Module that will provide a maximum of 1 amp of additional current for modular devices connected to the system.

A maximum of 8 keypads per partition and a total of 24 per system can be wired to the control module. These devices are used by the homeowner to control the security system and to receive system status information. Keypads range from an '8 *Zone* to a '48 *Zone* LED unit'.

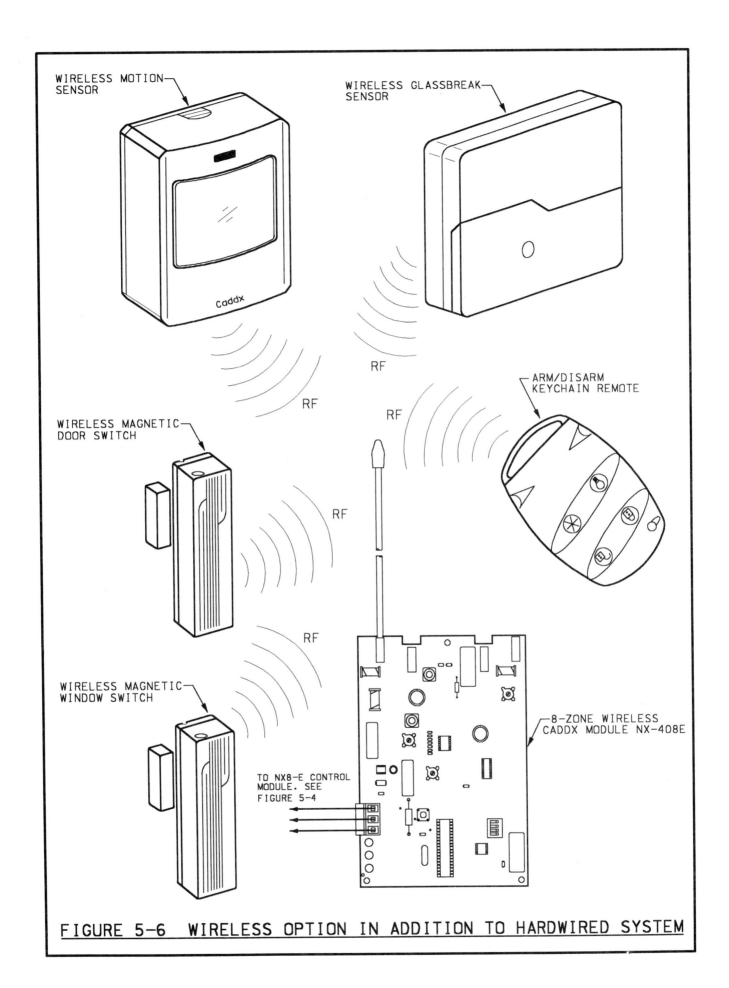

WIRELESS MOTION SENSOR

WIRELESS GLASSBREAK SENSOR

ARM/DISARM KEYCHAIN REMOTE

WIRELESS MAGNETIC DOOR SWITCH

WIRELESS MAGNETIC WINDOW SWITCH

RF

RF

RF

RF

RF

Caddx

8-ZONE WIRELESS CADDX MODULE NX-408E

TO NX8-E CONTROL MODULE. SEE FIGURE 5-4

FIGURE 5-6   WIRELESS OPTION IN ADDITION TO HARDWIRED SYSTEM

These devices provide function indicator lights, a siren and individual *Zone* indicator lights. There is also an LCD keypad available. This unit provides function indicator lights, word descriptions for *Zone* status and a built-in speaker/siren. This speaker is capable of frequencies that can produce "Ding Dong" sounds as well as an audible alarm.

There are 5 function buttons on all standard *Caddx* system keypads. These functions include: 'Stay', 'Chime', 'Exit, 'Bypass', and 'Cancel'. Pushing the 'Stay' button *Arms* the system as long as the quick *Arm* feature has been enabled. If it is not enabled, the homeowner must enter the access code prior to pressing the 'Stay' button. The 'Exit' button *Arms* the system. All 'Exit' type *Zones* are active at the end of the 'Exit Delay'. Similar to the 'Stay' function, pushing the 'Exit' button *Arms* the system as long as the quick *Arm* feature has been enabled. If it is not enabled, the user must enter the access code prior to pressing the 'Exit' button.

There are also 'Fire', 'Emergency' and 'Police' buttons on all keypads. A key must be pressed for a period of 2-seconds to initiate a function successfully. The 2-second requirement is used to avoid an accidental alarm condition if the user prematurely presses a button. The security system cannot be *Armed* until the 'Ready' light is ON. If the 'Ready' light is not ON, the homeowner must make sure all windows and doors are closed while avoiding areas that are covered by motion sensors.

Other features provided by the security system are the 'Entry' and 'Exit Delay' functions. Any number of *Zones* can be programmed for 'Entry' or 'Exit Delay' purposes and two timers are available per *Zone*. This type of *Zone* is for door openings that the homeowner uses for normal entry when arriving or for exiting the home. When the panel is *Armed* the 'Exit Delay' will begin. When the audible 'Exist Delay' is enabled, the keypad will beep every second until the 'Exit Delay' expires. The keypad will then beep rapidly for the last 10 seconds of the 'Exit Delay' period to warn the homeowner that the system is about to be *Armed*. 'Delay 1 Zone' provides an entry delay that will leave the homeowner sufficient time to manually *Disarm* the system upon entry. Keypads will initiate a

beeping sound to warn the occupants that the system needs to be *Disarmed* upon arrival. If the system is not *Disarmed* during the 'Entry Delay' period the system will alarm. The 'Delay 2 Zone' works the same as the 'Delay 1 Zone'; however, it is used when a different delay period of time is required. For instance; the 'Delay 2 Zone' is typically used for the garage door where a longer delay period is required to park, get out of the car and walk to the keypad to *Disarm* the system.

If the homeowner would like the *Caddx* NX8-E or NX8 security system to be *Armed & Disarmed* automatically when leaving and arriving home respectively, *Stargate* can provide this convenience as described in Section 5-2 that follows.

An 'Interior Zone' is typically used for interior protection of the home and is generally monitored by motion sensors. When the panel is *Armed*, the interior *Zone* will allow entry if a delay type *Zone* was violated first. If not, it will cause an instant alarm.

An 'Instant Zone' is generally used for windows, sliding glass doors and other home perimeter type *Zones* that are not used by the homeowner when arriving or leaving the home. When this type of *Zone* is violated the alarm will be activated instantly. The alarm can also be programmed to provide an audible or silent notification to the monitoring station.

**5-2 Automatic Security System Arm/Disarm:** *Arming* and *Disarming* the *Caddx* Security System through the *Stargate* Interactive Home Controller will provide the homeowner with added safety, security, convenience and control capabilities. By pressing a *JDS* Keypad button as the homeowner leaves the residence, the 'Leaving Home Mode' is initiated. This mode will change the state of desired electrical loads on the premises as well as *Arm* the security system.

Another mode called 'Arriving Home' is similarly used to change the state of desired electrical loads and *Disarm* the security system. The homeowner can choose one of several methods of initiating the 'Arriving Home Mode' including the use of a long-range push button transmitter from a car. This device ultimately provides a Digital Input to *Stargate* before *Stargate* knows to initiate the mode.

**5-3 Interfacing *Stargate* to *Caddx* NX8-E:** The first question that someone may ask is why would I want to interface *Stargate* to my security system? This question can be answered like this. The conventional home automation system will at times utilize a variety of sensors and transmitters to initiate control sequences or modes. The beauty behind interfacing the home automation controller (*Stargate*) with the security system is explained as follows: *Stargate* will be allowed to read the state of each security system sensor and whether the security system is *Armed, Disarmed* or in an alarm condition. If *Stargate* knows that the front door magnetic switch has opened upon arrival, *Stargate* will run the '*Arriving Home Mode.* With this method of activation, the owner would not want to include the security system *Disarming* function. Conditionally, this mode may turn ON a number of lights for safety only when it is after Sunset. It may also open vertical blinds, turn ON your favorite music only if it is before 10:00 PM on Friday or Saturday night. *Stargate* can also read the state of each motion sensor in the home so it will be able to control lights ON and OFF automatically when an occupant enters or exits a room.

If an intruder enters the front door or any other portion of the home, *Stargate* can be programmed to place a phone call to a pre-selected number that will notify the homeowner of the intrusion while the security system calls the monitoring station. *Stargate* can also track and record an intruder's steps through the home with the use of data received from the motion sensors. This may give the authorities information about the crime that may otherwise be unavailable. One can see that there are numerous functions that a home automation system can provide the owner with the use of inputs from one or more security sensors.

*Stargate* can read all of the *Caddx* security functions through the *Caddx* NX8-E RS-232 built-in interface. The standard *Caddx* NX8 security system can also interface with *Stargate*, however, functions can only be read through the optional NX584 Serial Interface. *Stargate* has the ability to perform functions and recognize conditions that follow.

1. *Arm* or *Disarm* the security system
2. Switch between Home and Away modes.
3. Bypass *Zones*
4. Turn the keypad chime mode ON or OFF
5. Monitor and act upon *Zone* changes
6. Automatically set the alarm panel's clock
7. Track the status of the security system
8. Detect alarm conditions
9. Sound the 'Fire Panic Mode'
10. Sound the 'Medical Panic Mode'
11. Sound the 'Police Panic Mode'
12. Detect *Zone* trouble conditions

Before attempting to interface *Stargate* with the *Caddx* security panel, the security system must first be operational. We recommend getting the security system up and running with all the bugs worked out before connecting it to *Stargate*. This will reduce the likelihood of system problems and make troubleshooting much easier if required. After the security system is operational and all is well, the interface cable connection between *Stargate* and *Caddx* can be made. *Stargate* interfaces with *Caddx* in the arrangement shown in Figure 5-7. Beginning at the *Stargate* connector, notice how the 6 conductor modular data cable (RS-232) connects to *Stargate's* COM 2 or COM 3 port. The other end of this cable is an RJ-11 to DB-9 male serial adapter that connects to the female DB-9 connector of the *Caddx* serial cable. The end connection is made to the *Caddx* security module in the location shown. After all connections have been made, it is time to configure *Stargate's* WinEVM software. Support for all *Caddx* panels requires WinEVM Version 3.00 or higher. The user will first open up the security system configuration screen in the software under the 'Define' menu. In the security system select box, the user would select '*Caddx NetworX'*. In the 'Serial port used box', the user would select the *Stargate* serial port number Com 2 or Com 3 where the security system is connected. For each security *Zone*, the user would enter a descriptive name like '*Front Door', 'Pool Slider', 'Garage Door'*, or '*Family Room motion detector'* to be used in *Stargate's* schedule.

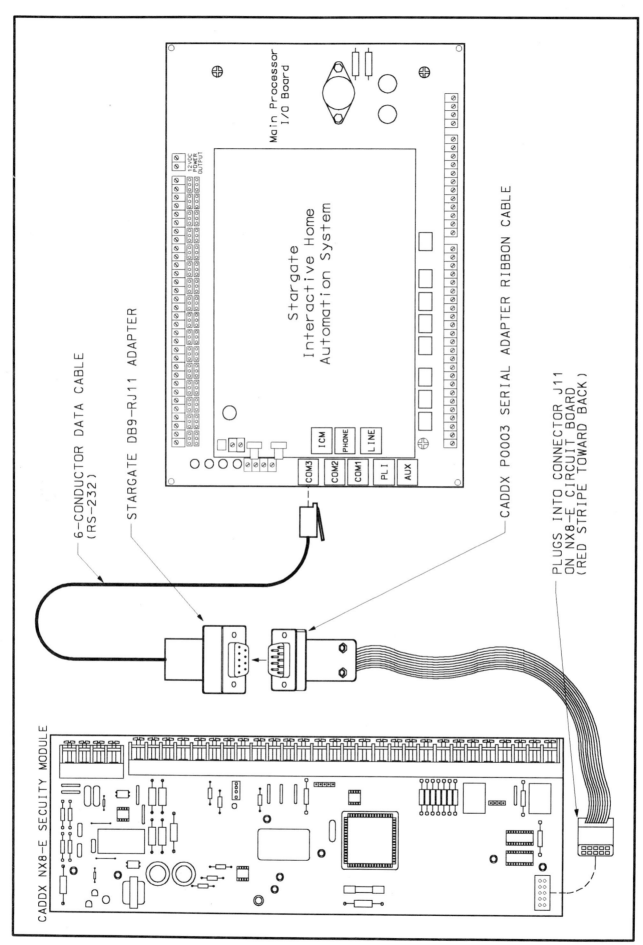

FIGURE 5-7 STARGATE INTERFACE WITH CADDX NX8-E SECURITY SYSTEM

By clicking 'OK', WinEVM will configure *Stargate's* serial port for use with the *Caddx* security system. At this point in the setup the user will be able to use the IF, THEN statements anywhere in *Stargate's* schedule. With *Stargate's* MegaController utility in the software, the user can monitor the security system's activity to verify that *Stargate* is communicating properly with the *Caddx* security system. Windows from the WinEVM software are shown in Figure 5-8 & 5-9. They display the security system conditions and commands that *Stargate* can use

in the IF, THEN statements anywhere in the schedule. At the start of every schedule pass, *Stargate* will process the information that the *Caddx* security panel has sent. Any changes to partitions or security *Zones* will cause an internal "transition" state that will be cleared at the end of the schedule. By selecting the "Transition Activated" checkbox, the IF condition will be true when the condition goes active, as opposed to when the condition is active. To explain this in the best way, see the 'Partition Armed' and 'Security Lights' Events on page 114.

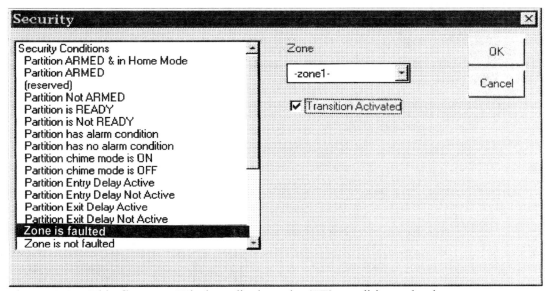

Figure 5-8   This *Stargate* Window displays the '**IF**' condition selections.

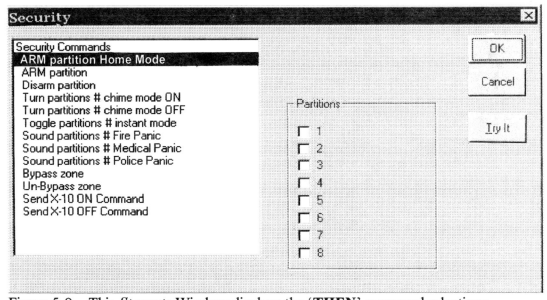

Figure 5-9   This *Stargate* Window displays the '**THEN**' command selections.

# *Stargate's* Event Programming When Using The *Caddx* RS-232 Interface

EVENT: **PARTITION ARMED**                               *Feature name*
   **IF**                                                 *if*
     Partition ARMED [Partition 1] TRANSITION       *If partition #1 has just become Armed*
   **THEN**                                         *then*
     LCD: Red LED ON                         *Turns ON Red LED on JDS Keypad*
End

Note: In this example the Red LED on *JDS* LCD Keypad's will turn ON at the time the security system panel gets *Armed*.

EVENT: **SECURITY LIGHTS**                          *Feature name*
   **IF**                                                 *if*
     Partition ARMED [Partition 1]           *If partition #1 is in the Armed state*
     and Sunset SMTWTFS             *and it is Sunset Sun. thru Sat.*
   **THEN**                                         *then*
     X-10: F-1 Front Porch Light ON         *Turns ON porch light*
End

Note: In this example the Front Porch light will turn ON if the security panel is *Armed* and it is Sunset as opposed to GOES *Armed*. If "Transition Activated" was used, the Event would be triggered only if the security panel became *Armed* at the same time as Sunset.

EVENT: **'LEAVING HOME' – ARMS SYSTEM**           *Feature name*
   **IF**                                                 *if*
     (F: LEAVING HOME) is Set       *If 'Leaving Home Mode' Flag is set from JDS Keypad*
   **THEN**                                         *then*
     (Partition ARM) [Partition 1]       *Arms security system Partition #1*
     (F: ARRIVING HOME) Clear       *Clears 'Arriving Home Mode' Flag*
End

EVENT: **'ARRIVING HOME' – DISARMS SYSTEM**      *Feature name*
   **IF**                                                 *if*
     (F: ARRIVING HOME) is Set       *If 'Arriving Home Mode' Flag is set from JDS Keypad*
   **THEN**                                         *then*
     (Partition DISARM) [Partition 1]       *Disarms security system Partition #1*
     (F: LEAVING HOME) Clear       *Clears 'Leaving Home Mode' Flag*
End

EVENT: **CCTV CAMERA**                              *Feature name*
   **IF**                                                   *if*
     Partition has alarm condition [Partition 1]       *If partition #1 alarms system*
   **THEN**                                         *then*
     (RELAY: CAM-1) ON       *Turns ON CCTV camera #1*
     (IR: RECORD) play 1 time(s) [Equipment Room]    *Starts video recorder located in Equip. Rm*
     Delay 0:30:00       *Waits 30 minutes*
     (IR: STOP) play 1 time(s) [Equipment Room]    *Stops video recorder located in Equip. Rm*
End

EVENT: **POLICE PANIC**                             *Feature name*
   **IF**                                                   *if*
     (F: Police) is Set       *If 'Police Panic' Flag is set from JDS Keypad*
   **THEN**                                          *then*
     Telephone Out: ^911       *Dials phone for help from the police*
     Voice Emergency       *Voice over the phone, a request for help*
     Telephone Out: +       *Hangs up*
     (F: Police) Clear       *Clears 'Police Panic' Flag*
End

**5-4 Monitoring any Security System Using Stargate:** Any hardwired security system can be monitored by *Stargate*. Monitoring a standard security system will allow *Stargate* to make control decisions based upon the present state of each security *Zone* and whether the security system is in an alarm condition. Although the methods of monitoring any wired security system described in the following paragraphs, falls short of the monitoring capabilities described in the *Caddx* RS-232 interface Section 5-3, it can provide a level of monitoring that is still useful for both security and home automation purposes.

To interface any hardwired security system the installer would wire each *Zone* in series with a *Stargate* Digital Input as shown in Figure 5-10. Notice the normally closed (N.C.) security contact switches wired to 'Digital Inputs 1' through 7. These contacts represent sensors such as magnetic switches, motion sensors, glassbreak sensors, etc. If the contacts from any sensor are opened by an intrusion and the bell/siren is energized, *Stargate* will read these conditions. *Stargate* receives this data from the affected *Zone(s)* (1-7) and the 'Bell outputs' connected to Digital Input 8 as shown in Figure 5-10. Even if the security system is *Disarmed*, individual open *Zone* contacts will be read by *Stargate*, which can be used to initiate automatic control responses. With the correct wiring along with *Stargate's* programmed Events, the automation capabilities of *Stargate* can be used to work in security modes that will provide some of it's own unique security features.

During an alarm condition, *Stargate* can turn ON lights after Sunset to allow occupants to egress safely. *Stargate* can also make audible announcements to try and scare off the intruder. CCTV cameras and a video recorder can be turned ON. Window coverings can be opened to allow the police to see into the home as they approach. By wiring all security *Zones* through *Stargate's* Digital Inputs, decisions can be made based on what particular *Zone(s)* has been violated. This will allow *Stargate* to provide a specific audible response to an intrusion for the purpose of helping the occupants avoid these areas of the home during egress.

In Figure 5-10, the security panel provides low voltage power to each Digital Input circuit while magnetic switches are closed. A 'Digital Input OFF' condition is detected by *Stargate* when a switch opens. The Digital Input jumpers must be Set to the 'Voltage' position as shown. A "end-of-line resistor may be required in each circuit to maintain the proper current. Contact the security system manufacturer for the maximum *Zone* current and resister requirements.

The security system can be *Armed* and *Disarmed* by wiring a standard keyswitch to any security *Zone* on the panel. A keyswitch is a security system device used to manually *Arm* and *Disarm* the system using a key. When the security system sees this particular *Zone* close and then open approximately one second later (momentary contact closure), the security system will *Arm*. The next time the security system sees a momentary closure it will *Disarm* the system.

When the homeowner wishes to *Arm* or *Disarm* 'any security system" with *Stargate's* automation capabilities an actual keyswitch is not used. Instead the switching action is performed by one of *Stargate's* Relay Outputs to provide a contact closure. By controlling the 'N.O. Relay Output 1' closed and then open, *Stargate* is able to mimic a keyswitch and automatically *Arm* or *Disarm* the security system. After the wiring is complete, security *Zone* 8 shown in Figure 5-10, must be programmed into the security system for a momentary contact closure. See the *Arm & Disarm* functions shown in the 'Leaving & 'Arriving Home' Events shown on page 117.

When *Disarming* the security system as one of many functions provided by the 'Arriving Home Mode', the integrity of the security system must be maintained. This is achieved by initiating the 'Arriving Home Mode' using a long range (200 feet or more) push button RF transmitter as the occupants approach the home. The RF receiver is wired to 'Digital Input 9' and will provide a maintained contact closure. This will inform *Stargate* to initiate the 'Arriving Home Mode'. This mode is designed to prepare the home for the occupants before they actually enter the home by turning ON select lighting, adjusting the HVAC temperature set-points, turning ON the water heater, turning ON some favorite music and could include the command to *Disarm* the security system.

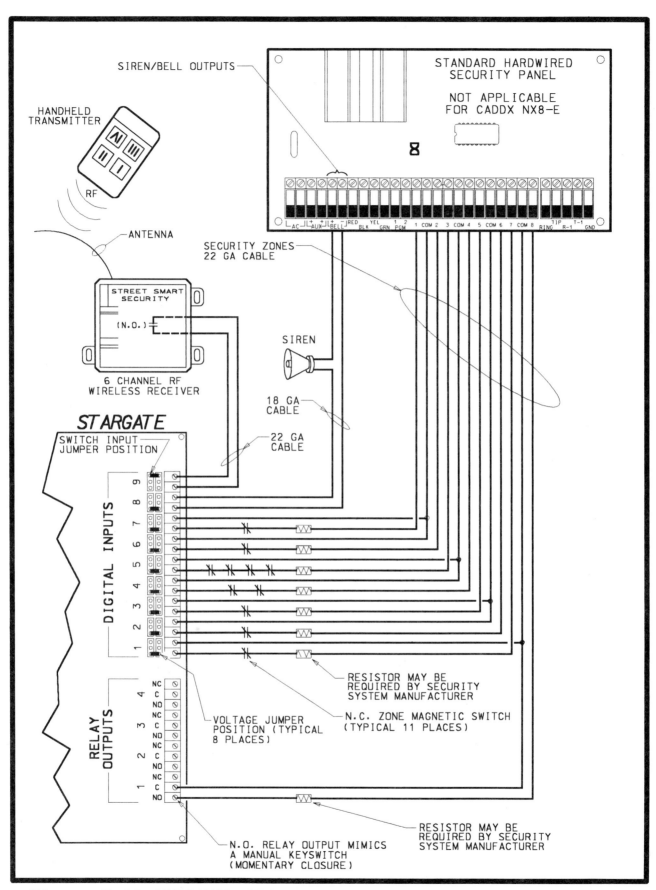

Figure 5-10 OPTIONAL SECURITY SYSTEM INTERFACE TO STARGATE

116

| STARGATE PROGRAMMING: | Description: |
|---|---|

EVENT: **'LEAVING' – ARMS SYSTEM** — *Mode name*
**IF** — *if*
  ( F: AWAY ) — *If 'Away' Flag is set from JDS Keypad*
**THEN** — *then*
  ( RELAY: ARM )  ON — *Close Relay Output*
  DELAY  0:00:01 — *Wait 1 second*
  **( RELAY: ARM )  OFF** — ***Open Relay Output (Arms security system)***
  *All other lines of Leaving Home Mode programming*
  "      "      "
End

EVENT: **ARRIVING HOME – DISARMS SYSTEM** — *Mode name*
 **IF** — *if*
  ( DI: ARRIVING )  is ON — *When a Digital Input triggered by RF Receiver contacts*
  and  ( F: AWAY )  is SET — *and the 'Away' Flag is Set*
**THEN** — *then*
  ( F: AWAY )  CLEAR — *Clear the 'Away' Flag to keep various modes from running*
  ( X10: GAR RECEPT )  ON — *Turn garage door receptacle power ON*
  DELAY  0:00:01 — *Wait 1 second*
  ( RELAY: GAR DR OPN )  ON — *Relay Output closes*
  DELAY  0:00:01 — *Wait 1 second*
  ( RELAY: GAR DR OPN )  OFF — *Open Garage door - Relay opens*
  ( X10: LIGHT GARAGE)  ON — *Turn garage lights ON*
  ( RELAY: DISARM )  ON — *Relay closes security Zone*
  DELAY  0:00:01 — *Wait 1 second*
  **( RELAY: DISARM )  OFF** — ***Disarm security system - relay opens***
  *All other lines of Arriving Home Mode programming*
  "      "      "
End

---

EVENT: **INTRUDER ON THE PROPERTY** — *Mode name*
 **IF** — *if*
  ( DI: ARRIVING 4 )  Goes  ON — *Digital Input 4 triggered by IR Beam sensor #1*
**THEN** — *then*
  Voice: " Halt, You Are On Private Property" — *First Message through outdoor speakers*
  ( X10: PERIMETER LIGHTING )  ON — *Turn perimeter property lights ON*
  ( X10: SECURITY LIGHTS )  ON — *Turn security lights ON*
  ( F: CAMERA)  Set — *Set Camera #2 Flag to avoid multiple mode activations*
  ( RELAY: CAMERA # 2)  ON — *Turn CCTV Camera #2 ON*
  ( IR: RECORDER ) play 1 time(s) [Equip. RM] — *Select Time-Lapse VHS VCR Recorder*
  ( IR: POWER ) play 1 time(s) [Equip. RM] — *Turn Time-Lapse VHS VCR Recorder ON*
  DELAY  0:00:02 — *Wait 1 second*
  ( IR: 7 ) play 1 time(s) [Front Dr] — *Select first digit of channel 74 to view front door camera*
  ( IR: 4 ) play 1 time(s) [Front Dr] — *Select second digit of channel 74 to view front door camera*
  ( IR: TV KIT ) play 1 time(s) [Kitchen] — *Select Kitchen TV*
  ( IR: POWER ) play 1 time(s) [Kitchen] — *Turn Kitchen TV ON to see video*
  End

**5-5 Security and Automation System Sensors:**
There are a number of standard issue security system sensors that provide the homeowner with a variety of home security levels. The minimum level of home security may only include a panel and a magnetic switch sensor protecting each door and window. Other systems may include a few motion sensors and maybe a glassbreak sensor or two. An above average security system may also include window screen sensors, outdoor motion sensors, outdoor infrared beam sensors, smoke detectors, CCTV cameras as well as other components. The more levels of home security a system provides, the less likely the homeowner will experience an undetected intrusion.

Home automation systems will often times incorporate a number of security system type sensors that are used to initiate a variety of home control responses. Home automation systems can also use a variety of sensors that are considered non-standard security system components but are common components for a home automation system. Sensors are very important components to a home automation system because in many cases they are the devices that inform *Stargate* to request control responses from a variety of electrical loads on the premises. Without these specific sensors the automatic response of the system would be limited while the occupant's safety and security could be compromised.

**5-6 Magnetic Switch Sensors:** As we have seen in the 'Example Home', magnetic switch sensors are primarily used in security systems to monitor perimeter doors and windows to detect a home intrusion. They are also used in home automation systems to provide a control input to trigger one or more control responses from *Stargate*.

Magnetic switches are used in a variety of applications shown in Figures 5-11 through 5-14. A magnetic switch is made up of two separate components. One component is a switch and the other is a magnet. When the magnet is placed next to a normally closed (N.C.) magnetic switch, the switch will close. When the magnet is moved away from the switch, the switch will open. The switch component is installed on each door frame, window frame or floor while the magnet is mounted on the moving object such as a door, window, gate, etc. In a standard security

system installation, magnetic switches are considered the first line of defense. They are designed to initiate an alarm condition before an intruder can enter the home. When a switch is wired directly to a *Stargate* Digital Input, it can be used to initiate lighting in the entryways when the front door or garage door is opened. They can also be used to initiate an audible response from *Stargate* to let parents know that their child has entered the pool area.

Magnetic switches are manufactured in both normally open (N.O.) and normally closed (N.C.) versions. Normally closed units are primarily used for security system applications, however, (N.O) units can be wired in parallel with a resistor to initiate a trouble call if a *Zone* cable has broken. (N.O.) switches are occasionally wired in series with a *Stargate* Digital Input to notify *Stargate* when a door is actually open or closed. This configuration is used for the 'Example Home' driveway access gate. In this installation, *Stargate* is able to read the present position of the gate so it will know whether to send a command to open or close the gate. The (N.O.) switch it also used to notify the security system that an intruder has opened the gate. The security system will sound the alarm and *Stargate* will turn on CCTV cameras, TVs and a video recorder. See Section 10-3 for more on this application.

**5-7 Interior Motion Sensors:** Interior motion sensors are considered the second line of defense for most home security systems. This is because they are generally used to detect an intruder that has some how entered the home undetected by a window or door magnetic switch.

There are three types of interior motion sensors: Passive infrared (PIR), Ultrasonic, and dual technology models. The most common type of motion sensor used in the security and home automation industries is the (PIR). This sensor detects the body heat from an intruder passing through its coverage area. The dual technology units use passive infrared and

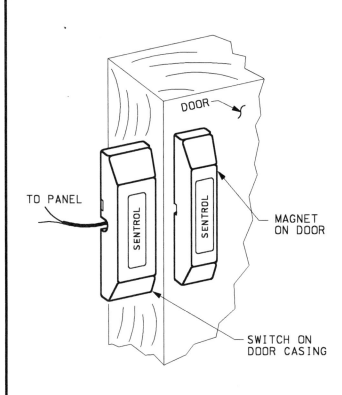

FIGURE 5-11    HARDWIRED DOOR/WINDOW
MAGNETIC CONTACTS

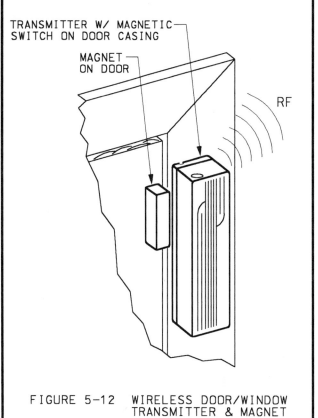

FIGURE 5-12    WIRELESS DOOR/WINDOW
TRANSMITTER & MAGNET

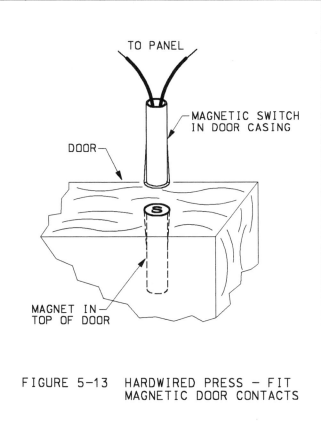

FIGURE 5-13    HARDWIRED PRESS - FIT
MAGNETIC DOOR CONTACTS

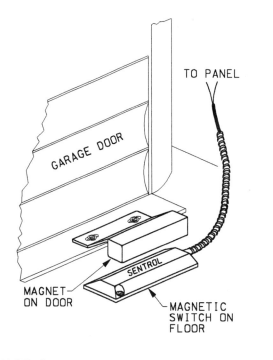

FIGURE 5-14    HARDWIRED OVERHEAD DOOR
MAGNETIC CONTACTS

microwave sensing technologies designed to detect an intruder passing through high frequency radio waves within the coverage area. In the 'Example Home', Ultrasonic 360-degree coverage motion sensors are located on the ceiling of each room and Hallway to detect intruders and to automatically control lighting ON & OFF. See Figure 4-8 for the locations of these motion sensors in the home. Dual purpose functions can be realized by wiring each motion sensor to a *Stargate* Digital Input.

In Figure 5-15, notice the motion sensor wired in series with the security panel and a *Stargate* Digital Input. These wires are connected to the motion sensor's normally closed (N.C.) set of contacts shown on the motion sensor. When an occupant enters the room the contacts in the motion sensor will open and both the security system and *Stargate* will read this condition. When the security system is *Armed,* the alarm will be activated while *Stargate* turns ON the appropriate *Zone* lighting. Even when the system is *Disarmed, Stargate* will recognize the open *Zone* and control specific lighting.

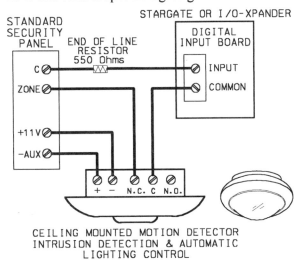

CEILING MOUNTED MOTION DETECTOR
INTRUSION DETECTION & AUTOMATIC
LIGHTING CONTROL

Figure 5-15    AUTOMATIC LIGHTING CONTROL
& INTRUSION DETECTION

**5-8 Outdoor Motion Sensors:** Outdoor motion sensors are used to detect an intruder approaching the home. Most of these type of sensors are passive infrared (PIR) devices that detect large heated objects moving across the yard. This type of sensor is normally immune to small animals and is designed to withstand harsh weather conditions and direct sunlight. Outdoor motion sensors are generally located to monitor the front and rear doors of the home, driveway gates, side gates or anywhere an intruder can enter the home. These devices can also be used to provide a Digital Input to *Stargate* when directly wired. This input can be used to control lighting in the correct areas of the property to hopefully scare off the intruder. Voice responses can also be initiated to warn an intruder that the authorities are on their way.

In the 'Example Home', there are outdoor (PIR) motion sensors located near the front door and rear patio identified as Z15 & Z16 respectively. These PIRs can be seen in Figure 5-3 & 5-5. They can also provide *Stargate* with RS-232 data through the *Caddx* interface. When *Stargate* receives this data, a *Stargate* Event will turn the appropriate exterior lights ON. If

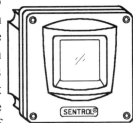

motion is not detected for 10-minutes after the initial detection, the lights will be turned OFF. Detection of motion can also initiate CCTV cameras located at the front door and patio areas and can be programmed to activate the security alarm when the system is *Armed*. An alarm can be initiated upon detection only if the occupants are away or if the 'Good Night Mode' has been initiated for the evening. The 'Example Home' has a fenced perimeter that is monitored by exterior Infrared Beam sensors. If an intruder gets past this first line of defense, detection by either (PIR) will warrant an alarm condition.

**5-9 Outdoor Infrared Beam Sensors:** Infrared beam sensors are used to create an invisible fence around the property. These devices are used in the 'Example Home' as shown in Figure 5-3. They are also shown in Figure 5-5 wired to *Zones* Z20 through Z23. Infrared Beam sensors are very difficult to get around or over without setting off

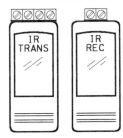

the alarm. This device consists of a transmitter that is positioned on one corner of the property and a receiver that is placed on the other corner of the property. An infrared beam is produced at the transmitter and is aimed at the receiver. If the security system is *Armed* and an IR beam receiver can no longer sense the transmitter beam (intruder passing), *Stargate* will initiate a voice response broadcast over an outdoor PA speaker while CCTV video is displayed on TVs in the home. If the intruder gets past an IR beam sensor, an exterior motion sensor will most likely pick the intruder up as they approach the home. Exterior Infrared Beam sensors are designed to be resistant to sunlight, fog, rain, snow and frost. They will continue to detect intruders even when the beam strength is reduced 99% due to bad weather. These sensors will automatically adjust the trigger sensitivity level for weather conditions that change slowly and also provide adjustments to the beam interruption time.

**5-10 Glassbreak Sensors:** Glassbreak sensors are used to detect an intruder breaking a window as a means of entering the home. This method is sometimes used by an intruder to avoid detection by magnetic switches that are normally installed at window and door locations. Glassbreak sensors

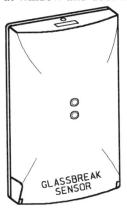

applied directly to the glass will detect the force of the glass breaking and will initiate an alarm condition. For rooms that have a large number of windows, a wall or ceiling mounted glass-break sensor is often used. These devices sense specific sound patterns produced when glass is breaking and can accurately detect breaking glass from up to 20 feet away. There are also dual technology glassbreak sensors that detect both shock and sound waves.

**5-11 Screen Sensors:** Magnetic switches that are installed to protect window and door openings are only useful when the window or door is closed. Some occupants prefer to sleep with one or more windows open at night, which can make them vulnerable to intruders. For this particular situation, screen sensors should be installed.

Screen sensors are woven into the screen structure. If an intruder cuts or removes the screen from the window, the alarm will go off. This type of sensor is delicate and can be easily damaged if not properly maintained.

**5-12 Smoke Detectors:** Smoke detectors are the most important sensor the occupants can have in the home because they save more lives than any other device in the home. These sensors are designed to alarm the security system and notify the occupants and/or monitoring station that fire or smoke is present in the home. Smoke detectors should be positioned in each bedroom and in the

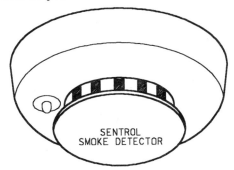

hallways leading to the bedrooms. These sensors should also be mounted at the ceiling level. Smoke sensors can be wired to both the standard security panel and Digital Inputs of *Stargate*. Programming of the security *Zones* served by these devices should sound an alarm tone that is different from the intrusion alarm tone. A 'voice response' from *Stargate* can also be used to notify the occupants why the alarm is sounding and where the fire is located. Refer to Figure 5-4 to see how the 'Example Home' Family Room smoke detector is wired to the security panel.

**5-13 Keychain Touchpad Remote:** When the homeowner wants to control the security system at his or her fingertips, the keychain touchpad is the answer. It can be carried around in ones pocket, purse or as a pendent. The user can wear this keypad at all times, even in the shower. Touchpads provide the homeowner with several convenient functions. They can be used to *Arm* the security system. The keychain touchpad can also *Arm* the system with no entry delay and *Disarm* the system while approaching the front door. Other control options include the activation of the Panic and Medical alarms. *Arming* the system is performed by pressing the locked button and *Disarming* the security

KEYCHAIN REMOTE

system is initiated by pressing the unlock button. When the lock and unlock buttons are pressed simultaneously, the system activates the Panic alarm. When the 'Light' and 'Star' buttons are pressed simultaneously, the Medical alarm is initiated. The 'Light' button *Arms* the security system in the 'Stay/Instant' mode. The 'Star' button performs the 'Exit' function.

**5-14 Security System Sirens:** Security sirens provide the homeowner and/or neighbors with an audible means of identifying an intrusion of the home or property. Eighteen gauge 2-conductor stranded wire is pulled from the security panel to each siren location. There are outdoor and indoor mounted sirens. An outdoor siren is normally located above the soffit and is directed towards the neighbors. They can also be installed in the

TO PANEL

OUTDOOR SIREN

attic next to the ventilation louver in the wall. There are three types of indoor sirens. Each type can be provided by a hardwired or wireless security system. Some sirens require a separate siren driver while other units have the driver built in. Interior sirens are generally located in the main body of the home at an elevation that can not be quickly accessed by an intruder. One type of interior siren provides audible siren tones only that are either steady or yelping. Another type of siren may provide either siren tones or an audible

word response of messages to the homeowner or intruder after a break in. The third siren type is located in the security keypad itself and normally provides an audible buzzing response to an intrusion.

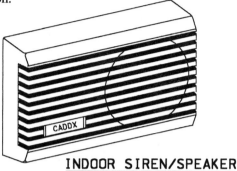

INDOOR SIREN/SPEAKER

**5-15 Carbon Monoxide Sensors:** Carbon monoxide produced from a failing gas stove, water heater, fireplace, furnace and other residential combustion appliances can cause sickness and even death. This odorless and colorless gas is the cause of approximately 300 deaths per year in residential homes. Even with this number of fatalities, the carbon monoxide sensor is considered the second most important sensor in the home. This is only because home fires cause even a greater number of deaths. Carbon monoxide sensors should be placed in each bedroom as well as in the hallways leading to the bedrooms. Sensors should also be mounted to the ceiling because carbon monoxide gas flows upward similar to the way smoke migrates.

**5-16 Water Leak Sensors:** Water leak sensors are used to monitor potential leaks in sink areas and near the dishwasher, cloths washer, water heater, toilets and air conditioner where condensate is drained. These sensors provide a means of communicating to the security system as well as to *Stargate* that there is water present. Water sensors should be installed at the low point of the floor where water will migrate. To protect the home, a solenoid valve can be installed in the supply water piping locally to automatically turn the water off when a leak is detected.

The wiring required to connect this device to the security system is a (22 GA, 2 connector) cable. Not only can a water sensor initiate the security alarm, but it can also initiate a 'voice response' from *Stargate* over the whole house audio system ("**water leak detected in kitchen**").

# Automated Whole House Audio &Video Sys ums

**6-1 Whole House Audio & Video Systems**: A 'Whole House Audio & Video System' is a centralized entertainment arrangement that pipes music and TV audio/video signals throughout the home. Since the system is centralized, the only components that are required in each room are the speakers, TVs, hand-held remote and an 'A/V In-Wall Controller'. The entertainment system designed for the 'Example Home' will be described and illustrated throughout this chapter to provide the reader with information on what is required during the pre-wiring stage and

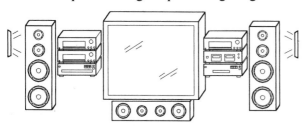

the system installation. The main system components that contribute to the 'Example Home' audio/video system are located in the Home Theater. They include the TV, Dolby Digital Receiver #1, Dolby Digital Receiver #2, *Kustom* 6 Amplifier #1, *Kustom* 6 Amplifier #2, Satellite Receiver, DVD Player, VCR, Cassette Tape Player and a Cable Box. The homeowner has the option of hiding these main system components away in an equipment room or an enclosure to provide a non-electronic look to the home. Equipment can also be configure so only the front panels of the components are exposed to the

Theater. In the 'Example Home' Theater the ladder configuration is incorporated.

The CD, DVD and VCR are all input devices of the 'Whole House Audio/Video System' that can provide entertainment within the room that the particular input device is located as well as provide entertainment to other rooms in the home. Besides the audio & video equipment located in the Home Theater, there are also separate components located in select rooms that include a DVD and/or VCR. These components are used primarily for convenience purposes. This means that the homeowner does not have to go to the Home Theater CD, DVD or VCR components to set-up the entertainment source if it is going to; for instance, be played in the Master Bedroom.

There are many different types of Whole House Audio/Video systems that the homeowner can choose from. There are systems that will provide superior sound and video at an absorbent price and there are systems that can provide high quality affordable entertainment. In the 'Example Home' we will describe and illustrate one method that provides quality entertainment for the average homeowner that could not afford a 'Whole House Audio/Video System' in the past.

**6-2 Whole House Audio:** The whole house audio portion of the 'Example Home' system is designed to provide audio from music sources as well as from TV programming to any room in the home. Sources that can provide audio include a CD or DVD players, tape players, tuners or satellite. The heart of the whole house audio portion of this system is the **Kustom 6 Amplifier** shown in Figure 6-1. In the 'Example Home' system illustrated in Figure 6-2, a quantity of two *Kustom 6 Amplifier* units are used to serve virtually every room in the home. Each of these units incorporate 6 discrete stereo amplifiers that are each rated at 20 watts per channel. To some audio enthusiasts, 20 watts per channel may not seem sufficient; however, it is more than enough to power speakers of a whole house audio system for applications where audio is played at reasonable listening levels. For Home Theater applications, a dedicated high wattage amplifier is generally used, which will often times provide a minimum of 100 watts per channel with heavy bass content for enhanced action packed movie audio. This dedicated high wattage amplifier is wired to the Home Theater audio & video components as shown in Figure 6-2.

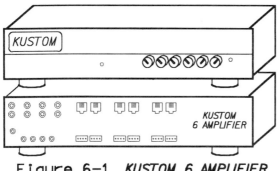

**Figure 6-1  KUSTOM 6 AMPLIFIER**

Other essential components used in this system are the wall mounted 'A/V Controllers'. An 'A/V Controller' is installed in each room to provide functions that include volume control, selection of four audio sources and a means of receiving and repeating IR signals. Independent LEDs light up on the face of these controllers to identify the input source selected. An 'A/V Controller' can be seen on the wall in each room as shown in Figure 6-2.

When wall mounted 'A/V Controllers' are used with a *Kustom 6 Amplifier,* family members can choose from the four different audio sources by pushing the volume knob on the 'Wall A/V Controller' or by pushing the appropriate button on a hand-held remote as illustrated in

Figure 6-3. The four audio sources are independent of the other rooms, which enables the users to listen to any of the four sources in different rooms at the same time.

The *Kustom 6 Amplifier* is designed to *use* one amplifier for each set of speakers to eliminate the need for impedance matchers or autoformers. (CAT 5, 4 UTP) cable is pulled during the construction phase of the home from the location where a *Kustom 6 Amplifier* will reside to each associated wall mounted 'A/V Controller' location. These cables are either part of the wire 'Bundle' drop in each room or are separate runs of cable used primarily for 'A/V Controller' communication. RJ-45 type phone plugs are installed on both ends of each cable pull to provide an easy method of termination. One RJ-45 connector is plugged into the rear of the 'A/V Controller' and the other end is plugged into the assigned jack of the *Kustom 6 Amplifier*. Each connection is shown in Figures 6-2 & 6-3.

The IR Receiver-Repeater located on the face of each 'A/V Controller' shown in Figure 6-3, receives IR command signals from a universal hand-held remote to make system function selections for greater convenience when watching a program from bed or the easy chain. Hand-held remotes must incorporate or learn the correct IR signal codes required to control the desired source input audio equipment functions. When an 'A/V Controller' receives the correct IR command signals from a remote, these signals will then travel over the CAT 5 conductors to a specific *Zone* connection (1 thru 6) located on the back of the appropriate *Kustom 6 Amplifier*. These signals will then travel through the component and out the IR Flasher Outputs (1 thru 4) that are also shown on the back of the *Kustom 6 Amplifier* in Figure 6-2. IR control signals can then be sent directly to the audio/video source equipment to access control functions; however, in the 'Example Home' we have incorporated an IR controller that will provide this system with automation capabilities as well. The IR controller we are referring to is the *IR-Xpander* that must be used along with the *Stargate* or other compatible home controller. (See Chapter Three for more on the *IR-Xpander.*) Instead of sending the IR control

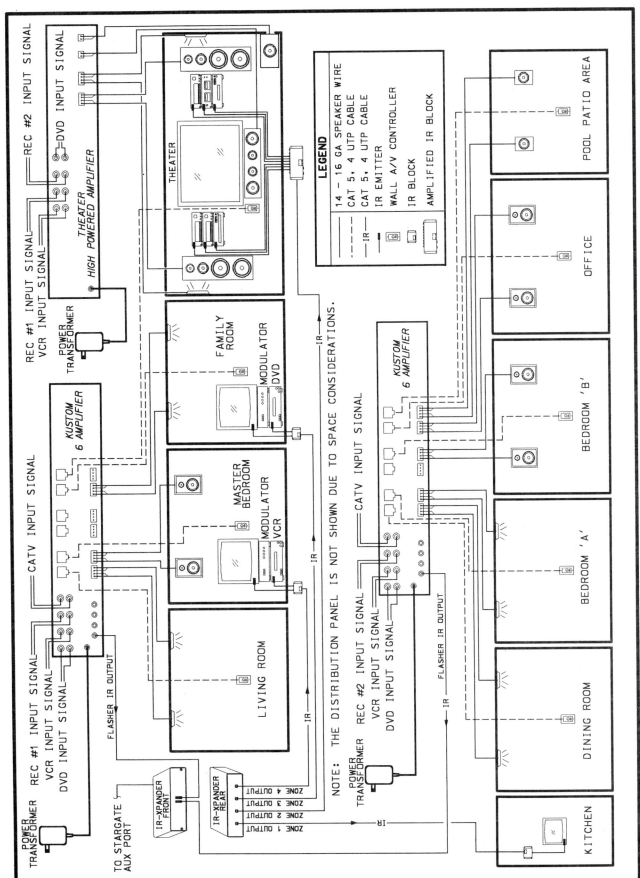

Figure 6-2 WHOLE HOUSE AUDIO & IR CONTROL SYSTEM

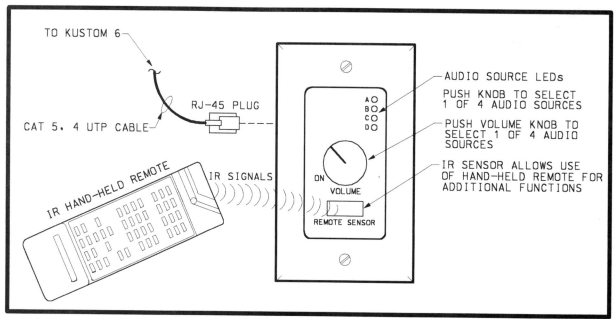

TO KUSTOM 6

CAT 5, 4 UTP CABLE

RJ-45 PLUG

IR HAND-HELD REMOTE

IR SIGNALS

AUDIO SOURCE LEDs
PUSH KNOB TO SELECT
1 OF 4 AUDIO SOURCES

PUSH VOLUME KNOB TO
SELECT 1 OF 4 AUDIO
SOURCES

IR SENSOR ALLOWS USE
OF HAND-HELD REMOTE FOR
ADDITIONAL FUNCTIONS

A
B
C
D

ON
VOLUME

REMOTE SENSOR

## Figure 6-3   IN WALL A/V CONTROLLER & HAND-HELD REMOTE

signals directly to the audio/video source equipment, these signals will travel to a mini-IR emitter that is attached to the 'IR receiver' located on the front panel of the *IR-Xpander*. This configuration can be seen in Figure 6-2. The *IR-Xpander* and the *Stargate* can now receive IR signals so they can make the proper control decisions and output specific IR signals to a designate *Zone(s)*. When the *Stargate* receives IR signals and when a programming Event's 'IF' statement becomes true, the 'THEN' statement will allow the *Stargate* to send IR signals to the appropriate *Zone* Outputs (1 thru 4), shown on the rear panel of the *IR-Xpander* in Figures 6-2 & 6-4. These signals are then carried by the (CAT 5, 4 UTP) conductors that are connected to the rear of the *Service Input Hub* shown in Figure 1-10 on page 12. IR signals are then jumpered from the front of the *Service Input Hub* to the *Family Room Hub* as shown in Figure 1-12 on page 15. From here the IR signals for *Zone* 3 will travel to a non-amplified IR block located in the Family Room as shown in Figure 6-2. From the IR block, signals will then travel to individual mini-IR emitters that are attached to an 'IR receiver' located on the front of each audio/video component. These signals will control the majority of the audio/video equipment functions such as, audio receiver ON/OFF commands, volume control, CD player ON/OFF commands, CD and track selections, satellite

receiver ON/OFF commands, satellite channel selections, TV ON/OFF commands, TV channel selections, etc.

The *Stargate* and *IR-Xpander* combination will allow the system to send one IR command or a whole string of different command signals to any *Zone* in the home separate from the other three *Zones*. This is an important feature because homes that generally incorporate Whole House Audio/Video Systems will often times have A/V equipment that respond to the same IR signal codes. This will generally be the case when the same brand TVs, audio receivers, DVDs, VCRs and others are used in different rooms of the home. The homeowner may want to have the *Stargate* initiate a Macro that contains IR signals used to turn ON the Family Room TV, Dolby Digital Receiver #1 and the VCR. Without separate outputs to individual IR *Zones*, audio/video components will not be properly controlled and will become a nuisance.

Notice the *Zone* 2 output from the *IR-Xpander* shown in Figure 6-2. This *Zone* connects to an amplified block shown below the TV screen in the Home Theater. This block receives IR signals, amplifies the signals and splits the signals to individual mini-IR emitters that are attached to individual IR receivers located on the front of the A/V components. The amplified block is required any time there are more than four IR outputs needed in a room.

More than four IR signal outputs from a block requires amplification to provide sufficient IR signal strength so the appropriate audio/video components will respond reliably.

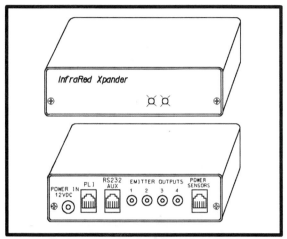

Figure 6-4 IR-XPANDER

**6-3 System Equipment Configuration:** The most versatile design configuration is one that locates all audio/video equipment inside an *Equipment Room* with the front panels of the audio/video equipment visible from the Home Theater. This will allow access to the rear of the audio/video equipment to make initial wire connections and to perform system modifications for years to come. As in most homes including the 'Example Home', this configuration is not possible so the designer must look for another means of attaining access to the back of the system components. An alternate method is to provide a narrow access way behind the system components by building the entertainment center out away from the main room wall. This will provide room for someone to shimmy their way in back of the components for access purposes. This 'access way' should be a minimum of 2'-0" wide with an access door on either end of the 'access way'. This is a good option if the Home Theater is large enough to accommodate this configuration; however, if the room size is marginal it may not be desirable to the homeowner.

For most audio/video installations, access to the rear panels of the A/V equipment can be obtained by installing a 'Slide-Out In-Wall A/V **Shelve**' unit or 'Slide-Out In-Wall A/V **Rack**' unit. The 'Slide-Out In-Wall A/V **Shelve**' unit shown in Figure 6-5, slides out of an opening in the wall and rotates to provide the necessary access to the rear of the components. This unit is generally designed to support between 200 to 280 pounds of equipment. The minimum wall opening required is approximately 20 inches wide and 19 inches deep to allow sufficient room to install and rotate this assembly. 'Slide-Out In-Wall A/V **Shelves**' are generally available in 5, 6 & 9 shelve units. They also provide shelve adjustments that can be made for different height A/V components.

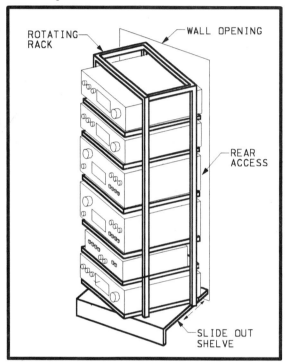

Figure 6-5 SLIDE OUT SHELVES

'Slide-Out In-Wall A/V **Racks**' are also available; however, these units do not rotate. When access to the rear of the equipment is required, support legs and slide-out rails must be retracted and placed on the floor in front of the rack to temporaly support the weight of the equipment. This rack can then be pulled out of the wall opening to a distance that will allow access to the rear panels of the components. This type of configuration requires the rack to extend out away from the wall opening farther than the rotating shelve unit because the 'Slide-Out **Rack**' units do not incorporate rotation capabilities. Rack units do; however, support up to 650 pounds of equipment compared to the maximum capacity of 280 pounds for the 'Slide-Out In-Wall A/V **Shelve**' assemblies.

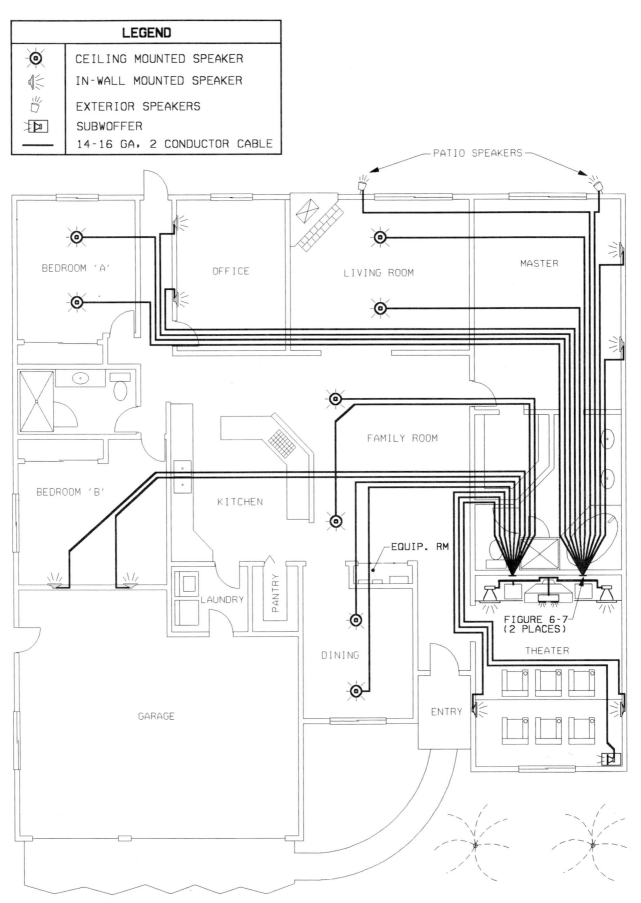

**LEGEND**

| | |
|---|---|
| ⊙ | CEILING MOUNTED SPEAKER |
| ◁ | IN-WALL MOUNTED SPEAKER |
| ▽ | EXTERIOR SPEAKERS |
| ▷ | SUBWOFFER |
| —— | 14-16 GA, 2 CONDUCTOR CABLE |

PATIO SPEAKERS

BEDROOM 'A'

OFFICE

LIVING ROOM

MASTER

FAMILY ROOM

BEDROOM 'B'

KITCHEN

EQUIP. RM

FIGURE 6-7
(2 PLACES)

LAUNDRY

PANTRY

DINING

THEATER

GARAGE

ENTRY

FIGURE 6-6   AUDIO SPEAKER SYSTEM CONTROL PLAN

**6-4 System Speaker Installation:** There are five different types of speakers installed in the 'Example Home' system shown in Figure 6-6. Speaker wire types and gauge requirements are dependent on the RMS wattage requirement of a specific speaker and the length of wire pulled from the amplifier to the speaker. It is always best to follow the speaker manufacturer's recommendations for wire type and gauge.

The 'Example Home' in-wall speakers are installed in the Master Bedroom, Office, Bedroom 'B' and Home Theater. These are areas of the home where the homeowner will enjoy a high quality sound that can be played at higher volume when desired. In-wall speakers are generally higher capacity speakers (40 to 100 watts RMS) that can handle more wattage than the smaller ceiling speakers that are used in other areas of the home. In most homes, 16 gauge, 2-conductor speaker cable is generally sufficient for both in-wall and ceiling mounted speakers. All speaker cables are pulled from the entertainment center (Theater in this case) where the *Kustom 6 Amplifiers* are located, to each speaker location in the home. Individual speaker wire connections at the rear panel of each *Kustom 6 Amplifier* are shown in Figure 6-2. Since the rear portion of an in-wall speaker is located inside the wall, the speaker wire terminals will end up inside the wall as well. This configuration requires the speaker wires to be pulled from the *Equipment Room* and through the attic to the top plate of the wall where a speaker will be installed. A pre-drilled 1/2" diameter hole in the top plate of the wall will allow each speaker cable to be pulled down between the wall studs. After pulling a speaker cable, it should be attached to a wall stud at the height and location where the speaker will be installed. This will tell the drywall installer where to pull the wire through the drywall during construction. This height will generally be between 5 and 7 feet. The next step is to draw guidelines in pencil on the wall before cutting the opening in the drywall where the speaker will be installed. Speaker wall openings must be cut with a sharp utility knife. Wall openings must also be smaller than the speaker frame in order to provide enough drywall material to firmly mount the speaker up against.

When 'in wall' speakers need to be installed in an existing home, a 30" long security system type drill bit can be used to drill a 1/2" diameter hole in the top plate of the wall above where the speaker will be installed. Once the speaker opening is cut out of the drywall, the drill bit and drill can normally be placed up inside the wall opening to drill the hole up through the top plate. This approach is used when speakers are installed at an elevation of 6 feet or more above the floor in an 8-foot tall wall. After the hole is drilled in the top plate, the speaker cable can be snaked down through the hole from the attic and between the wall studs to the speaker wall opening. The cable will need to be attached to a wall stud near the opening so it will not be pulled out of position during the cable installation. The installer will then pull the other end of the cable through the attic and over to the top of the wall where the *Kustom 6 Amplifiers* are installed. The speaker cable is then routed through a pre-drilled hole in the top plate of the wall and down between the wall studs until is can be seen through the mud-ring opening. Wires are then pulled out through the mud-ring opening to prepare the conductors for termination to speaker binding posts similar to the ones shown in Figure 6-7. All speaker wires must be properly labeled so when the final connections are made, the installer will know what speaker connects to what set of *Kustom 6 Amplifier* outputs.

In the 'Example Home', Figure 6-7 illustrates two 2-gang mud-rings installed behind the *Kustom 6 Amplifiers* for a total quantity of 20 modular speaker binding posts. These are required to connect all in-wall, ceiling, and patio speakers to the *Kustom 6 Amplifier(s)*. Notice the cross sectional view of the modular binding posts shown in Figure 6-9. Each speaker requires a 2-conductor cable. One is connected to the positive terminal (red) and the other is connected to the negative terminal (black). This is true when connecting wires to speaker terminals, to the binding posts, and to the appropriate *Kustom 6 Amplifier* connectors. Speaker cables that were previously pulled to the binding posts shown in Figure 6-9, must first be cut to length before stripping ½" of insulation off the end of each conductor. Each conductor is then inserted into the end of the appropriate binding post before

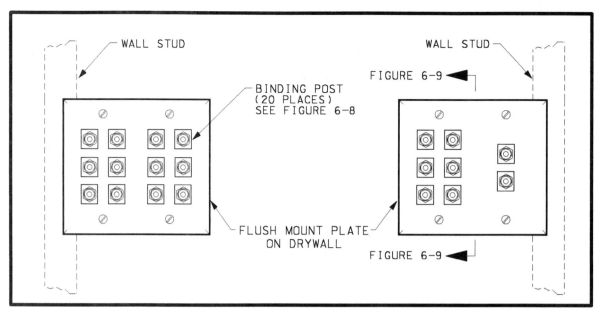

Figure 6-7   2-GANG SPEAKER BINDING POSTS

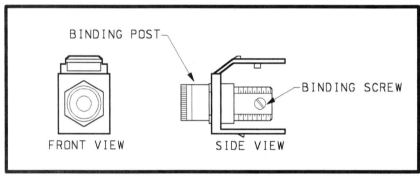

Figure 6-8 MODULAR BINDING POST

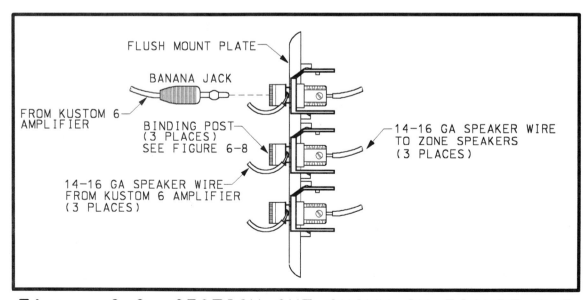

Figure 6-9   SECTION CUT SHOWN IN FIGURE 6-7

tightening the binding screw that is shown close up in Figure 6-8. This portion of the binding post is inside the wall. The other end of the binding post is mounted to the flush mount plate located inside the room. Short lengths of speaker cable are connected to the designated *Kustom 6 Amplifier* terminals and the modular binding posts to provide audio to each speaker. Each speaker conductor is terminated to the binding post front connector by first stripping off ½" of insulation. Each conductor is then inserting through the hole located in the binding post front connector before turning down the finger knob to bind the wire in place as shown in Figure 6-9. The installer also has the option of using a banana jack on the end of each conductor that slips into a connector hole on the front of the binding post as shown.

An in-wall speaker and backing plate supplied with each speaker assembly is placed inside the pre-cut speaker wall opening. Mounting screws are then tightened to draw the backing plate up to the drywall to hold the speaker securely in place. It is important to mount this type of speaker correctly because a poor installation can cause the speaker to vibrate and produce buzzing noises.

Ceiling speakers are another type of speaker used in the home. Most ceiling speakers are designed for music that is played at moderate volume levels, which in most cases is sufficient for whole house audio systems. This speaker type is normally available in power ratings of 40 to 80 watts RMS. Ceiling speakers are easier to install in an existing single level home compared to in-wall speakers because the speaker wires do not need to penetrate the top wall plate and do not need to be snaked to the speaker wall opening. A ceiling speaker is inserted within a penetration that is cut out of the ceiling material. It is always a good idea to draw the proper size penetration on the ceiling before making the cut. This penetration is made by first cutting a starter hole in the ceiling and then using a bare hacksaw blade for the finishing cut. Speaker wire is then crimped onto slip-on terminals that connect to the speaker terminals before placing the speaker with the backing plate into the ceiling opening. Each speaker is then firmly mounted to the ceiling material by tightened the mounting screws.

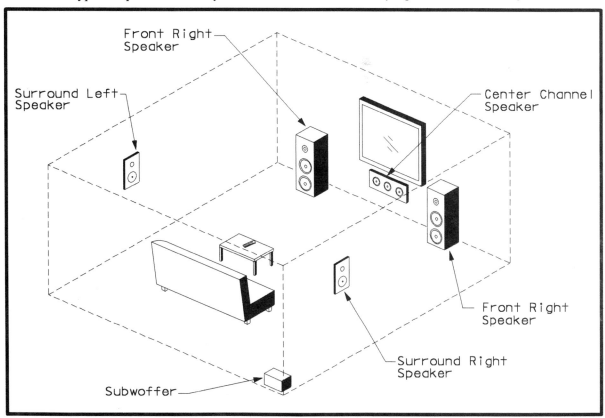

Figure 6-10   Audio & Video Room Speaker Arrangement

16 GA speaker wire is sufficient for most ceiling speakers because they do not have high wattage requirements and the wire can be routed 75-100 feet in length without introducing a significant amount of resistance. Speaker wire is then connected to the appropriate *Kustom 6 Amplifier Zone* terminals in a similar fashion as previously described for the in-wall speakers.

Weatherproof outdoor speakers are the third type of speaker used in the 'Example Home'. These speakers are located on the pool patio to provide entertainment while sun bathing or enjoying a swim. They can be mounted either on the exterior wall or in the soffit. The use of 16 gauge wire is generally sufficient for 40 to 100 watts RMS speakers.

Speaker wire is routed from the *Kustom 6 Amplifier* location through the attic and over to the top of the exterior wall near the patio. In an existing home, the speaker cable will then penetrate the soffit, which is often times the easiest way to get the wires to where the speaker will be mounted. For new home construction, these speakers are normally mounted right to the exterior wall.

When a framed home is under construction, the speaker cable can easily be routed down inside the exterior wall to penetrate the wall where the speaker will be mounted. If the exterior wall is constructed of concrete block, the speaker cable will need to be routed on the interior surface of the rigid board insulation between the furring strips. In the location where each speaker will be mounted, a 1/2" diameter pre-drilled hole through the exterior block wall is used to pass the speaker wire through for termination purposes. All speaker wire wall penetrations should be filled with expandable foam insulation before the final finish is applied to the exterior wall surface.

The last four types of speakers used in the 'Example Home' are located in the Theater as shown in Figure 6-10. The Theater uses a dedicated Dolby Digital Surround Sound 400 watt receiver/amplifier that is used to drive the front left and right speakers, the center channel speaker, the rear left and right surround sound speakers and a subwoofer. The receiver/amplifier combination is equivalent to a 5.1 channel digital sound system used in movie Theaters. The front

left and front right speakers are the primary speakers in the Theater. These speakers deliver the majority of the 'movie audio' created by; for instance, aircraft, explosions, cars, breaking glass, etc. The center channel speaker is designed to enhance clarity in dialogue. This speaker is normally located directly on top or below the TV screen. The left & right surround sound speakers are located on the rear side walls of the room and provide audio that seems to move from left to right and visa versa in relation to moving objects on the TV screen. These speakers are designed to provide a sense of realism and the feeling that you are actually there.

The last speaker type used in this room is the subwoofer. This speaker provides audio base while watching a movie. It is designed to furnish the listener with audio that can be felt through percussion primarily when viewing action packed entertainment.

**6-5 Whole House Video:** The Whole House Video Distribution System Plan is shown in Figure 6-12. This Plan illustrates the RG-6 Quad Shield video cables that are routed from each **video source** (Video Inputs) to the *Distribution Panel* located in the *Equipment Room*. Video Input sources include the cable TV service (CATV), satellite video service, TV antenna broadcasts, and CCTV video camera signals. DVD and/or VCR players also provide Video Inputs to the *Distribution Panel*. Video Input cables are shown as dash lines in this Plan. Video Output cables are also shown routed from the *Distribution Panel* to TVs and VCRs located throughout the home. These cables are shown as solid lines, or dashed lines to VCRs. All cables pulled in the home should follow the procedures laid out in Section 1-24 on page 44.

In most cases, video input & video output . cables pulled from the *Distribution Panel* to each room are contained by the *Structured Wiring* 'Bundles'. Separate RG-6 cables supply Video Inputs from sources that include CATV, satellite, TV antenna and CCTV video cameras. Reference *Zone Hub* and *Service Input Hub* cable connection diagrams in Chapter One to identify specific video cables required for each room.

When looking at Figure 6-12, keep in mind that in this manual, Video Input signals received by the *Distribution Panel* originate from a source. Once Video Input signals are received by the *Distribution Panel*, they are distributed as Video Outputs to specific rooms that contain or have the potential to contain TVs or VCRs. When these signals reach a specific room, they become Video Inputs to a TV and/or VCR. This means that a Video Output cable from the *Distribution Panel* is also an Video Input cable to a TV or VCR. VCRs receive Video Input signals for recording purposes.

Video Outputs can also originate from VCRs and DVDs; however, they are received as Video Inputs by the *Distribution Panel* for re-distribution to the other rooms in the home for shared entertainment purposes.

When looking at the **rear view** of the *Interactive Receptacle* shown in Figure 6-11, the Video **Output** cable pulled from the *Distribution Panel* connects to the Video **Input** F-connector. In the front view of Figure 6-11, one end of a short RG-6 cable connects to the front F-connector labeled Video Input and the other end connects to the Video Input connector of the VCR and/or TV. The Video Output cable located on the back of a VCR or DVD connects to the Video Output F-connector on the front of the *Interactive Receptacle*. The Video Output cable that connects to the back of the *Interactive Receptacle* is also the Video **Input** cable to the *Distribution Panel*.

To allow the homeowner and other occupants to view VCR, DVD, and CCTV camera video in any room when the 'Input' source is from another area of the home, a device called a modulator is required. A modulator allows the homeowner to assign specific channels to specific Video Input programming so any of the TVs in the home can view video from specific areas of the home or property. If the homeowner would like to watch a

movie in the Living Room when a DVD is not present in this location, all he/she needs to do is place the disc in any DVD player in the home and use the hand-held remote from the Living Room to start the movie after selecting channel 78. Once the movie is started, any TV in the home will be able to view this movie by selecting channel 78.

Video from CCTV cameras located in the infant's room, pool area, front door and driveway gate locations can be viewed on TVs by simply selecting the channel assigned to the specific camera angle. In Figure 6-13, notice how the cables from the CCTV cameras are connected to the Video Input F-connectors on the modulator. The modulator assigns input channels (68, 70, 72 & 74) and sends this video to the *Service Input Hub* in the *Distribution Panel*. CCTV video is then distributed to the *Interactive Receptacles* located throughout the home. When an occupant wants to view the pool area, channel 70 must be selected on any of the four TVs in the home.

Notice the 12V DC power conductors shown in Figure 6-13. They are routed from the CCTV cameras to a low voltage power source located in *Equipment Room* above the modulators as shown Figure 1-8 on page 9. Low voltage power is provided to this terminal strip from a transformer that plugs into the 120V AC power strip. A quantity of four 18 gauge, 2-conductor cables are connected to this low voltage power source and each is pulled along with a RG-6 coax cable to each CCTV camera location. Also notice in Figure 6-13, that the low voltage conductors are wired in series with a Relay Output from the *Stargate*. The *Stargate* is used to control the CCTV cameras ON & OFF based on a Digital Input from motion detector, vehicle detector, or by other conditional control inputs.

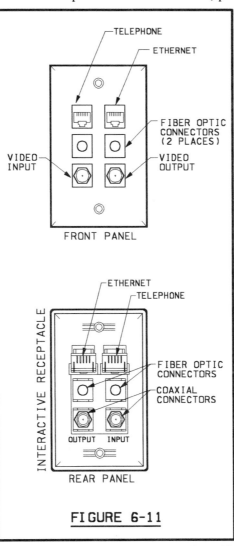

FIGURE 6-11

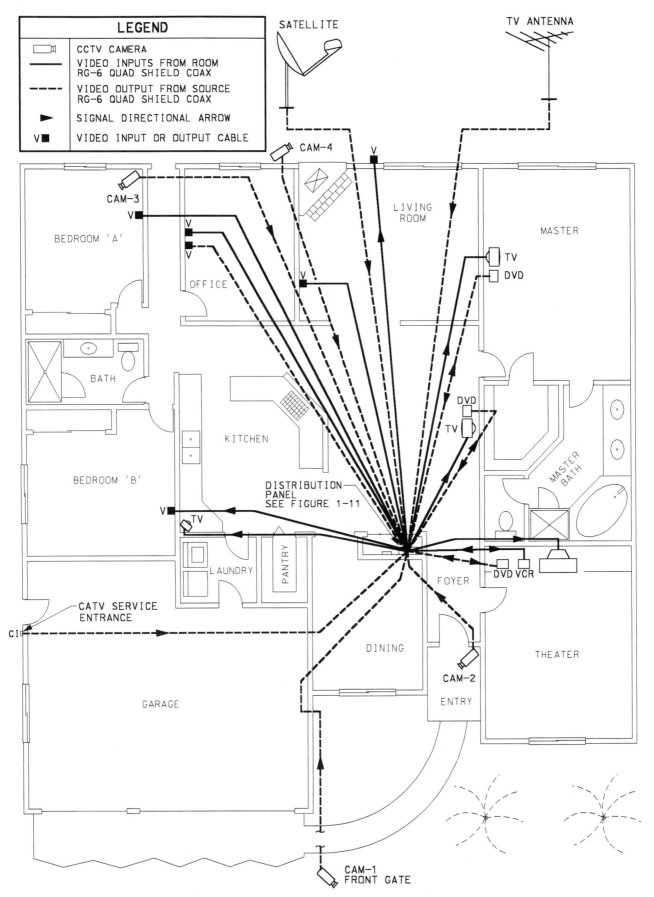

**LEGEND**

| | |
|---|---|
| 🎥 | CCTV CAMERA |
| —— | VIDEO INPUTS FROM ROOM RG-6 QUAD SHIELD COAX |
| - - - | VIDEO OUTPUT FROM SOURCE RG-6 QUAD SHIELD COAX |
| ▶ | SIGNAL DIRECTIONAL ARROW |
| V■ | VIDEO INPUT OR OUTPUT CABLE |

SATELLITE

TV ANTENNA

CAM-4

CAM-3

BEDROOM 'A'

LIVING ROOM

MASTER

TV

DVD

OFFICE

BATH

DVD

TV

KITCHEN

MASTER BATH

BEDROOM 'B'

DISTRIBUTION PANEL SEE FIGURE 1-11

TV

LAUNDRY

PANTRY

FOYER

DVD VCR

CATV SERVICE ENTRANCE

CI

DINING

CAM-2

THEATER

ENTRY

GARAGE

CAM-1
FRONT GATE

# Figure 6-12   WHOLE HOUSE VIDEO DISTRIBUTION PLAN

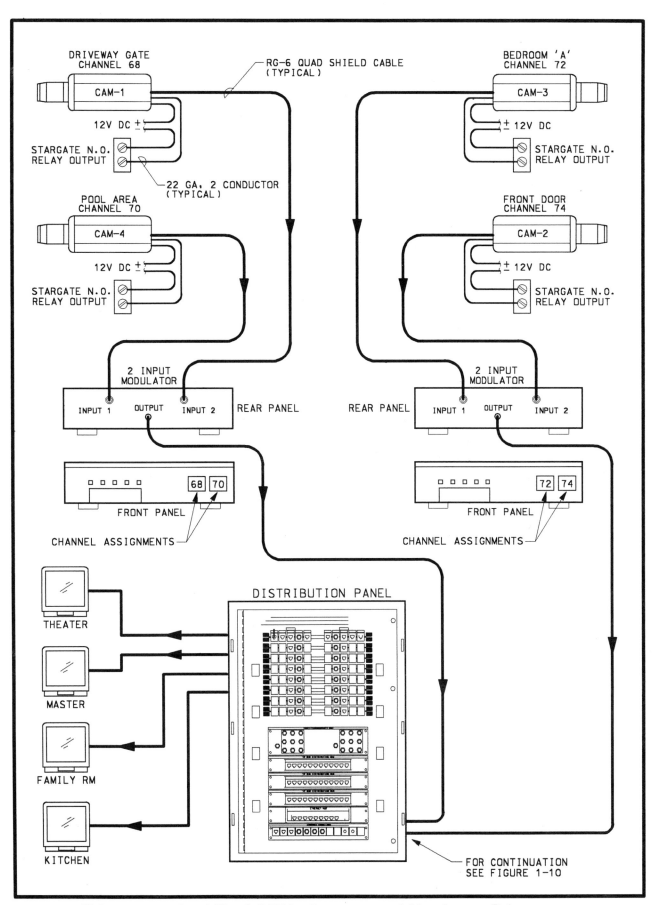

# Figure 6-13 CCTV Camera Wiring Diagram

# THEATER MODE

**6-6 Theater Mode:** The 'Theater Mode' can be initiated by a hand-held IR remote, push button *JDS* Keypad, Digital Input or touch-tone phone. This mode will turn ON the satellite receiver; for instance, to channel 80 before turning ON the TV, Dolby Digital processor and VCR. This mode will also close the motorized Verticals, turn OFF the lights in adjacent rooms to the Theater, and dim the Theater lighting to a desirable brightness level for movie viewing. (See programming shown below). This mode will dim the Theater lighting only when the 'Theater Mode' is initiated **after** sunset. **Before** sunset, all functions are performed as previously described except the lights and Verticals are unaffected. The 'Theater Mode' **'IF'** statement requires a 'Theater Mode' command and an **after** sunset condition to trigger the '**THEN**' statement. If it is **before** sunset, the '**IF**' statement will not be true and a (nested) '**THEN**' portion of the Event will Run instead. The nested portion of the Event programming is not shown due to space considerations. The 'Theater Mode' **Sets** the 'Theater Flag' to let the *Stargate* know that the audio/video equipment is turned ON. If the TV; for instance, is turned ON directly from a hand-held remote, the *Stargate* will not know this and therefore will not know the ON or OFF state of the device. If the occupants leave the home and initiated the 'Leaving Home Mode', the *Stargate* would not know to turn the TV or other A/V component OFF. To avoid this problem, the user needs to turn the entertainment components ON & OFF through the *Stargate* & *IR-Xpander* because the *Stargate* maintains a record of what audio/video components are ON or OFF. Since the '**Example Home**' utilizes the *IR-Xpander*, power status sensors could be incorporated in order to positively report the ON or OFF status of up to four components regardless of how the audio/video components are controlled ON & OFF.

# THEATER MODE PROGRAMMING

## *STARGATE PROGRAMMING*

| | |
|---|---|
| EVENT:  **THEATER MODE - ON** | *Mode name* |
| **IF** | *if* |
| ( THEATER MODE ) | *If 'Theater Mode' is selected on JDS Keypad* |
| and **After Sunset**  .SMTWTFS. | *and it is after sunset  Sunday thru Saturday* |
| **THEN** | *then* |
| (F: THEATER )  SET | *Set the 'Theater' Flag* |
| (IR: TV )  play  1  time(s) [Theater] | *Select Theater TV* |
| (IR: POWER )  play  1  time(s) [Theater] | *Turn TV ON* |
| (IR: 0 )  play  1  time(s) [Theater] | *First digit of channel 03* |
| (IR: 3 )  play  1  time(s) [Theater] | *Second digit of channel 03* |
| (IR: SAT )  play  1  time(s) [Theater] | *Select satellite receiver* |
| (IR: POWER )  play  1  time(s) [Theater] | *Turn satellite receiver ON* |
| (IR: 5 )  play  1  time(s) [Theater] | *First digit of channel 53* |
| (IR: 3 )  play  1  time(s) [Theater] | *Second digit of channel 53* |
| (IR: ENTER )  play  1  time(s) [Theater] | *'**Enter**' command* |
| (IR: REC #1 POWER ) play 1 time(s) [Theater] | *Turn Living Rm Rec #1 ON* |
| (IR: TV-AUDIO ) play 1 time(s) [Theater] | *Select **tv-audio** function to maintain stereo movie audio* |
| (IR: VOLDN )  play  15  time(s) | *Turn Rec #1 amplifier volume fully off* |
| (IR: VOLUP )  play  6  time(s) | *Turn Rec #1 amplifier volume UP to desired level* |
| (IR: VCR )  play  1  time(s) [Theater] | *Select VCR* |
| (IR: POWER )  play  1  time(s) [Theater] | *Turn VCR ON* |
| (RELAY: THEATER R1)  ON | *Close Theater Roller Shade* |
| DELAY  0 : 00 : 02 | *Delay stopping of the roller shades for 2 seconds* |
| (RELAY: THEATER R1)  OFF | *Stop Theater Roller Shades* |
| ( LIGHT FOYER  C-5 )  OFF | *Turn Foyer lights OFF* |
| ( LIGHT  THEATER  A-5 )  30 % | *Turn ON Theater low voltage lighting to 30% bright* |
| End | |

**STARGATE PROGRAMMING:**                                    *Description:*

EVENT:  **FRONT DOOR CCTV Camera**                            *Feature name*
  **IF**                                                             *if*
    (DI: MOTION Z15 )  is  ON                    *front door Zone 15  motion detector detects motion*
    and ( CAM #2 FLAG )  is Clear               *and CCTV camera Flag is Clear*
        -OR-                                   *or*
    (DI: VEHICLE DETECTOR )  is  ON            *If vehicle detector Digital Input is ON (vehicle detected)*
    and ( CAM #2 FLAG )  is Clear               *and CCTV camera Flag is Clear*
  **THEN**                                                         *then*
    (F:  CAMERA FLAG )  Set                     *Set Camera #2 Flag to avoid multiple mode activations*
    (RELAY: CAMERA # 2)  ON                     *Turn CCTV Camera #2 ON*
    (IR: RECORDER ) play 1 time(s) [Theater]    *Select Time-Lapse VCR Recorder*
    (IR: POWER ) play 1 time(s) [Theater]       *Turn Time-Lapse VCR Recorder ON*
    DELAY   0:00:02                             *After 2 seconds perform next line*
    (IR: 7 ) play 1 time(s) [Frt Dr]            *Select first digit of channel 74 to view front door camera*
    (IR: 4 ) play 1 time(s) [Frt Dr]            *Select second digit of channel 74 to view front door camera*
    (IR: RECORDER ) play 1 time(s) [Theater]    *Select Time-Lapse VCR Recorder function*
    (IR: TV KIT  ) play 1 time(s) [Kitchen]     *Select Kitchen TV*
    (IR: POWER ) play 1 time(s) [Kitchen]       *Turn Kitchen TV ON*
    DELAY   0:00:02                             *After 2 seconds perform next line*
    (IR: 7 ) play 1 time(s) [Kitchen]           *Select first digit of channel 74 to view front door camera*
    (IR: 4 ) play 1 time(s) [Kitchen]           *Select second digit of channel 74 to view front door camera*
    (IR: TV MS BED  ) play 1 time(s) [Master Bedroom]   *Select Master Bedroom TV*
    (IR: POWER ) play 1 time(s) [Master Bedroom]   *Turn Master Bedroom TV ON*
    DELAY   0:00:02                             *After 2 seconds perform next line*
    (IR: 7 ) play 1 time(s) [Master Bedroom]    *Select first digit of channel 74 to view front door camera*
    (IR: 4 ) play 1 time(s) [Master Bedroom]    *Select second digit of channel 74 to view front door camera*
  * (TIME 11 )  LOAD  with  00:05:00              *Timer 11 will count down from 5 min to 0 min*
End

EVENT:  * TIME  11                                           *Timer name*
  **IF**                                                             *if*
    (T: TIME  11)  is  Expiring                 *When 12 minute Timer has expired*
  **THEN**                                                         *then*
    ( RELAY: CAMERA #2 )  OFF                   *Turn front door CCTV Camera #2 OFF*
    (IR: RECORDER) play 1 time(s) [Theater]     *Select Recorder*
    (IR: REC  STOP ) play 1 time(s) [Theater]   *Stop Recorder recording*
    (IR: POWER ) play 1 time(s) [Theater]       *Turn Recorder OFF*
    (IR: TV  ) play 1 time(s) [Living Rm]        *Select Kitchen TV*
    (IR: POWER ) play 1 time(s) [Living Rm]     *Turn Kitchen TV OFF*
    (IR: TV  ) play 1 time(s) [Master Bedroom]   *Select Master Bedroom TV*
    (IR: POWER ) play 1 time(s) [Master Bedroom]   *Turn Master Bedroom TV OFF*
    (F: CAMERA  FLAG )  Clear                   *Clear 'CAMERA' Flag to allow CCTV Event to Run next time*
End

**6-7 Vehicle Detector:** The vehicle detector could provide the homeowner of the 'Example Home' with automatic control of the gate when leaving the home; however, the 'Exit loop' described in Section 10-3 on page 201 controls this function. Instead, the vehicle detector is used for security and surveillance purposes as we will describe in the following paragraphs.

The probe portion of the vehicle detection system detects distortion of the earth's magnetic field caused by objects made of iron, steel and other ferrous metals that pass by the probe. The probe is generally buried next to or under the driveway 6 to 8 inches below the surface. This probe is then wired to the console using burial conductors supplied by the manufacturer.

The vehicle detection system is used to detect both authorized an unauthorized vehicles approaching the home. When an authorized vehicle is allowed to pass through the property gate and drives by the buried probe portion of the detector, a signal is transmitted to the Vehicle Detector Control Console located in the *Equipment Room* as shown in Figure 1-8 on page 9. The console will then close an internal auxiliary relay wired to Digital Input 11 of the *Stargate*. The Digital Input cable is a (CAT 5, 4 UTP) as shown in Figure 6-14. The 'Surveillance'

Event 'IF' statement will then be true, which will allow the *Stargate* to turn ON the CCTV camera located at the front door along with the TV located in the Kitchen and Master Bedroom. The TVs will also be automatically switched to the appropriate channel for viewing this particular camera angle.

If the property gate is opened by an unauthorized means, the security system's magnetic contact switch located on the property access gate will close and set off the alarm when the security system is in the *Armed* state as described in Section 10-3 on page 202. In this condition, the CCTV camera at the front door will turn ON, the TVs will turn ON, and the Time-Lapse Recorder will turn ON to record the events. As the vehicle approaches the home, it is detected as it travels up the driveway and by the probe. At this point the homeowner will immediately receive a 'Voice Response' from the *Stargate* over the whole house audio system announcing "*Unauthorized Vehicle is Approaching*". This informs the homeowner that there is definitely a security concern and not just a equipment malfunction. The *Stargate* will also immediately place a phone call to the security monitoring station when the home is either occupied or unoccupied at the time.

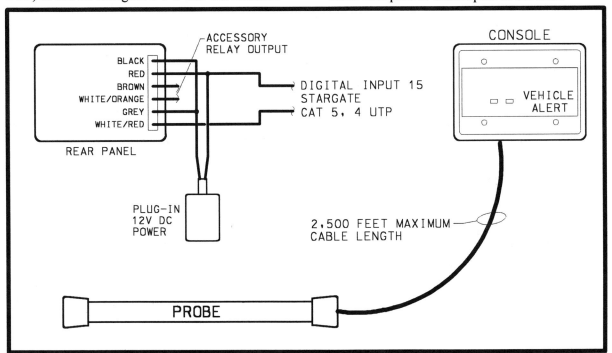

## Figure 6-14 VEHICLE DETECTOR

# Automated Heating & Cooling Systems

**7-1 Automated HVAC:** The majority of residential heating and air conditioning systems will condition all of the rooms in the home while operating. There are also systems that condition areas or rooms of the home individually as needed. If the entire home is air conditioned and controlled by one thermostat, this system is considered a single *Zone* system. If areas of the home are conditioned individually as required, this is considered a Multi-Zone system. Naturally Multi-Zone systems are more economical to operate because only specific areas of the home that are calling for heating or cooling will receive conditioned air.

The 'Example Home' is heated and cooled by a Heat Pump (HP) that is located on the outside of the home. This system also includes an Air Handler (AH) that is located in the garage as shown in Figure 7-1. Notice in Figure 7-2, other system components that include the Multi-Zone Control Panel, *Zone* thermostats, outside air (OA) temperature sensor, motorized volume dampers, supply and return ductwork, supply air diffusers, return air grille and the assistance of the *Stargate* Home Controller. Since this manual establishes the wiring infrastructure for all of the other sub-systems in the Example Home', we will identify the following wiring requirements for the air conditioning system as well. (18 GA unshielded,

5 conductor cable) is used to connect the Multi-Zone Control Panel to the Heat Pump and the Air Handler. (18 GA shielded, 4-conductor cable) is used to connect each thermostat to the Multi-Zone Control Panel. (18 GA unshielded, 2-conductor cable) is used to connect each control damper to the Multi-Zone Control Panel. (CAT 5, 4 UTP) cable is used to connect the *Stargate* to the Multi-Zone Control Panel through the RS-485 interface as shown. Even through only 2 pairs of the CAT 5 are used, the additional 2 pairs can be very useful if one or more conductors are damaged during the life of the control system.

The HVAC designer must be careful when combining rooms to establish an air conditioning *Zone*. This is because each room has a different cooling and heating load. Notice the thermostat locations in Figure 7-1 for the following rooms; Bedroom 'A', Family Room, Master Bedroom, and Theater. The Bedroom 'A' thermostat is located within *Zone* 1. Notice how the supply air (SA) ductwork serving *Zone* 1 also serves the Bathroom and Bedroom 'B'. Also notice the *Zone* 1 control damper (ZN1) located above Bedroom 'B'. This damper is basically an air valve that is controlled open and closed by *Stargate* to flow the proper rate of conditioned air to satisfy either the heating or cooling temperature setpoint.

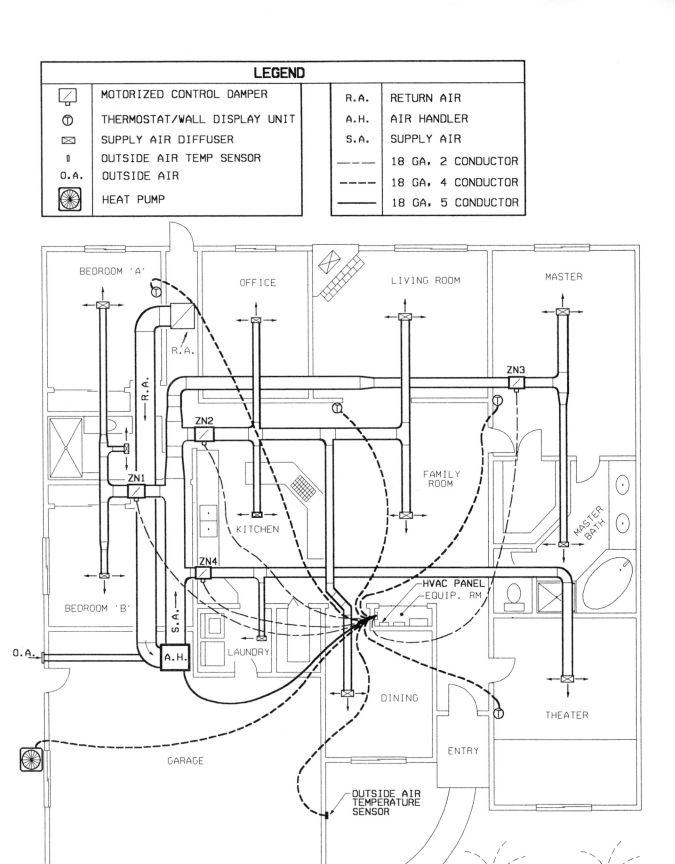

# FIGURE 7-1  HVAC MULTI-ZONE SYSTEM PLAN

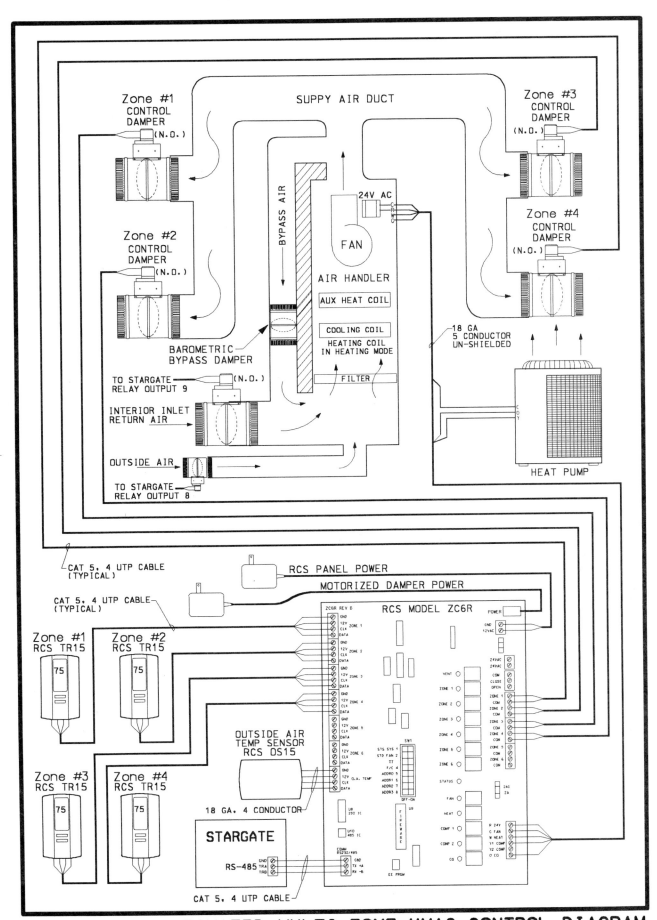

# FIGURE 7-2 AUTOMATED MULTI-ZONE HVAC CONTROL DIAGRAM

Since the *Zone* 1 thermostat needs to satisfy all three rooms, it should be placed in the room that requires the most accurate temperature control. In this case the thermostat is placed in Bedroom 'A'. This is because Bedroom 'A' is the baby's room, which the parent's wish to keep under tight temperature control to make sure the infant stays healthy. Although conditioned air is supplied at the same temperature to the other two rooms in *Zone* 1, they may not be maintained at the same temperature setpoint. This is because each room in this *Zone* experiences a different heating and cooling load.

The designer selected Bedroom 'A', the Bathroom and Bedroom 'B' to make up *Zone* 1 because all three rooms are located on the same exterior wall, which means that each room will experience the same wall heat transmission loads per square foot of wall area. The other types of loads to consider in these rooms are the lighting and other internal loads such as computers. Each room has similar lighting loads; however, Bedroom 'B' has a computer. Since the computer is primarily used in the evenings, the heat load will not be significant. The last item to consider is where the rooms are located in relation to each other. This is important because rooms that are far apart will generally not be good candidates to establish a *Zone*. This is because long sections of ductwork cost more to install and the additional air pressure loss in the ductwork will often require a larger Air Handler. In this particular *Zone,* short lengths of ductwork are possible because all three rooms are fairly close together. With all points considered, these three rooms will establish a well-balanced *Zone*.

In order to help maintain the rooms of a *Zone* within 1° F of each other, a supply and return air balance is required in each room so they will receives the proper air flow rate (CFM) when the control damper is positioned open.

In *Zone* 2, conditioned air is supplied through the ductwork to serve the Office, Living Room, Kitchen and Family Room. This is considered a large *Zone* so the designer must take extra care in selecting a location where the thermostat will best serve all four rooms. In this particular case the Family Room was selected to receive the thermostat because this room is the most prominent room within *Zone* 2 and is

occupied most of the time. Notice the control air damper (ZN2) located above the Kitchen in Figure 7-1. This damper will be controlled open & closed to maintain the temperature setpoint in *Zone* 2. This *Zone* unfortunately is not well balanced because the Office experiences higher internal loads and may not receive enough conditioned air. Since the Family Room is where the thermostat is located it will control this room well; however, the Office may operate a few degrees warmer when the Office equipment is in use. This 2°F to 3°F temperature difference can be countered by running a ceiling fan to provide additional comfort for the occupant(s). This room could have been placed in a *Zone* by itself; however, the additional cost to do so was not in the budget. Instead the designer decided to partially counter the extra cooling load by increasing the supply air (CFM) in the Office.

Since each and every room in the home has a different heating and cooling load, it would be optimal to provide each room with it's own thermostat, *Zone* control damper and ductwork. This configuration would maintain the best temperature control throughout the home; however, it would also be very expensive. This is why rooms are grouped together to provide the most comfort while staying within budget.

Depending on the home's room configuration, homes under 2500 square feet can generally be properly air conditioned using 2 to 3 *Zones*. Homes between 2500 and 4000 square feet can generally be properly controlled using 4 to 6 *Zones*.

To continue on with the 'Example Home' design, *Zone* 3 is made up of the Master Bedroom and the Master Bath. The control air damper labeled (ZN3) is located above the entrance to the Master Bedroom as shown. This *Zone* is clean cut and will provide the homeowner with a dedicated thermostat and *Zone* damper for superior control.

The *Zone* 4 control air damper (ZN4) is located above the Kitchen and supplies conditioned air to the Theater and Laundry Room. The HVAC designer decided to install the thermostat in the Theater because of the large internal heat load that is dissipated from all of the audio and video equipment and the added comfort level desired while being entertained.

142

The Multi-Zone HVAC control system used in the 'Example Home' centers around the *RCS* 6 *Zone* HVAC Controller model ZC6R as shown in Figure 7-2. Although this Multi-Zone controller is capable of controlling up to 6 *Zones*, we will only use it to control 4 *Zones* in the 'Example Home' for simplicity purposes. The ZC6R is designed to control a standard Gas/Electric or Heat Pump HVAC mechanical system with one stage heating and one stage cooling. This controller also controls two stage heating and one stage cooling for Heat Pump systems.

The *Stargate* Home Controller is used in conjunction with the ZC6R to provide HVAC automation capabilities. The *Stargate* communicates and controls all functions of the *RCS* Multi-Zone Controller via the RS-485 remote interface. The RS-485 interface is located on the lower bottom section of the ZC6R as shown in Figure 7-2. The RS-485 interface on the *Stargate* is shown in Figure 3-2 on page 64.

The *Stargate* has the capability of selecting the Heating Mode, Cooling Mode, Auto Mode, System Off as well as others. It can change the temperature setpoints for both the heating and cooling modes. It can also turn the air handler fan ON/OFF and 'set-back' the temperature when the occupants leave the home. The *Stargate* can also request the current temperatures, temperature setpoints and Mode for each *Zone* as well as the air handler fan status. The remote system RS-485 interface has a 9600-Baud rate and the remote system software uses ASCII based freeform character strings for communications.

The thermostats used in this system are actually wall display units that furnish the homeowner with a user interface. This will allow local control selections to be made manually. The wall display unit located in each *Zone* is a TR15 as shown on page 139. These devices are connected to the ZC6R Multi-Zone Control Panel in a 'Home Run' wiring topology using (CAT 5, 4 UTP) cable as shown in Figure 7-2. Each wall display unit uses these conductors for data communications, clock, 12V power and ground.

The sequence of operation used to control temperature within each *Zone* is as follows: If the TR15 is in Cooling Mode and the temperature setpoint in *Zone* 1 is; for instance,

75°F the thermostat/wall display will monitor the temperature within this *Zone*. When the temperature reaches 76°F, the thermostat will send this data to the ZC6R HVAC Multi-Zone Controller and the *Stargate*. This will initiate the ZC6R to close *Zones* 2, 3 & 4 control dampers and then start the Heat Pump and Air Handler Fan. The return air from the home will enter the air handler and flow through the cooling coil as it supplies air to *Zone* 1. This will continue to occur until the thermostat senses a 74°F temperature within *Zone* 1. The thermostat will send this data to the ZC6R and turn OFF the Heat Pump along with the Air Handler Fan and close the *Zone* 1 damper. If one or more of the other *Zones* required cooling during the time of the process just described, the ZC6R would open the appropriate *Zone* damper(s) in order to provide the required conditioned air. When *Zone* 1 is satisfied and the other *Zone*(s) are not, the ZC6R would continue to monitor and control the system until all *Zones* are satisfied. If one or more of the *Zones* called for heating when the system was operating in the Cooling Mode, the cooling operation would be satisfied first before the Heat Pump is turned OFF and restarted in the Heating Mode after a short time delay.

The barometric air bypass damper is a mechanical device used to bypass varying quantities of air depending on the number of *Zone* control dampers that are open during a cooling or heating process. When all of the *Zone* control damper are open, the pressure will not be enough to open the bypass damper. When there is only one, two or three *Zone* dampers open during a cooling or heating process, the air pressure in the ductwork will rise and open the barometric air bypass damper until a constant pressure is established in the system.

There is also an outside air temperature sensor connected to the ZC6R panel as shown. This system component will provide outside air temperature data to both the ZC6R and the *Stargate*. The *Stargate* can read the outside air temperature and decide whether to take in outside air based on one or more *Zone* temperature setpoints. If the outside air; for instance, is equal to or less than 70°F and the *Zone* cooling temperature setpoint is 75°F, the *Stargate* will recognize this condition and allow outside air to enter the home to provide free cooling. This will save energy by utilizing the cooler outside air instead of bringing on the heat pump in the Cooling Mode. A detailed sequence of operation is as follows. Also see the outside air cooling Event programming shown on page 146.

When the outside air temperature is equal to or less than 70°F and one or more *Zones* are calling for cooling, the *Stargate* will read this data and initiate a command to turn OFF the Heat Pump. This will keep the ZC6R controller from turning on the heat pump prematurely in the Cooling Mode. The *Stargate* will then energize I/O Relay Output 8 to open the outside air control damper, denergize I/O Relay Output 9 to close the return air damper before initiating a command to turn ON the air handler fan to draw outside air into all *Zone(s)*.

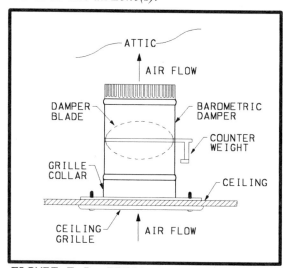

**FIGURE 7-3  PRESSURE RELIEF DAMPER**

To allow cooling to take place using outside air there must be a way of providing pressure relief in the home since there is no return air going through the air handler. Without pressure relief, the outside air will increase the pressure in the home to the point that no more outside air will be able to enter the home. Pressure relief is provided by installing a barometric damper in the ceiling of the home as shown in Figure 7-3. This will allow air to escape into the attic to properly control the positive pressure inside the home. The barometric damper is a mechanical device that is adjusted to open when the pressure on the internal damper blade reaches approximately .03 inches of water pressure (.03 in-wg).

Now that *Stargate* can interface the ZC6R Multi-Zone Controller and receive status requests as well as control the HVAC system, the *Stargate* can now include the operation of the HVAC system as part of the automated home control functions. For instance; there are times of the day or night that the homeowner may require a change in the temperature setpoint for the Cooling Mode or the Heating Mode. In the 'Morning Mode' the cooling setpoint requested by the homeowner may be 75°F until the 'Leaving Home Mode' is initiated. This Mode will change the setpoint to 83°F if there is no one left at home for the purpose of saving energy. When the homeowner initiates the 'Arriving Home Mode', this will change the cooling temperature setpoint back to 75°F in all *Zones*. In the evening the 'Good Night Mode' will change the cooling temperature setpoint to 77°F; for instance, in all bedrooms while also changing the setpoint to 83°F in all unoccupied rooms. These control functions are performed to provide both comfort and energy savings. During the winter months the heating setpoint can also be change in different *Zones* by using similar Modes to save energy. See the temperature setpoint change programming shown on the next page.

Another way of controlling the air conditioning is automatically when people first enter a room, when they remain present in the room and when they leave the room. To provide this control capability, the designer can utilize the occupancy sensors located in each *Zone* to determine when people are actual there. These sensors are also used to automatically control lighting and to detect intruders as discussed in Chapters Four and Five. If a person walks into any room that is part of a *Zone* and maintains their presents for at least 1-minute, a Digital Input from the motion sensor will be recognized by *Stargate*. *Stargate* will then send command signals to the ZC6R Multi-Zone Control Panel. These signals are ASCII based characters that will control the appropriate supply air damper open to satisfy the cooling or heating temperature setpoint. When people are leaving the *Zone*, the cooling temperature setpoint will automatically be setback to 80°F in the Cooling Mode or 66°F in the heating mode to save energy.

## AUTOMATIC TEMPERATURE SET-BACK THRU RS-485

**NOTE**: When the occupants leave the home, the 'Leaving Home Mode' will Run and **Set** the '**Away**' Flag. This will allow the temperature to change to a higher than normal setting for energy conservation purposes. When the owners arrive back home, the 'Arriving Home Mode' **Clears** the 'Set-Back' Flag and '**Away**' Flag to allow the set-back function to work the next time they leave the home.

### *STARGATE PROGRAMMING:*                          *Description:*

EVENT: **COOLING & HEATING SET-BACK  83°F/ 64°F**          *Feature name*
  **IF**                                                           *if*
    (AWAY FLAG) is SET                          *'Away' Flag is Set by the 'Leaving Home' Mode*
    and  (SETBK FLAG)  is CLEAR         *and the 'Set-back' Flag is Clear - keeps event from re-running*
  **THEN**                                                     *then*
    (HVAC: ZONE 1 )   COOL Mode            *Switch to cooling mode*
    (HVAC: ZONE 1 ) = 83°F                  *Select cooling temperature setpoint of **83°F***
    (HVAC: ZONE 1 )   HEAT Mode            *Switch to heating mode*
    (HVAC: ZONE 1 ) = 64°F                  *Select heating temperature setpoint of **64°F***
    * similiar for the next 3 Zones*
    (HVAC: ZONE 1 ) Mode is AUTO           *Switch to auto mode*
    *similiar for the next 3 Zones*
    (F: SETBK  FLAG)  SET          *Set 'Set-back' Flag - so Event will Run only once after leaving home*
End

## AUTOMATIC TEMPERATURE RESET THRU RS-485

**NOTE**: When the occupants arrive home, the 'Arriving Home Mode' will Run and **Clear** the '**Away**' Flag and '**Set-back**' Flag. The 'Leaving Home Mode' **Clears** the 'Reset' Flag to allow the cooling & heating reset temperature setpoint changes to be performed as shown below.

### *STARGATE PROGRAMMING:*                          *Description:*

EVENT: **COOLING & HEATING RESET 70°F/ 75°F**             *Feature name*
  **IF**                                                           *if*
    (AWAY FLAG)  is CLEAR                    *'Away' Flag is Cleared, occupants have arrived*
    and  (RESET FLAG)  is CLEAR            *and the 'Reset' Flag is Clear - keeps event from re-running*
  **THEN**                                                     *then*
    (HVAC: ZONE 1 )   COOL Mode            *Switch to cooling mode*
    (HVAC: ZONE 1 ) = 75°F                  *Select cooling temperature setpoint of **75°F***
    (HVAC: ZONE 1 )   HEAT Mode            *Switch to heating mode*
    (HVAC: ZONE 1 ) = 70°F                  *Select heating temperature setpoint of **70°F***
    *similiar for the next 3 Zones*
    (HVAC: ZONE 1 ) Mode is AUTO           *Switch to auto mode*
    *similiar for the next 3 Zones*
    (F: RESET  FLAG)  SET         *Set 'Reset' Flag - so Event will Run only run one time after arriving*
End

# AUTOMATIC COOLING OF ZONES USING OUTSIDE AIR

**NOTE**: The outside air 'Cool' Flag must be Set by the 'Cooling Required Mode' shown below for the 'Outside Air Cooling' Mode to run. If the Flag is Set, this means that one or more *Zones* are calling for cooling.

| | |
|---|---|
| EVENT: **OUTSIDE AIR COOLING** | *Feature name* |
| **IF** | *if* |
| (COOL FLAG ) is SET | *cooling is required in any Zone* |
| and (HVAC OUTSIDE ) <= 70 | *and the outside air temperature sensor reads 70°F or less* |
| **THEN** | *then* |
| ( HVAC: FAN ON ) | *Turn the air handler fan ON* |
| ( RELAY: OSA DAMPER) ON | *Opens Outside Air control damper* |
| ( RELAY: RET AIR DAMPER) OFF | *Closes Return Air control damper* |
| End | |

| | |
|---|---|
| EVENT: **COOLING REQUIRED** | *Feature name* |
| **IF** | *if* |
| (HVAC MASTER ) System Mode is COOL | *Master Bedroom is in the cooling mode* |
| or (HVAC ZONE 1 ) System Mode is COOL | *or Zone 1 is in the cooling mode* |
| or (HVAC ZONE 2 ) System Mode is COOL | *or Zone 2 is in the cooling mode* |
| or (HVAC ZONE 3 ) System Mode is COOL | *or Zone 3 is in the cooling mode* |
| or (HVAC ZONE 4 ) System Mode is COOL | *or Zone 4 is in the cooling mode* |
| **THEN** | *then* |
| ( F: COOL ) SET | *Sets 'Cool' Flag for IF condition in Outside Air Cooling Mode above* |
| End | |

# HVAC PHONE CONTROL COMMANDS & PROGRAMMING:

**NOTE:** To change a temperature setpoint or HVAC Mode, the occupant must first select HVAC *Zone* 1, 2, 3 or 4 by keying *31, *32, *33 or *34 respectively as shown below. After selecting an HVAC *Zone*, a mode and a new temperature setpoint can be selected together as shown below. When making a temperature setpoint change in the Cooling Mode, the available selections are between 75°F & 83°F. . When making a temperature setpoint change in the Heating Mode, the available selections are between 64°F & 74°F. Any selection within either range will automatically select the corresponding Cooling Mode or Heating Mode.

### SELECT HVAC *ZONE 1* BEFORE MAKING CHANGE TO COOLING SETPOINT:
Phone command - key-in *31 to Select HVAC *Zone 1*

## *PROGRAMMING:*

| | |
|---|---|
| EVENT: **SELECT HVAC *ZONE* 1** | *Feature name* |
| **IF** | *if* |
| (XSEQ: C-1 C-ON ) Received within 4 second | *If keying *31 by phone* |
| **THEN** | *then* |
| (F: ZONE 1 FLAG ) SET | *Sets Zone 1 Flag to allow temperature setpoint change* |
| End | |

| | |
|---|---|
| EVENT: **CHANGE T0 75°F IN *ZONE 1*** | *Feature name* |
| **IF** | *if* |
| (XSEQ: G-5 G-ON) Received within 4 second | *If keying *75 by phone* |
| and (F: ZONE 1 ) is Set | *and if Zone 1 Flag is Set from Event shown above (identifies Zone)* |
| **THEN** | *then* |
| (HVAC: ZONE 1 ) COOL Mode | *Switch to Cooling Mode* |
| (HVAC: ZONE 1 ) = 75°F | *Selects cooling temperature setpoint of 75°F* |
| (F: ZONE 1 ) CLEAR | *Clears Zone 1 Flag so Event will not repeat* |
| End | |

**SELECT AC *ZONE 2* BEFORE MAKING CHANGE TO HEATING SETPOINT:**

Phone command - key-in \*32 to Select HVAC *Zone 2*

## *PROGRAMMING:*

EVENT:   **SELECT HVAC *ZONE* 2**                                    *Feature name*
  **IF**                                                                                  *if*
    (XSEQ: C-2 C-ON ) Received within 4 second          *If keying \*32 by phone*
  **THEN**                                                                            *then*
    (F: ZONE 2 FLAG )   SET                          *Sets Zone 2 Flag to allow temperature setpoint change*
End

---

EVENT:   **CHANGE T0 70°F IN *ZONE* 2**                              *Feature name*
  **IF**                                                                                  *if*
    (XSEQ: G-0 G-ON) Received within 4 second           *If keying \*70 by phone*
    and (F: ZONE 2 ) is Set                    *and if Zone 2 Flag is Set from Event shown above (identifies Zone)*
  **THEN**                                                                            *then*
    (HVAC: ZONE 2 )   **HEAT** Mode                        *Switch to Heating Mode*
    (HVAC: ZONE 2 ) = 70°F                          *Selects cooling temperature setpoint of 70°F*
    (F: ZONE 2 ) CLEAR                              *Clears Zone 2 Flag so Event will run only once*
End

---

## SELECT HVAC AUTO MODE:

**NOTE:** To select the HVAC Auto Mode for all *Zones*, key-in **\*38** by phone

EVENT:   **HVAC ZONE 1, 2, 3 & 4 AUTO MODE**                        *Feature name*
  **IF**                                                                                  *if*
    (XSEQ: C-8 C-OFF ) Received within 4 second         *If keying \*38 by phone*
  **THEN**                                                                            *then*
    (HVAC: ZONE 1 )   AUTO Mode                        *Zone 1 Switch to Auto Mode*
    (HVAC: ZONE 2 )   AUTO Mode                        *Zone 2 Switch to Auto Mode*
    (HVAC: ZONE 3 )   AUTO Mode                        *Zone 3 Switch to Auto Mode*
    (HVAC: ZONE 4 )   AUTO Mode                        *Zone 4 Switch to Auto Mode*
End

---

## SELECT HVAC OFF MODE:

**NOTE:** To select the HVAC Off Mode for all *Zones*, key-in **\*39** by phone

EVENT:   **HVAC ZONE 1, 2, 3 & 4 OFF  MODE**                       *Feature name*
  **IF**                                                                                  *if*
    (XSEQ: C-9 C-OFF ) Received within 4 second         *If keying \*39 by phone*
  **THEN**                                                                            *then*
    (HVAC: ZONE 1 )   OFF Mode                         *Zone 1 Switch to Off Mode*
    (HVAC: ZONE 2 )   OFF Mode                         *Zone 2 Switch to Off Mode*
    (HVAC: ZONE 3 )   OFF Mode                         *Zone 3 Switch to Off Mode*
    (HVAC: ZONE 4 )   OFF Mode                         *Zone 4 Switch to Off Mode*
End

**7-2 Automated Fireplaces:** The Heat-N-Glo fireplace is a direct vent natural gas fireplace designed to operate with 100% of the air siphoned from outside the home for combustion purposes. All exhaust gases are discharged to the home's exterior through an exhaust duct located in the top portion of the duct as shown in Figure 7-4. The bottom portion of the duct provides the outside air intake. A tightly sealed

**AUTOMATED FIREPLACE**

firebox combined with the combustion air drawn in from the outside is designed to keep the warm air in and the cold air out. These attributes will commonly provide a thermal efficiency of approximately 70% along with maintaining good indoor air quality (IAQ). A 'heat out duct outlet' can be used on occasions when the owner wishes to display the fireplace without having all of the warm air flow into the home. There will generally be an optional duct that can be installed off of the firebox to carry heat to other rooms or even to the basement when the requirement arises. There is also an optional variable speed blower system that is used to induce additional airflow into the convection air intake from the room to be warmed and reintroduced to heat the room. A hand-held remote will provide the following control functions: Turn the fireplace ON and OFF, adjust the room temperature setpoint, vary the blower speed and allow the automatic sleep timer to turn

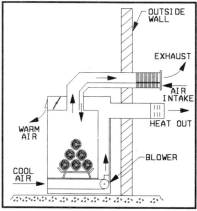

**FIGURE 7-4    AIR FLOW**

the fireplace OFF. The natural gas control system that is generally available with this type of unit includes: 'Standing Pilot' and 'Direct Spark Ignition' (DSI). In order to automate and integrate this fireplace as part of a 'whole house home automation system', the designer should select a unit that incorporates a Direct Spark Ignition (DSI). This allows a safe means of controlling the fireplace when using the *Stargate* or other comparable controller. To automate the firing function of this fireplace, a Relay Output from the *Stargate* is used to turn the fireplace ON & OFF by wiring it in series with the 24V DC low voltage control circuit shown in Figure 7-5. When an occupant selects the 'Fireplace ON' control function from the *JDS* Keypad located in Living Room, the normally open (N.O.) Relay Output contacts are closed by the *Stargate*. This will provide power to the gas control valve and the Direct Spark Ignition (DSI) to start the fireplace. See the Fireplace ON/OFF programming shown on page 150. Notice that a 2 hour 'Timer 10' is initiated when the fireplace is turned ON. After 2 hours has passed, the fireplace will be automatically turned OFF for safety purposes in case the occupants fall asleep. When the 'Fireplace OFF' function is selected from the *JDS* Keypad, the Relay Output will be turned OFF (contacts open), which will no long supply power to the fireplace control circuit. The system *Integrator* should always check with the fireplace manufacture when interfacing the fireplace control circuit to a centralized control system. He should also make sure the gas valve will close automatically (fail closed) when power is lost or removed.

To automate the blower function, a slave relay is required to switch the 120V AC power ON & OFF. This device should be installed in series with the blower, speed control device and the temperature sensor switch as shown in Figure 7-5. The slave relay should have single pole 120V AC normally open (N.O.) contacts with an amperage rating = 1.25 x (motor amperage) and a 12V DC coil. The 12 DC coil is wired to another *Stargate* Relay Output to energize and de-energize the slave relay to control the blower ON & OFF. See the blower ON/OFF

Event programming shown on page 150. An optimum speed must be selected initially on the dial of the blower speed controller. Remote control of the blower speed is not part of the automated system because of the difficulty associated with variable speed control. Control of the fireplace can now be included as part of a Macro called 'Romance Mode'. This mode will dim the lights, turn on some music, close the vertical blinds, start the fireplace and the blower all by selecting 'Romance' on the Living Room *JDS* Keypad, touch screen or from a hand-held remote.

If the smell of gas is present, do not try and light any appliance or use the telephone. Manually turn OFF the gas to the home or have the Gas Company do so. Always follow the manufacturer's instructions and recommendations when installing and operating a fireplace.

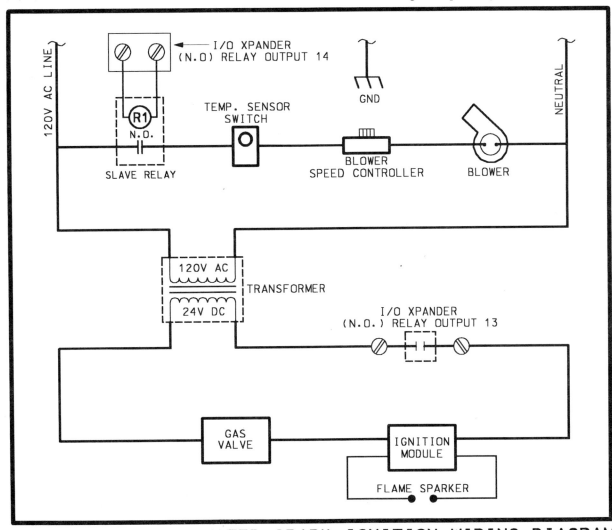

Figure 7-5    AUTOMATED SPARK IGNITION WIRING DIAGRAM

# **Stargate** Controlled - Automated Fireplace Programming

| Programming | Description |
|---|---|
| EVENT:  **FIREPLACE - ON** | *Feature name* |
| **IF** | *if* |
| (FIREPLACE) ON | *If Living Room JDS Keypad-'Fireplace ON' function is selected* |
| **THEN** | *then* |
| (RELAY: FIREPLACE) ON | *Turns ON fireplace* |
| (Timer 10 ) LOAD with 2 : 00 : 00 | *Start 2 hour timer (see Time 10 Event below)* |
| End | |

| | |
|---|---|
| EVENT **TIME 10** | *Event name* |
| **IF** | *if* |
| (T: TIME 10 ) is Expiring | *Timer counts down to zero seconds* |
| **THEN** | *then* |
| (RELAY: FIREPLACE) OFF | *Turns OFF fireplace* |
| (RELAY: BLOWER) OFF | *Turns OFF blower* |
| End | |

| | |
|---|---|
| EVENT:  **FIREPLACE - OFF** | *Feature name* |
| **IF** | *if* |
| (FIREPLACE) OFF | *If Living Room JDS Keypad-'Fireplace OFF' function is selected* |
| **THEN** | *then* |
| (RELAY: FIREPLACE) OFF | *Turns OFF fireplace* |
| End | |

| | |
|---|---|
| EVENT:  **BLOWER - ON** | *Feature name* |
| **IF** | *if* |
| (BLOWER) ON | *If Living Room JDS Keypad-'Blower ON' function is selected* |
| **THEN** | *then* |
| (RELAY: BLOWER) ON | *Turns ON blower* |
| End | |

| | |
|---|---|
| EVENT:  **BLOWER - OFF** | *Feature name* |
| **IF** | *if* |
| (BLOWER) OFF | *If Living Room JDS Keypad-'Blower OFF' function is selected* |
| **THEN** | *then* |
| (RELAY: BLOWER) OFF | *Turn OFF blower* |
| End | |

# PBX Digital Telephone Systems

**8-1 Digital Hybrid Telephone Systems:** The Panasonic KX-TD1232 Hybrid Telephone System is a powerful digitally advanced design that can manage any home or business telephone requirements. It is designed to provide the versatility that is often required in present day applications while having the capabilities that will be essential in the future.

To gain an understanding of where the system components are located in the 'Example Home', refer to the floor plan shown in Figure 8-1. This Plan is intended to portray a typical home with telephone requirements in the Living Room, Family Room, Kitchen, three bedrooms, Office, Home Theater, Garage, Entryway, Access Gate and the pool area. Notice the 'Bundle' drop locations in each room identified by round dots as shown. These 'Bundle' drops include two (CAT 5, 4 UTP) cables that are used for telephone service, the Ethernet network, Internet service, fax machine, credit card reader and communications required by the satellite receivers. Also notice the individual (CAT 5, 4 UTP) cable drops (triangular dots) that are dedicated to provide additional telephone service locations.

To demonstrate how this telephone system is integrated into the Example Home', we will introduce the main components of the system and provide the wiring requirements to support

the entire Hybrid Telephone System.

The installation begins by locating the main Telephone Control Panel in the *Equipment Room* as shown in Figure 8-1. The *Equipment Room* is in a centralized location of the home where the majority of the 'home control equipment' is located. Also refer to Figure 1-8 shown on page 9, to see an elevation view of what this system will look like once it is mounted. This Figure illustrates the main Telephone Controller along with the Voice Processor mounted to a plywood sheet attached to the *Equipment Room* wall. The Telephone Controller and Voice Processor frames can be grounded to the third wire of the power outlet located in the *Equipment Room*; however, in the 'Example Home', these units are connected to a grounding post on the *Structured Wiring Distribution Panel*. This is because there is a grounding cable that was pulled directly from the *Distribution Panel* location to the grounding rod located outside the home. This ground is superior because of its low resistance and its direct connection to ground.

After the Telephone Controller and Voice Processor are mounted, all of the telephone cables that were pulled during the construction stage are in place and ready to terminate. Cable connections will establish the system wiring

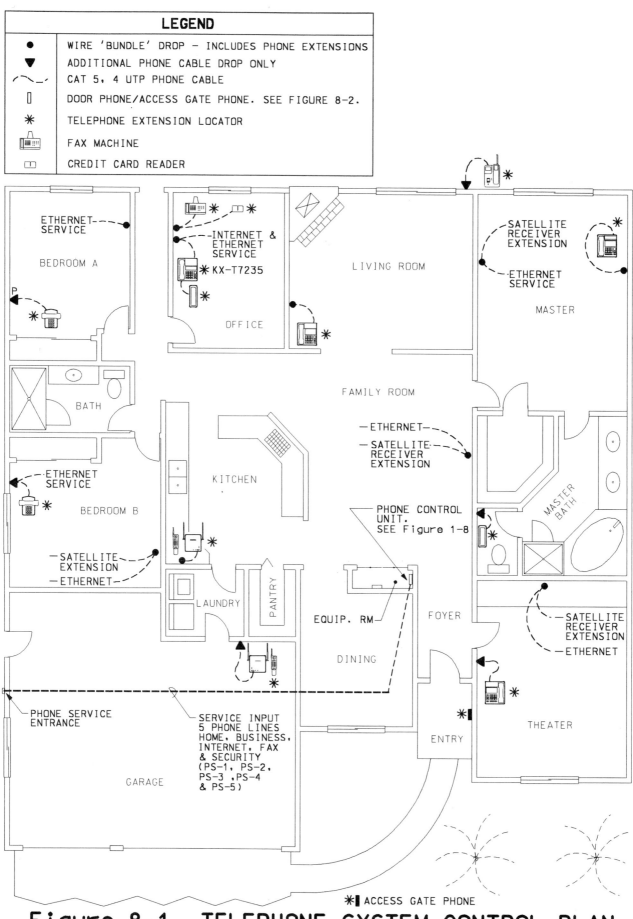

## LEGEND

●    WIRE 'BUNDLE' DROP – INCLUDES PHONE EXTENSIONS

▼    ADDITIONAL PHONE CABLE DROP ONLY

〜    CAT 5, 4 UTP PHONE CABLE

▯    DOOR PHONE/ACCESS GATE PHONE. SEE FIGURE 8-2.

✳    TELEPHONE EXTENSION LOCATOR

▥    FAX MACHINE

▭    CREDIT CARD READER

ETHERNET SERVICE

BEDROOM A

P

BATH

INTERNET & ETHERNET SERVICE

KX-T7235

OFFICE

LIVING ROOM

SATELLITE RECEIVER EXTENSION

ETHERNET SERVICE

MASTER

FAMILY ROOM

—ETHERNET

—SATELLITE RECEIVER EXTENSION

ETHERNET SERVICE

BEDROOM B

KITCHEN

—SATELLITE EXTENSION

—ETHERNET

LAUNDRY

PANTRY

EQUIP. RM

PHONE CONTROL UNIT. SEE Figure 1-8

MASTER BATH

FOYER

—SATELLITE RECEIVER EXTENSION

—ETHERNET

DINING

THEATER

ENTRY

—PHONE SERVICE ENTRANCE

SERVICE INPUT 5 PHONE LINES HOME, BUSINESS, INTERNET, FAX & SECURITY (PS-1, PS-2, PS-3 ,PS-4 & PS-5)

GARAGE

✳▯ ACCESS GATE PHONE

# Figure 8-1   TELEPHONE SYSTEM CONTROL PLAN

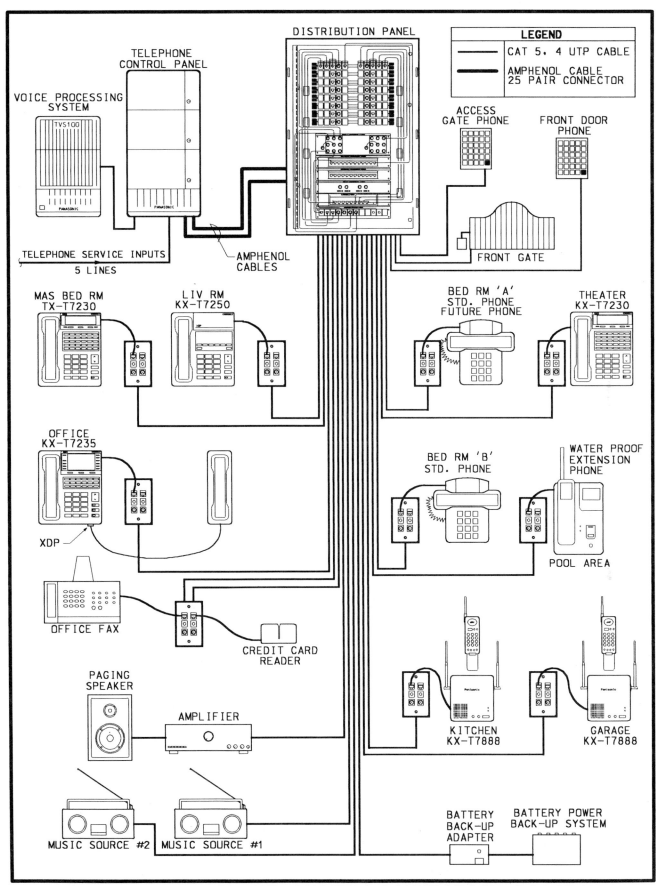

# Figure 8-2   PHONE SYSTEM CONNECTION DIAGRAM

configurations shown in Figures 8-2 & 8-7. The first lines to connect to the Telephone Controller are the telephone service input cables that were pulled to the service entrance location shown in Figure 1-7 on page 7. This is where the telephone company connects their service wiring to the customer's service input cable(s). These connections are made inside the service entrance enclosure mounted to the exterior wall by the Telephone Company. The service input cables run from this enclosure to the *Equipment Room* to be connected to the telephone system.

In Figure 1-8 shown on page 9, notice the telephone service input cables routed from the attic and down the wall. This will allow the service input cables to be connected to the Telephone Controller. In Figure 8-3, notice 4 telephone jacks that contain two 'service inputs' each. This accommodates 8 separate service input lines. The two center pins shown in the enlarged illustration of the jack provides a Tip (T1) and Ring (R1), which makes up line 1. T2 and R2 makes-up line 2. The three subsequent jacks will furnish lines 3 & 4, 5 & 6 and 7 & 8.

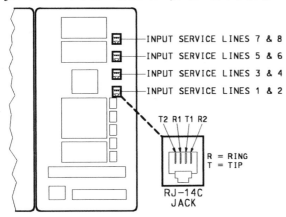

**FIGURE 8-3 TELEPHONE CONTROLLER SERVICE INPUT CONNECTIONS**

An interface cable is installed between the Telephone Controller and the Voice Processor. The Voice Processor provides mailboxes, messages and other telephone services that are useful to properly manage and receive incoming calls.

An Amphenol connector is a network interface device that provides all the necessary connections to support communications through the *Structured Wiring Distribution Panel* and out to each telecom extension. The Amphenol connectors connect to the inside panel of the Telephone Controller as shown in Figure 8-4.

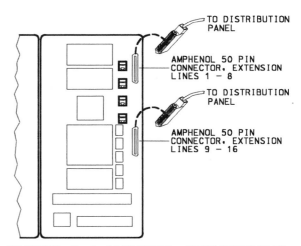

**FIGURE 8-4 AMPHENOL CONNECTIONS**

An Amphenol connector located on the other end of both cables are routed to the rear of a *TP Bus Distribution Hub* (*Telephone Hub*) that is mounted to the frame of the *Distribution Panel*. These connections can be seen in Figure 1-10 on page 12. The top Amphenol connector connects to one of the *Distribution Panel's* 8 Port/3 Line *Telephone Hub* providing extensions one (1) through (8). The bottom Amphenol connector connects to the second 8 Port/3 Line *Telephone Hub* providing extensions nine (9) through sixteen (16). This connector type can be seen close-up in Figure 8-5.

The telephone extension jumper cables connected to the front of the *Telephone Hub* Hubs are also connected to specific *Zone Hubs* that require telephone extensions. An example of this wiring configuration can be seen in the 'Office Hub Connection Diagram' shown in Figure 1-11 on page 13. The remaining jumper connections from the *Telephone Hub* to the remaining *Zone Hubs* can be seen in the individual 'Zone Connection Diagrams' for the other rooms of the home. (See Chapter One).

Figure 1-11 illustrates the following extension lines required for the Office: Home telephone, business telephone, Internet/Ethernet, credit card reader, and fax machine. These extensions are provided by using the two (CAT 5, 4 UTP) cables contained in each wire 'Bundle' along with three separate (CAT 5, 4 UTP) cables. Two wire 'Bundle' drops were pulled to the Office as shown in Figure 8-1. Each 'Bundle' drop is terminated to an *Interactive Receptacle* shown in Figure 1-28. The home telephones, business telephones, Internet, Ethernet, credit card reader and fax

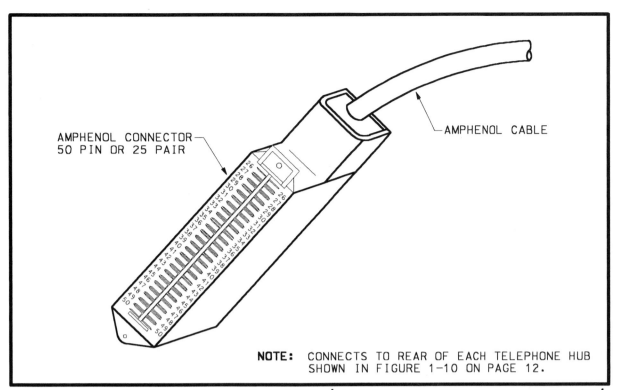

AMPHENOL CONNECTOR
50 PIN OR 25 PAIR

AMPHENOL CABLE

**NOTE:** CONNECTS TO REAR OF EACH TELEPHONE HUB
SHOWN IN FIGURE 1-10 ON PAGE 12.

## Figure 8-5 50 PIN, 25 PAIR 'AMPHENOL-TYPE CONNECTOR'

machine all receive cords that plug into their corresponding *Interactive Receptacle* jacks in order to receive service. All of the other *Zones* in the home will typically follow the same wiring scenario in order to receive telecom service as well.

Other extension lines included in this system are for the security system panel and the *Stargate*. The security panel requires telecom service so it can make outside telephone calls to a monitoring service company when the system detects an intrusion. The *Stargate* also uses an extension to notify the homeowner by phone that a specific home control function has occurred or has not occurred. These particular telecom cables can be seen in Figures 1-10, and 1-11.

Power required by both the Telephone Controller and the Voice Processor are provided through power transformers that are plugged into a 120V power strip as shown in Figure 1-8. Also notice that the power strips are plugged into a power source that is protected by a surge suppressor.

The *Distribution Panel* provides the capability of truly customizing each telephone drop (extension) in each room. The telephone wiring arrangement of the *Distribution Panel* allows the installer or homeowner to change the location of a drop by simply removing the

jumper from one *Zone* Hub and repositioning it to another as required. Figure 8-6 illustrates and example pin-out wiring diagram for a single telephone extension. A telephone cord with a minimum of 3 pairs is shown connected to the jack on the telephone using RJ-14C connector plugs on each end of the cord. RJ-45 connector plugs and a 4 pair telephone cord is optional. In Figure 8-6, notice there are only 3-pairs of wires required for this particular telephone extension that provides three CO service lines. If 4 CO lines are required, a 4-pair (CAT 5, 4 UTP) distribution cable, a RJ-45 modular jack as part of the *Interactive Receptacle,* along with a 4-pair telephone cord with RJ-45 plugs are required to furnish this additional line.

There are three digital telephone models used in the 'Example Home' design as described in the System Components Section 8-2. The Office utilizes the KX-7235 proprietary phone because this phone is used for business purposes and allows the users to maximize the system's capabilities. The Theater, Master Bedroom and Bedroom 'B' utilize the KX-7220 proprietary phone because only some of the advanced capabilities are desired in these areas. The Kitchen and Garage feature the KX-T7888 wireless phone because the owners require the mobility that this phone offers in these areas.

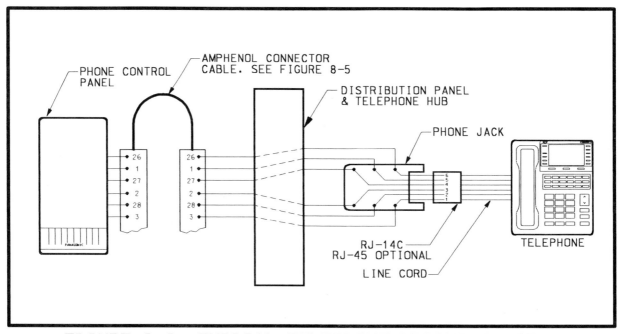

# FIGURE 8-6 TYPICAL TELEPHONE WIRING DIAGRAM

In areas of the home that require basic telephone service, the use of standard phones is sufficient. See Section 8-2 for some of the specifications and features provided by specific proprietary phones. Each of the digital telephones listed requires a minimum of 2-conductor cable. The pin connections used for digital telephones are 'D1' and 'D2'. 'D1'= Low and 'D2' = High. Another two conductors are required if the Extra Device Port (XDP) connection on a proprietary telephone phone is used for a single line device such as a second phone, fax machine, etc. The pin connections used for single line devices are 'T' and 'R'.

Notice the Office telephone drop layout shown in Figure 8-1. A separate (CAT 5, 4 UTP) cable was pulled from the *Distribution Panel* to an Office Drop to provide telephone service. A Proprietary Digital Telephone KX-T7235 is connected to this Office *Interactive Receptacle* using a 2-pair telephone cord. A second 1-pair telephone wire is connected from the Extra Device Port (XDP) located on the back of the KX-T7235 to a one line standard telephone as shown in Figure 8-2. The 2-pair telephone cord connects to pins 'D1' and 'D2' for the KX-T7235 and the one pair telephone cord connects to pins 'T' and 'R' for another single line device. Note that when using the Extra Device Port (XDP), each device has a different extension number and the (KX-T7235) considers them as two completely different extensions.

To demonstrate the features and capabilities of the KX-TD1232 Digital Hybrid System, the following family scenario will be presented to show how the 'Example Home' occupants typically utilize the system.

Say hello to John, Jane, Jackie, Joe and little J Smith. John works for an Architectural Engineering firm and plans to do some of his work at home. Jane is a full time mother and a part-time sales person and she too is looking forward to working at home in their new office. Joe is a full-time student at the local Junior Collage, Jackie is a senior in high school and little J is 10 months old.

It's Monday morning and John is thinking about his architectural project. John knows he doesn't have much time before his boss will require the finished product, but he feels confident that working at home will maximize his available time. It's mid morning and John is hard at work on his computer making some last minute changes to his design drawings; however he needs one more piece of information. John is expecting an important call from a product vendor with the critical information required. By programming his proprietary telephone to utilize the ***Discriminating Ring*** feature, he is able to identify his important incoming calls separate from all other calls by using a specific ring pattern. This will give him the opportunity to instantly know which call is the one he is waiting for. Another method used to identify the

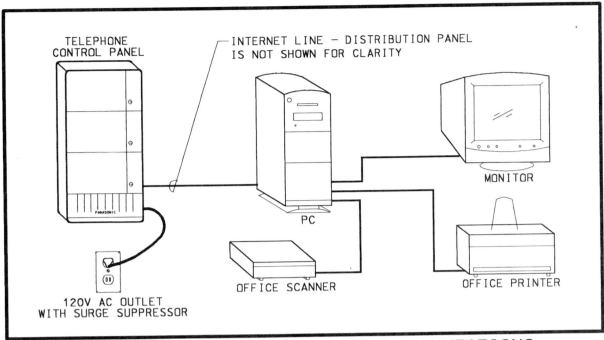

## Figure 8-7   REMAINING SYSTEM CONNECTIONS

caller is the **Caller ID** feature. This feature will display the caller's name and telephone number on the proprietary telephone in the office. John is amazed with how powerful his new Panasonic KX-TD1232 Digital Hybrid System really is! He is able to program all of his preferred features directly from any proprietary telephone in the home. All of a sudden John receives a call and quickly responses to the **Discriminating Ring**. During this call, he realizes that he will need to record the conversation for his records. This is accomplished by utilizing the **One Touch Record** feature. With this feature John can record the conversion and play it back at his convenience and save the recording for future use. While on the phone, John also realizes he must e-mail this information to the home office for his boss to review. He quickly switches to **Hands-free Operation** that allows John to dial and talk to the product vender without lifting the handset. He takes advantage of this feature to e-mail the data while talking on the phone. Now that John has received his important call and has e-mailed the home office, he can focus on completing his project.

A few hours later it is time for John's favorite Radio Business News. John will be able to listen to this program by utilizing the **Background Music** feature. This feature allows a proprietary telephone user to listen to background music or other radio programs from the monitor speaker on the telephone.

After awhile, John's wife Jane returns home from taking Jackie to school and from running a few errands. Jane has a very important meeting with a client today where she hopes to close on a big sale. Jane realizes that it is almost lunchtime and has just enough time to prepare a quick lunch for the family. Suddenly the telephone rings and by utilizing the **Live Call Screening** feature, Jane is able to determine if the call is important enough for her to stop what she is doing to pick up the telephone. Lucky for her she didn't pick up the telephone or she would have wasted part of her lunchtime trying to brush-off that Carpet Cleaning Company. After lunch is made, Jane is ready to call the family for lunch by utilizing the **Hands-free Operation** and **Paging-All** features. Since her hands are full, this feature allows Jane to dial and talk to John and Joe without lifting the handset. This will allow her to make a voice announcement from the speaker on the proprietary telephone or from any external paging device. During lunch, the telephone rings again and John quickly realizes that it is a fax because he again used the **Discriminating Ring** feature and was able to identify the incoming call by the specific ringing pattern. During lunch, John discusses the **Automatic Route Selection** feature with Jane. He states that this programmable system feature automatically select the least expensive route available at the time for outgoing long distance calls. After all, now that John and Jane are both working at home, this feature will definitely save them money on long distance business and personal telephone service.

By early afternoon, Jane is on her way to her meeting. Knowing that she might receive some last minute changes to the contract for the meeting, she forwards all her incoming calls to her cell phone by utilizing the system's *Call Forwarding* feature. By doing so, she is guaranteed not to miss any of her calls wherever she may be.

Later that afternoon John decides to take a break and watch the world business news in the Home Theater. Excited about what he just heard on the news, John decides to sell some of his top performing stocks to try an cash in on the Bull Market. John quickly grabs his laptop computer and connects it to the proprietary telephone in the Home Theater. This is accomplished by utilizing the *Extra Device Port* located on the back of the telephone. After the connection is made, John quickly brings up the Internet, places a sell order with his online broker while still be able to receive telephone calls on the Home Theater extension.

Later that evening as the family joins together to discuss their day. John and Jane feel their children are spending far too much time on the telephone and at times call long distance without asking first. To avoid these problems, John tells his children about the new features he has setup for them. The first feature is called *Limited Call Duration.* This is a system programmable feature that disconnects a call when a specified period of time has expired. A tone is sent to warn the children of a telephone call termination at 15 seconds, 10 seconds, and 5 seconds before the time limit expires. Another

feature he talked about is called *Toll Restriction.* This is also a system programmable feature that will prohibit certain extension users from placing unauthorized long distance calls. After the father's little speech on telephone control, the kids quickly point out some of their favorite system features. Jackie the high school student can't remember how she managed her social life without the *Call Splitting* feature. This feature allows her to alternate between two other parties. This is accomplished by placing the current call on hold to allow her to have a conversation with the other party. Another feature on her favorites list is *Call Pickup, Directed.* This feature allows her mom or anyone else in the home to answer a call ringing at Jackie's extension. Joe has his own favorite features too that greatly differs from his sister. Joe started taking about his favorite feature *Call Hold, Exclusive-CO Line.* (CO) refers to a line from the Central Office or the telephone company facility where the telephone lines are joined to the switching equipment for connection purposes. The *Call Hold, Exclusive-CO Line* feature allows the proprietary telephone user to prevent any other extension users from retrieving a held CO call. Now this feature is designed so Jackie can't pickup those calls and start talking to Joe's girl friends to let them know about the real Joe. After John's conversation with the family, he realizes that everyone has their own unique way of utilizing the capabilities of their new telephone system. So as a final note John reminds the family that the Panasonic KX-TD1232 Digital Hybrid Telephone System can be tailored to meet all of the families telephone needs with a wide number of features listed in Sections 8-3 & 8-4.

**8-2 System Components:**

| | Model | Description |
|---|---|---|
| Service Unit | KX-TD1232 | Digital Super Hybrid System (Main Unit) |
| Telephone | KX-T7235 | Digital proprietary telephone with large tilt-up display, 6-line LCD with 24 character per line, 10 function buttons and speaker phone. |
| | KX-T7230 | Digital proprietary telephone with small display, 2-line LCD with 16 charters per line, speakerphone. |
| | KX-T7220 | Digital proprietary telephone, no display, speakerphone |
| Voice Processor | TVS100 | Voice Processing System provides 64 mailboxes and 16 hours of recording time. |

**8-3 System Highlights:** This section will highlight some general information and system capabilities of the Panasonic KX-TD1232 Digital Super Hybrid System.

- *System Capacity:*
  The Panasonic KX-TD1232 Digital Super Hybrid System supports eight (8) lines and sixteen (16) digital extensions. It can be expanded to twenty-four (24) lines and sixty-four (64) digital extensions.

- *Super Hybrid System:*
  This system supports the connection of both digital and analog proprietary telephones, DSS Consoles and single line devices such as single line telephones, fax machines, and data terminals.

- *Module Expansion:*
  Expansion modules are used to increase the capacity of the system. One CO line module can be added to the basic telephone system to provide four additional CO lines and two extension modules can add 16 extensions.

- *Extra Device Port:*
  Each extension jack in the telephone system supports the connection of a digital proprietary telephone and a single line device. Each device has a different extension number and is treated as two completely different extensions.

- *Paralleled Telephone Connection:*
  Every jack in the system supports the parallel connection of a proprietary telephone and a single line device. Each device shares the same extension number and is considered by the system to be one extension.

- *System Connection:*
  With the addition of an optional System Inter Connection Card, two Digital Super Hybrid Systems can be connected together to expand the system to a maximum of 24 CO lines and 64 extensions. The two systems function as one; however, some functions such as PAGING and MUSIC ON HOLD are duplicated.

- *Digital Proprietary Telephones:*
  The system supports four different models of digital proprietary telephones that cover the range from a monitor set to a large display hands free version.

- *Programming System:*
  The system can be programmed from any proprietary telephone or from a personal computer.

- *Voice Mail Integration:*
  The system supports Voice Processing Systems with in-band DTIMF signaling. The Panasonic Voice Processing System provides automated attendant, voice mail, interview and bulletin board services.

- *Automatic Route Selection:*
  This feature automatically selects the pre-programmed least expensive route for outgoing toll calls.

- *Caller ID:*
  This feature allows the user to see the name or telephone number of the caller on the telephone display before answering.

- *Remote Station Lock Control:*
  This feature allows an operator to lock an extension so that outgoing calls cannot be made.
  8-4 System Features:

- *Alternate Calling - Ring/Voice*

  This system offers two methods of Intercom Calling-Ring-Calling and Voice-Calling. Ring-Calling informs the called party of an incoming call with a ring tone, while the Voice-Calling uses the calling party's voice. The called extension user, if on a proprietary telephone, can select tone or voice calling. If the user selects Voice-Calling, the calling party can talk to the user immediately after the confirmation tone.

- *Answering, Direct CO Line*

  Allows the proprietary telephone user to answer an incoming call by simply pressing the appropriate CO button without having to lift the handset.

- *Background Music*

  This feature allows the proprietary telephone user to listen to background music from the monitor speaker located on the telephone.

- *Busy Station Signaling*

  When attempting to call a busy extension, Busy Station Signaling allows you to signal the user on the telephone to answer your call. The called extension user hears a Call waiting tone and is able to answer the call.

- *Call Forwarding - All Calls*

  This feature is used when you want all your calls to be automatically re-directed to another extension.

- *Call Hold - CO Line*

  Allows the extension user to put a CO call on hold. The held call can be retrieved from the user who held it or from any other extension.

- *Call Pickup*

  Allows any extension user to answer a call ringing at any other extension.

- *Call Splitting*

  Allows the extension user to alternate between two other parties. Placing the current call on hold allows the user to have a conversation with the other party.

- *Call Transfer, Screened*

  Allows the proprietary telephone user to voice-announce to the external party and transfer the call.

- *Call Waiting*

  While in conversation, a call waiting tone informs the user of another incoming call that is waiting. He or she can answer the second call by disconnecting or placing the current call on hold. Call waiting tone can be enabled or disabled by dialing the appropriate feature number.

- *Caller ID*

  Provides the proprietary telephone user with a caller's information; such as their name and number.

- *Conference*

  The system supports three-party conference calls, including outside or inside parties. During a two-party conversation, the extension user can add a third party to their conversation, thereby establishing a conference.

- *Consultation Hold*

  Allows the extension user to place a call on hold temporarily to transfer it or make a Conference call or use the Call Splitting feature. The held call can also be retrieved from other extensions.

- *Direct In Lines*

  Enables an incoming CO call to go directly to one or more answering points. This CO line can be used by multiple extension users to make calls but can be used by only one extension to receive calls.

- *Display, Time and Date*
  Offers the display proprietary telephone user a display of either the present time and the date or the date and the day of the week. It is displayed while on-hook.

- *Flash*
  The FLASH button is used to allow a proprietary telephone user to disconnect from the current call and originate another call without hanging up first.

- *Full One-Touch Dialing*
  Allows the proprietary telephone user to make a call or have access to a system service with one button.

- *Hands-free Operation*
  Allows the proprietary telephone user to dial and to talk to a party without lifting the handset. Pressing an appropriate button provides hands-free mode.

- *Intercom Calling*
  Allows the extension user to call another extension user within the system.

- *Limited Call Duration*
  Limited Call Duration is a system programmable feature that disconnects a CO call when a specified timer expires. A warning tone is sent to the extension user 15 seconds, 10 seconds, and 5 seconds before the time limit. Limiting the call duration can be enabled or disabled by Class of Service for each extension.

- *Off-Hook Call Announcement*
  Allows the user to inform a busy extension that another call is waiting by talking through the built-in speaker of the called party's proprietary telephone. If the existing call is using the handset, the second conversation is made with the speakerphone so that the called party can talk to two parties independently.

- *Paging - All*
  Allows you to make a voice announcement from the speakers of the proprietary telephones and from the external paging devices (external pagers). If one of the paged persons answers your page, you can talk to the person through the connected line.

- *Redial, Automatic*
  This is a special feature for the proprietary telephones that provide automatic redialing of the last dialed, saved number or call log, if the called party is busy. If the Last Number Redial, Saved Number Redial or Call Log operation is performed hands-free, the telephone set will hang up and try again after a pre-determined period of time.

- *Redial, Last Number*
  Every telephone in the system automatically saves the last telephone number dialed to a CO line and allows the extension user to dial the same number again.

- *Ringing, Discriminating*
  Allows the extension user to identify the incoming call by the ringing pattern.

- *System Speed Dialing*
  A list of the names stored for System Speed Dialing is displayed on the phone. This allows the user to dial by name without having to know the telephone number. All the user needs to do is to press the button associated with the desired name.

**Note**: System highlights and features shown above are minimized due to space considerations.

NOTES:

# CHAPTER
# NINE

## Automated Water Systems

**9-1 Automated Swimming Pool and Spa:** When a homeowner decides to purchase a swimming pool, it is for a number of basic reasons that may include, entertainment, relaxation, exercise or therapy. During cool periods of the year a pool without heat will be uncomfortable for swimming, which makes an expensive investment virtually unusable during these times. To extend the swimming season, most owners incorporate some form of pool & spa heating. Heating the pool & spa can be an expensive operating cost when the wrong type of heating method is used. Most of the energy used to heat a pool/spa is lost to the surrounding air so the most efficient method of heating is desirable as long as it can meet other homeowner require-ments. The best heating method for a pool or spa depends on the location, budget and usage requirements.

The three most common methods of heating a pool or spa are as follows. The most popular form of heat is supplied by a solar panel system. A solar heating system will cost approximately $2,800 installed for a 15,000 gallon pool. It is the most economical to operate and requires minimal maintenance. The disadvantage of a solar heating system is its inability to properly heat the pool during the cooler months. This is even more evident when trying to heat the spa.

An electric heat pump is the second most efficient method of heating. It will cost approximately $3,200 installed for a 15,000

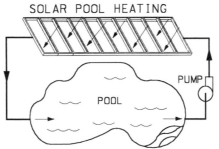

SOLAR POOL HEATING

PUMP

POOL

gallon pool. A natural gas heating system, costs approximately $1,600 installed. The advantage of the heat pump and natural gas heating systems over the solar heating system are as follows. Both the heat pump and natural gas systems can heat the pool or spa all year long in most parts of the country. If the pool has a spa and the homeowner wishes to use the spa during the cold months of the year, a natural gas heater should be used. A heat pump can be used effectively to heat the pool or spa when the outside air temperature is more than 40°F. The natural gas heating system will heat the pool or spa much faster than a heat pump system; however, it will cost up to 70% more to operate.

To provide the reader with an idea of how much it may cost to operate a pool and spa, we will provide the following costs based on assumptions. A circulation pump is required to maintain any pool even when the pool is not heated. If we assume that a 1½ HP pump is used and it operates for 8 hours per day or 240 hours per month and the cost of electricity is 8 cents per kilowatt-hour (kW-HR), the cost to operate this pump each month will be approximately $22. If we also assume that the pool is heated 2°F per day by the sun and then looses 5°F during the night, the pool will need to be heated 3°F during the day to maintain the setpoint temperature. If the pool holds 15,000 gallons and we use a heat pump with a coefficient of performance (COP) equal to 5.24, it will cost approximately $1.60 per day or $48 per month to heat the pool.

If we look at how much it may cost each time the spa is heated by a heat pump, let us first assume the that the spa holds 650 gallons and the water temperature will rise from 75°F to a temperature setpoint of 103°F within the first hour. If the heat pump maintains this temperature for two hours and it costs 8 cents per (kW-HR), it will end up costing the homeowner approximately $2.00 each time the spa is used for the same length of time.

**9-2 Solar Panels:** There are two basic types of solar collectors used for pool heating. One is a solar panel and the other is a solar mat. Both types of heat absorbing devices incorporate carbon black as part of their makeup for the purpose of maximizing their energy absorbing capacity. For simplicity purposes, we will refer to both types of heat collectors as solar panels. Solar panels also contain solar inhibitors within the panel material to help prevent deterioration over time. Most solar panels are made of polypropylene plastic or thermoplastic rubber that generally comes in 4' x 8' sections. Panels will generally last about 10 to 20 years with minimal maintenance costs.

Solar panels are generally installed on the roof of a home where the energy from the sun can be absorbed during the hours of 9:00 AM and 5:00 PM. In areas of the country where freezing temperatures may occur, solar panels should be elevated above the pool surface to allow the water to drain back into the pool when the system is turned OFF. Panels are normally mounted at a minimum of 15 degrees from horizontal, which will also provide additional elevation to properly drain the system when required. Solar panels should ideally face due south; however, they can be oriented within 20 degrees east or west of due south without causing a significant loss in energy absorbing performance. The optimum panel orientation will vary based on the latitude of the pool and if heating is required all year long or just during the cooler months.

Solar heating systems are designed to heat large volumes of water and when the system is properly designed, it will return water back to the pool 2°F to 5°F higher in temperature on each pass. After multiple passes, the heating system

should be able to raise the water temperature 10°F to 15°F. To properly size the pool solar heating system, the designer needs to consider a few items. If the pool is in the sun much of the day and is covered at night with a solar blanket, the panel area requirement should be approximately 50% of the pool's surface area. It is a good idea to use a solar blanket because it will reduce the loss of heat and evaporation from the pool surface. However, for most homeowners, removing and reinstalling the blanket will end up being just too much trouble. There are companies that offer motorized and automated pool covering systems, which are very convenient and can save energy while also helping to keep the pool clean. When a cover is not placed over the pool surface at night, the solar panel area should be sized for approximately 75% of the pool's surface area. If the pool is not covered and is partially in the shade during the peak solar hours of the day or is located in-doors, the solar panel area may need to be as large as 100% of the pool's surface area to provide the homeowner with sufficient heating capacity.

**9-3 'Pool Mode':** Solar panels are naturally the major component of a solar heating system. Other system components include: The pool pump, solar panel temperature sensor, pool return water temperature sensor, and motorized control valves shown in Figure 9-1. The solar panel temperature sensor is located on the roof to the left of the solar panel, and the return water temperature sensor is located in the return water line on the suction side of the pump. See the Event called **'Pool Mode ON'** shown on page 169. This mode is initiated by selecting the 'Pool Mode' from any *JDS* wall mounted Keypad in the home. This mode will first turn ON some music that the homeowner has pre-selected, cycles the control valves and Clears the 'Spa Flag', which will keep both modes from attempting to run at the same time. The 'Pool Flag' is then Set to allow automatic temperature control of the pool. The 'Pool Mode' is automatically initiated at 10:00 AM and turns OFF at 6:00 PM Sunday through Saturday by Events shown on page 173. This period of time is when the pool can be heated. Once the 'Pool Mode' is established, the motorized control valves will be positioned to control the water temperature.

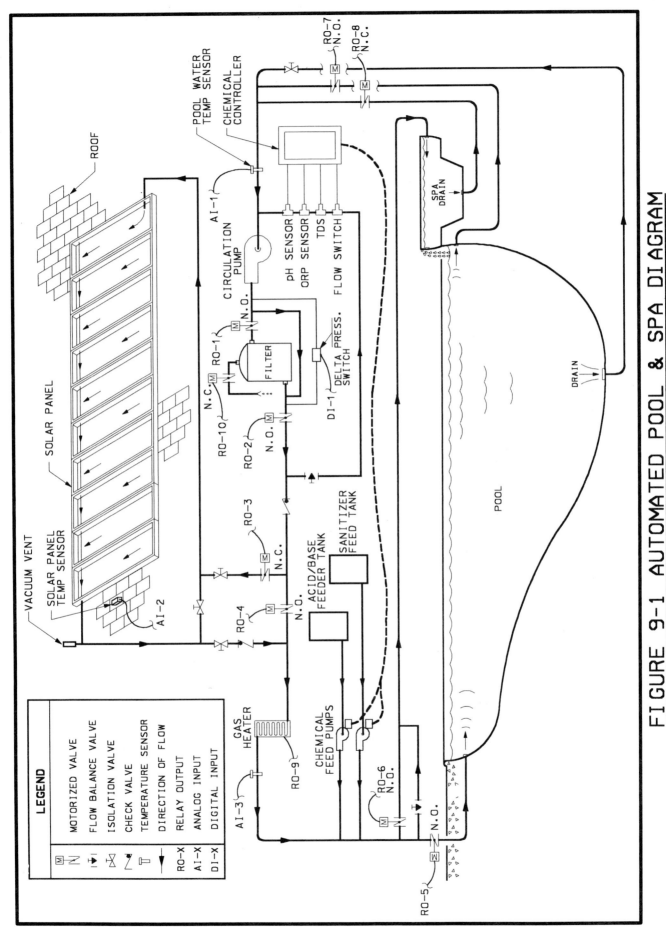

FIGURE 9-1 AUTOMATED POOL & SPA DIAGRAM

165

See the **'Automatic Pool Heating When Solar Energy is Available'** Events shown on page 170. Now that the 'Pool Flag' is Set, the *Stargate* will be allowed to automatically heat the pool when the water temperature is less than 79°F (< 79) and when the solar panel water temperature is more than 89°F. These conditions are all listed in the 'IF' statement shown in the Event called **'Pool Temperature Control – Heat ON'** shown on page 170. When all of these conditions are true, the programming lines listed under the 'THEN' statement will be initiated by *Stargate*. *Stargate* will energize Relay Output (RO-3) to open this normally closed (N.C.) control valve and also energizes Relay Output (RO-4) to close this normally open (N.O.) control valve. This will allow the pool return water to flow through the solar panel to absorb heat and return at a higher temperature back to the pool. Please note that all conductors wired to the control valves are connected to normally open (N.O.) Relay Outputs of *Stargate*. Figure 3-2 on page 64 illustrates the *Stargate* Home Controller and the (N.O.) and (N.C.) Relay Outputs on the bottom left hand corner of the diagram.

Normally open (N.O.) and normally closed (N.C.) control valves are selected based on two requirements. If the valve is in the open position the majority of the time, a (N.O.) valve should be selected when possible to minimized the length of time that a *Stargate* Relay Output is (Hot). If the valve is required to be in the closed position the majority of the time, a (N.C.) valve should be selected. The valve wired to (RO-4) shown in Figure 9-1, is a (N.O.) device because the pump needs to bypass water around the solar panel most of the time and the designer does not want Relay Output 4 to be energized to keep the valve open. This is the same reason why the control valve wired to (RO-3) was selected as (N.C.). Another reason for selecting a (N.O.) or (N.C.) control valve is whether the valve should fail in an open or closed position. For pool and spa control applications, we prefer that a valve failure allow the water to continue flowing through both the pool and the spa until the failed component is replaced.

The 'Pool Mode' is programmed to flow water through the pool and the spa. The *Stargate* will de-energizes (opens N.O. control valve RO-5, RO-6 & RO-7), and de-energizes (closes N.C. control valve RO-8). Control valve RO-6 (Spa Valve) is controlled open in the 'Pool Mode' because water must flow through the spa to sanitize the water with chlorine. It is also opened to allow water to flow over the spa's water fall.

Normally open control valves RO-5 & RO-6 are used because if the pump is ON and if either control valve RO-5 or RO-6 should fail, they will fail in the open position and allow water to continue flowing through the pool or spa to avoid dead heading the pump. Since control valve RO-5 and RO-6 are (N.O.), they will also allow water to drain out of the solar panel and into the pool each time the pump is turned OFF. This function is designed to prevent damage to the solar panels during freezing temperatures.

These are examples of how the designer must look at the pool configuration and programming logic and weigh the advantages against the disadvantages in order to select either a (N.O.) or (N.C.) control valve for each function.

When the pool is being heated and a water temperature setpoint of (80°F + or - 1°F) is established, *Stargate* will read this temperature from the return water temperature sensor AI-1 (Analog Input 1). *Stargate* will then de-energize RO-3 & RO-4 in order to bypass water around the solar panel to pause the heating process. (See the **'Pool Temperature Control - Heat OFF'** Event shown on page 170).

When the low end of the pool temperature setpoint of (79°F) cannot be establish or maintained by the solar heating system due to an insufficient temperature difference between the pool setpoint temperature and the solar panel temperature, the natural gas heater will be utilized instead. See the **'Automatic Pool Heating With 'Natural Gas Heater'** Event shown on page 171. Notice in the **'Heat – ON'** 'IF' statement, when the pool water temperature is less than 79°F (< 79) and the solar panel sensor (AI-2) reads less than 89°F (< 89) and the 'Pool Flag' is Set, the control valves will cycle to flow water through the natural gas heater.

Before the natural gas Heater can turn ON, the water must be flowing through the heater and sensed by the heater's internal flow sensor. This will be the case between 10:00 AM an 6:00 PM each day. Once the heater is ON and the water temperature in the pool rises to more than 81°F ( > 81 ) and the 'Pool Flag' is Set, the 'IF' statement will become true and the 'THEN' statement will initiate a command to turn the heater OFF. The 'Pool Flag' is Set to maintain automatic pool temperature control until this Flag is Cleared when an occupant selects the 'Spa Mode ON' Event shown on page 170.

**9-4 'Spa Mode':** When the homeowner selects the 'Spa Mode' from any *JDS* Keypad, the 'Pool Flag' is Cleared and the 'Spa Flag' is Set. (See the 'Spa Mode' programming on page 170). The 'IF' statement will then be true and allow automatic temperature control of the spa. See the Event called' **Spa temperature Control - Heat ON'** shown on page 171.

When the spa water temperature is less than 100°F (< 100) and the solar panel water temperature is more than 110°F ( > 110), the control valves in the system are cycled to potentially flow water through the solar panel before the pump is started. When the spa temperature setpoint of 103°F is established, the appropriate control valves will cycle in order to bypass water around the solar panel while the pump continues to flow water through the spa jets. If the solar panel will not provide sufficient heating to maintain the water temperature setpoint, the natural gas heater will operate as shown in the Event called **'Spa Temperature Control-Heat ON'** shown on page 172. Although the solar panel will provide sufficient heat to effectively operate the spa during the summer months, the owner will need to use a natural gas heater or heat pump as soon as the weather begins to cool down. This is why the 'Example Home' incorporates both the solar panel and gas heating systems. A heat pump could be substituted for the natural gas heater for periods of the year that are just to cool to provide solar heating; however, if it gets below 40°F, it

will either take hours to heat the spa or become ineffective. If the owner has an outdoor pool and spa and he wants to heat the spa during cold periods of the year, he should go with the natural gas heating system. It would also be unpractical to try and heat the pool using the heat pump when it is below 40°F outside. If the owner lives in the southern states where it rarely gets below 40°F and he can do without the use of the spa when it does get below 40°F, the heat pump and solar panel combination would provide the lowest operating costs throughout the year. In either case, having to purchase two types of heating systems will be expensive and generally does not payoff unless the owner plans to live in the home for at least 7 years. In most cases, only one heating system will be purchased due to the high initial equipment and installation costs.

**9-5 Automatic Pool Cooling Feature:** If high ambient temperatures raise the pool water temperature above the setpoint temperature, the pool's temperature control system will automatically cool the pool back to the setpoint temperature at night. This is accomplished by running the solar heating system (solar cooling system in this case) at night to reject heat from the pool water. As the water flows through the solar panel, the heat from the water is rejected to the atmosphere. This will cool the water that flows through the panel and drop the temperature in the pool by running the **'Pool Cool ON'** Event shown on page 172. 'IF' the pool water temperature is more than 84°F and it is after Sunset and the 'Spa Flag' is Clear, 'THEN' cycle the control valves and turn the pump ON to flow water through the solar panel for cooling purposes. When the pool temperature sensor reads a reduction of water temperature that is equal to 80°F, the pump is turned OFF while the control valves are cycled to divert the water flow around the solar panel and opens valves RO-5 & RO-6 to drain the solar panel water into the pool for freeze prevention purposes.

**9-6 Automatic Freeze Prevention Feature:** In locations of the country where there is a possibility of freezing temperatures, the solar panel water is drained at night to avoid damage to the solar panel if the water freezes inside the panel. When the circulation pump is stopped at

6:00 PM each day, the vacuum vent located at the high point of the solar panel piping shown in Figure 9-1, will automatically open to allow air to enter the system. This will in turn allow the water filled solar panel to drain all of its contents into the pool when valves RO-5 & RO-6 are open and the pump is OFF. The **'IF' statement in the 'Freeze Prevention'** Event shown on page 173, is true when the outside temperature is less than 37°F (sensed by AI-2). This condition will allow *Stargate* to open the control valves for 30 minutes to drain the solar panel before starting the pump to flow water through all other pool equipment to prevent freezing.

**9-7 Automatic Filter Cleaning Feature:** Over a period of operating time, the pool's sand filter will start to fill up with debris that was removed from the pool water. To clean the debris out of the filter, the system will need to go into a back wash cycle by reversing the flow of water through the sand filter to blow the debris to grade. *Stargate* is programmed to back flush the sand filter based on the water pressure difference measured across the sand filter when the water is flowing. When the difference in pressure rises from 5 PSIG (clean filter) to 15 PSIG (dirty filter) the

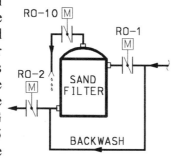

'delta pressure switch' shown in Figure 9-1, will close and initiate Digital Input '**(DI: FILTER ) ON'** as shown in the **'Filter Cleaning'** Event on sheet 173. The *Stargate* will then close control valves (RO-1) & (RO-2) and open control valve (RO-10). These valve positions will direct the water backward through the sand filter to lift the debris off the top of the sand and out through dump valve (RO-10) to grade. The back flushing function will operate for 3 minutes to sufficiently clean the filter before the control valves are reversed to establish normal directional water flow and filtering.

**9-8 Pump Control:** The pool/spa water circulation pump uses a starter relay that ultimately switches the pump ON & OFF. This starter relay is energized & de-energized by

*Stargate* through a (N.O.) *IO Xpander* Relay Output to control the pump. This starter relay is selected based on a 1 1/2 HP, 240V pump motor. As shown in Figure 9-2, this starter relay must have a 1 1/2 HP continuous duty rating along with a 12V DC relay coil. The starter relay coil is energized by closing the control circuit and denergized by opening the circuit. This starter relay is shown wired to the *I/O-Xpander* in Figure 9-2. A (N.O.) Relay Output along with a (N.O.) starter relay are used because it is best to have both types of relays fail open to automatically stop the pump if any portion of the pump controls should fail.

**9-9 Pool/Spa Water Treatment:** By constantly monitoring the pH of the pool and spa water along with the activity of the sanitizer, chemical automation will make it possible to maintain clean and safe water with a significant reduction in the cost of chemicals and maintenance time. A Chemtrol® programmable pool controller is used in the 'Example Home' to manage the pool's water treatment process and is shown in Figure 9-1. It is an independent stand along pool controller from *Stargate,* which means that *Stargate* does not interface or control this sub-system. When the pool pump is running, the pool controller takes water samples off of the return water piping to test the total dissolved solids (TDS) or conductivity of the water. The temperature of this water sample is also measured along with the Oxidation-Reduction Potential (ORP) and pH. There is also a flow switch that is used to prove that the water is flowing before adding chemicals. Also notice in Figure 9-1, the Acid/Base chemical feeders, the Sanitizer/Chlorine feed pumps and the chemical storage tanks.

Remote operation of this system can be accomplished from a PC, which displays an exact screen of the localized controller screen with full access to all menus. All operations on the computer are immediately executed by the on-site controller. The Chemtrol® pool controller can also be accessed with a touch-tone phone to obtain instant voice status reports and operational settings can be modified subject to a password identification. Up to six phone numbers can be specified for automatic dialing and report of alarm conditions.

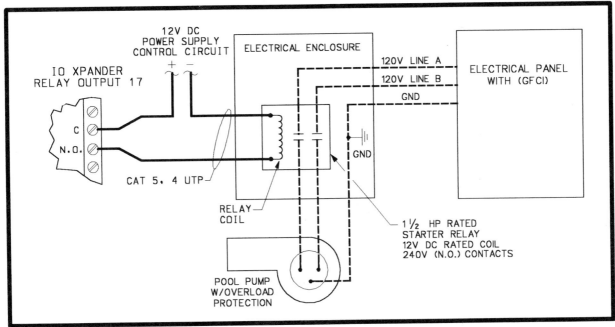

FIGURE 9-2   POOL PUMP WIRING DIAGRAM

## *Stargate* AUTOMATED SPA & POOL PROGRAMMING

EVENT: **POOL MODE - ON**

| | |
|---|---|
| **IF** | *Mode name* |
| (POOL MODE ON) | *if* |
| | *If 'Pool Mode ON' Event is selected from JDS Keypad* |
| **THEN** | *then* |
| (IR: CD ) play 1 time(s) [Theater] | *Select CD player* |
| (IR: CD POWER ) play 1 time(s) [Theater] | *Turn CD player ON* |
| DELAY  0:00:02 | *After 2 seconds perform next line* |
| (IR: DISK 4 ) play 1 time(s) [Theater] | *Selects CD #4* |
| (IR: TRACK 1) play 1 time(s) [Theater] | *Select CD Track #1* |
| (RELAY: VALVE 5) OFF | *Open (N.O.) valve (RO-5) - de-energize to flow water thru pool* |
| (RELAY: VALVE 6) OFF | *Open (N.O.) valve (RO-6) - de-energize to flow water thru spa* |
| (RELAY: CIR PUMP ) ON | *Turn water circulation pump ON* |
| (F: SPA FLAG) Clear | *Clears the 'Spa Flag'* |
| (F: POOL FLAG) Set | *Sets 'Pool Flag' (See pool temp. control Events IF conditions)* |
| End | |

**Note:** See pages 170 & 171 for pool water temperature control Events.

EVENT: **POOL MODE - OFF**

| | |
|---|---|
| **IF** | *Mode name* |
| (POOL MODE OFF) | *if* |
| | *If 'Pool Mode OFF' Event is selected from JDS Keypad* |
| **THEN** | *then* |
| (F: POOL FLAG) Clear | *Clears 'Pool Flag'* |
| (IR: CD POWER ) play 1 time(s) [Theater] | *Turn CD player OFF* |
| (RELAY: CIR PUMP ) OFF | *Turn water circulation pump OFF* |
| (RELAY: VALVE 5) OFF | *Open (N.O.) valve (RO-5) – de-energize to drain solar panel* |
| (RELAY: VALVE 6) OFF | *Open (N.O.) valve (RO-6) - de-energize to drain solar panel* |
| (RELAY: VALVE 7) OFF | *Open (N.O.) valve (RO-7) – de-energize* |
| (RELAY: VALVE 8) OFF | *Close (N.C.) valve (RO-8) - de-energize* |
| End | |

**Note :** This mode is generally used after swimming or when the pool and/or spa is shut down for repair.

EVENT: **SPA MODE - ON**                                          *Mode name*
  **IF**                                                      *if*
    (SPA MODE-ON)                      *If 'Spa Mode ON' Event is selected from JDS Keypad*
  **THEN**                                                    *then*
    (F: POOL FLAG) Clear                        *Clear 'Pool Flag'*
    (F: SPA FLAG) Set                   *Sets 'Spa Flag' so temp control operates*
    (RELAY: VALVE 5) ON          *Close (N.O.) valve (RO-5) – energize to block flow to pool*
    (RELAY: VALVE 6) OFF          *Open (N.O.) valve (RO-6) – de-energize to flow to spa*
    (RELAY: VALVE 7) ON        *Close (N.O.) valve (RO-7) – energize to block flow from pool*
    (RELAY: VALVE 8) ON        *Open (N.C.) valve (RO-8) – energize to draw water from spa*
End
**Note 1**: See pages 171 & 172 for spa water temperature control programming.
**Note 2**: During periods when solar energy is not sufficient, the natural gas heater is used. See Gas Heating Events shown on page 172.

---

EVENT: **SPA MODE - OFF**                                         *Mode name*
  **IF**                                                      *if*
    (SPA MODE-OFF)                    *If 'Spa Mode OFF' Event is selected from JDS Keypad*
  **THEN**                                                    *then*
    (F: SPA FLAG) Clear                      *Clears the 'Spa Flag'*
    (RELAY: HEATER) OFF                 *Turn natural gas heater OFF*
    DELAY 0 : 01 : 00          *Allow the pump to operate for one minute after the heater turns OFF*
    (RELAY: CIR PUMP ) OFF          *Turn water circulation pump OFF*
    (RELAY: VALVE 5) OFF          *Open (N.O.) valve (RO-5) – de-energize to drain solar panel*
    (RELAY: VALVE 6) OFF          *Open (N.O.) valve (RO-6) - de-energize to drain solar panel*
    (RELAY: VALVE 7) OFF          *Open (N.O.) valve (RO-7) – de-energize*
    (RELAY: VALVE 8) OFF          *Close (N.C.) valve (RO-8) - de-energize*
End
**Note**: This mode is generally initiated after using the spa.

---

## ***AUTOMATIC *POOL* HEATING WHEN SOLAR ENERGY IS AVAILABLE***

EVENT: **POOL TEMPERATURE CONTROL – Heat ON**                   *Mode name*
  **IF**                                                      *if*
    (A/D: T-SENSOR 1) < 79          *If water temperature sensor (AI-1) senses less than 79°F*
    and (A/D: T-SENSOR 2) > 89       *and if roof temperature sensor (AI-2) senses more than 89°F*
    and (F: POOL FLAG) is Set        *and the pool Flag is Set, (Set by the 'Pool Mode')*
  **THEN**                                                    *then*
    (RELAY: VALVE 3) ON          *Open (N.C.) valve (RO-3) - energize to flow water thru solar panel*
    (RELAY: VALVE 4) ON          *Close (N.O.) valve (RO-4) - energize to flow water thru solar panel*
End
**Note**: The circulation pump and all other control valves are controlled by the 'Pool Mode'.

---

EVENT: **POOL TEMPERATURE CONTROL – Heat OFF**                  *Mode name*
  **IF**                                                      *if*
    (A/D: T-SENSOR 1) > 81          *If water temperature sensor (AI-1) senses more than 81°F*
    and (F: POOL FLAG) is Set        *and the 'Pool Flag' is Set, (Set by 'Pool Mode')*
  **THEN**                                                    *then*
    (RELAY: VALVE 3) OFF          *Close (N.C.) valve (RO-3 ) - de-energize*
    (RELAY: VALVE 4) OFF          *Open (N.O.) valve (RO-4) - de-energize*
End

## ***AUTOMATIC _POOL_ HEATING WITH NATURAL GAS HEATER***

**Note:** When temperature sensor (AI-2) on the roof does not senses sufficient solar heat, the natural gas heater will take over.

**EVENT: POOL TEMPERATURE CONTROL – Heat ON**            *Mode name*

**IF**                                                                          *if*

   (A/D: T-SENSOR 1) < 79                     *If water temperature sensor (AI-1) senses less than 79 °F*

   and (A/D: T-SENSOR 2) < 89              *and if roof temperature sensor (AI-2) senses less than 89 °F*

   and (F: POOL FLAG) Set                       *and if the 'Pool Flag' is Set, (Set by the 'Pool Mode')*

**THEN**                                                                     *then*

   (RELAY: VALVE 3) OFF            *Close (N.C.) valve (RO-3) de-energize to flow water thru gas heater*

   (RELAY: VALVE 4) OFF            *Open (N.O.) valve (RO-4) de-energize to flow water thru gas heater*

   (RELAY: CIR PUMP ) ON             *Turn water circulation pump ON – RO-17 - energized*

   (RELAY: HEATER) ON                   *Turn natural gas heater ON – RO-9 - energized*

End

**Note**: Heater internal flow switch proves water flow before heater will turn ON.

**EVENT: POOL TEMPERATURE CONTROL – Heat OFF**          *Mode name*

**IF**                                                                            *if*

   (A/D: T-SENSOR 1) > 81                     *If water temperature sensor (AI-1) senses more than 81 °F*

   and (F: POOL FLAG) Set                       *and the 'Pool Flag' is Set, (Set by the 'Pool Mode')*

**THEN**                                                                       *then*

   (RELAY: HEATER) OFF                      *Turn natural gas heater OFF*

End

## ***AUTOMATIC _SPA_ HEATING WHEN SOLAR ENERGY IS AVAILABLE***

**EVENT: SPA TEMPERATURE CONTROL – Heat ON**              *Mode name*

**IF**                                                                            *if*

   (A/D: T-SENSOR 1) < 100                   *If water temperature sensor (AI-1) senses less than 100 °F*

   and (A/D: T-SENSOR 2) > 110            *and if the solar panel temperature sensor (AI-2) senses more than 110 °F*

   and (F: SPA FLAG) Set                         *and the 'Spa Flag' is Set, (Set by the 'Spa Mode')*

**THEN**                                                                       *then*

   (RELAY: VALVE 3) ON               *Open (N.C.) valve (RO-3) - energize to flow water thru solar panel & spa*

   (RELAY: VALVE 4) ON               *Close (N.O.) valve (RO-4) - energize to flow water thru solar panel & spa*

End

**Note**: Pump remains ON to continue water flow thru spa. Valves RO-5 & RO-6 remain in spa mode positions. Temperature control will remain operational until the 'Spa Mode OFF' or 'Pool Mode' is initiated.

**EVENT: SPA TEMPERATURE CONTROL – Heat OFF**            *Mode name*

**IF**                                                                            *if*

   (A/D: T-SENSOR 1) > 103                   *If water temperature sensor (AI-1) senses more than 103 °F*

   and (F: SPA FLAG) Set                         *and the 'Spa Flag' is Set, (Set by the 'Spa Mode')*

**THEN**                                                                       *then*

   (RELAY: VALVE 3) OFF            *Close (N.C.) valve (RO-3 ) - de-energize (bypass solar panel)*

   (RELAY: VALVE 4) OFF            *Open (N.O.) valve (RO-4) de-energize to bypass the solar panel*

End

**Note:** Pump remains ON to continue water flow through the spa. Valves RO-5 & RO-6 remain in Spa Mode positions. Temperature control will remain operational until the 'Pool Mode' is initiated or if it is 6:00 PM when the pump is automatically turned OFF.

## ***AUTOMATIC _SPA_ HEATING WITH NATURAL GAS HEATER:***

**EVENT: SPA TEMPERATURE CONTROL – Heat ON**        *Mode name*

**IF**                                                 *if*

    (A/D: T-SENSOR 1) < 100           *If water temperature sensor (AI-1) senses less than 100 °F*

    and (A/D: T-SENSOR 2) < 110     *and if roof temperature sensor (AI-2) senses less than 110 °F*

    and (F: SPA FLAG) Set              *and the 'Spa Flag' is Set, (Set by the 'Spa Mode')*

**THEN**                                             *then*

    (RELAY: VALVE 3) OFF        *Close (N.C.) valve (RO-3) de-energize to flow water thru gas heater*

    (RELAY: VALVE 4) OFF        *Open (N.O.) valve (RO-4) de-energize to flow water thru gas heater*

    (RELAY: CIR PUMP ) ON       *Turn water circulation pump ON – energize RO-17*

    (RELAY: HEATER) ON          *Turn natural gas heater ON – energize RO-9*

End

---

**EVENT: SPA TEMPERATURE CONTROL – Heat OFF**      *Mode name*

**IF**                                                 *if*

    (A/D: T-SENSOR 1) = 103        *If water temperature sensor (AI-1) senses 103 °F*

    and (F: SPA FLAG) Set           *and if the 'Spa Flag' is Set, (Set by 'Spa Mode')*

**THEN**                                            *then*

    (RELAY: HEATER) OFF        *Turn natural gas heater OFF – de-energize RO-9*

End

---

## ***AUTOMATIC COOLING OF POOL WATER USING SOLAR PANEL***

**EVENT: COOL POOL - ON**                *Mode name*

**IF**                                                 *if*

    (A/D: T-SENSOR 1) > 84         *If water temperature sensor (AI-1) senses more than 84°F*

    and after Sunset               *and it is after sunset*

    and (F: SPA FLAG) is Clear     *and the 'Spa Flag' is Clear*

**THEN**                                           *then*

    (RELAY: VALVE 3) ON        *Open (N.C.) valve (RO-3) - energize to flow water thru solar panel*

    (RELAY: VALVE 4) ON        *Close (N.O.) valve (RO-4) - energize to divert flow water thru solar panel*

    (RELAY: CIR PUMP ) ON       *Turn water circulation pump ON – energize RO-17*

End

---

**EVENT: COOL POOL - OFF**              *Mode name*

**IF**                                                 *if*

    (A/D: T-SENSOR 1) = 80         *If water temperature sensor (AI-1) senses 80°F*

    and after Sunset               *and it is after sunset*

    and (F: SPA FLAG) is Clear     *and the 'Spa Flag' is Clear*

**THEN**                                           *then*

    (RELAY: VALVE 3) OFF        *Close (N.C.) valve (RO-3) - de-energize*

    (RELAY: VALVE 4) OFF        *Open (N.O.) valve (RO-4) - de-energize*

    (RELAY: VALVE 5) OFF        *Open (N.O.) valve (RO-5) – de-energize to drain solar panel*

    (RELAY: VALVE 6) OFF        *Open (N.O.) valve (RO-6) - de-energize to drain solar panel*

    (RELAY: CIR PUMP ) OFF      *Turn water circulation pump OFF - de-energize RO-17*

End

## ***AUTOMATIC FILTER CLEANING BACKFLUSH PROGRAMMING***

EVENT: **FILTER CLEANING**                                    *Mode name*
  **IF**                                                *if*
    (DI: FILTER ) is ON                *If pool/spa filter differential pressure switch is ON (dirty filter)*
  **THEN**                                             *then*
    (RELAY: VALVE 1) ON          *Close (N.O.) valve (RO-1) – energize, reverses water flow thru filter*
    (RELAY: VALVE 2) ON          *Close (N.O.) valve (RO-2) – energize, reverses water thru filter*
    (RELAY: VALVE 10) ON        *Open (N.C.) valve (RO-10) – energize, dumps water to grade*
    (T: TIME 11 ) LOAD with 0 : 03 : 00   *After 3 minutes, initiate TIME 11 shown below*
End

EVENT: **TIME 11**                                              *Mode name*
  **IF**                                                *if*
    (T: TIME 11 ) is Expiring         *If Timer 11 is over*
  **THEN**                                             *then*
    (RELAY: CIR PUMP ) OFF     *Turn water circulation pump OFF – de-energize RO-17*
    (RELAY: VALVE 1) OFF         *Open (N.O.) valve (RO-1) – de-energize - flows water straight thru filter*
    (RELAY: VALVE 2) OFF         *Open (N.O.) valve (RO-2) – de-energize- flows water straight thru filter*
    (RELAY: VALVE 10) OFF       *Close (N.C.) valve (RO-10) – de-energize,*
End

## ***FREEZE PREVENTION PROGRAMMING***

EVENT: **FREEZE PREVENTION**                                 *Mode name*
  **IF**                                                *if*
    (A/D: OUTSIDE TEMP ) < 37      *If the solar panel temperature sensor (AI-2) senses less than 37°F*
  **THEN**                                             *then*
    (RELAY: VALVE 5) OFF         *Open (N.O.) valve (RO-5) – de-energize to drain solar panel*
    (RELAY: VALVE 6) OFF         *Open (N.O.) valve (RO-6) - de-energize to drain solar panel*
    (T: TIME 2 ) LOAD with 0 : 30 : 00   *When Timer 2 expires after 30 minutes start pump*
End
**Note:** Drains water from solar panel to pool and starts pump after 30 minutes to prevent equipment from freezing.

## POOL PUMP - SCHEDULED TIME EVENT PROGRAMMING

EVENT: **POOL PUMP RUN 10:00 AM**                            *Feature name*
  **IF**                                                *if*
    Time is 10:00 AM . SMTWTFS .      *If the time is 10:00 AM Sunday - Saturday*
    and (A/D: OUTSIDE TEMP ) > 37    *and if the solar panel temperature sensor (AI-2) senses more than 37°F*
  **THEN**                                             *then*
    (RELAY: CIR PUMP ) ON       *Turn water circulation pump ON - energize RO-17*
    (RELAY: VALVE 5) OFF         *Open (N.O.) valve (RO-5) – flow water thru pool*
    (RELAY: VALVE 6) OFF         *Open (N.O.) valve (RO-6) – flow water thru spa*
End

EVENT: **POOL PUMP OFF 6:00 AM**                             *Feature name*
  **IF**                                                *if*
    Time is 6:00 AM .SMTWTFS .        *If the time is 6:00 AM Sunday - Saturday*
  **THEN**                                             *then*
    (RELAY: CIR PUMP ) OFF      *Turn water circulation pump OFF – de-energize RO-17*
End

# Automated Water Heater

**9-10 Gas-fired Water Heater:** Electric and natural gas fired water heaters are the two primary types of water heaters used in residential applications. Electric water heaters are commonly automated; however, gas fired water heaters are normally not automated. This is partially due to higher efficiencies associated with operating this type of appliance. Using natural gas allows the homeowner to heat domestic water for less than half the cost of heating water using electricity. This diminishes the potential savings a homeowner can receive by turning the gas fired water heater OFF when away from the home or at night. Although some gas fired units can be automated under the right circumstances, installation costs and potential control interface difficulties along with possible safety concerns can diminish the justification of automating this device. Automating a gas water heater is generally not recommended unless the home is frequently unoccupied for weeks at a time. The only gas fired water heater that should ever be considered an automation candidate is a water heater with electronic ignition.

**9-11 Electric Water Heater:** Automated control of the water heater is part of the energy management requirements of the 'Example Home'. The 'Example Home' water heater is located in the Garage as shown in Figure 9-7 on page 182. This is an electric 40 gallon water heater that provides 6000 watts or 6kW of water heating capacity. This level of power must be handled by a switching device that is designed and rated for a least 6 kW. Figure 9-3 illustrates the use of 240V AC rated slave relay contacts with a 12V DC rated coil. Relay contacts are controlled open & closed by energizing & de-energizing the relay coil. This  is accomplished by controlling one of *Stargate's* Relay Outputs ON and OFF. When selecting the proper 240V rated slave relay, one must consider what state the contacts will return to if the control

circuit or relay coil should fail. In the 'Example Home', the slave relay should fail closed. This will allow the water heater to continue operating to provide hot water even though the control system has failed. This is accomplished by selecting a slave relay that has normally closed (N.C) 240V contacts. The control coil side of this relay should be connected to a normally open (N.O.) Relay Output of *Stargate*. This will also allow the low voltage control circuit to fail open and maintain the heating process shown in Figure 9-3. To size this slave relay properly, the amperage draw of the 6 kW water heater must be calculated. Since the water heater is a resistive load, the power factor (**PF**) is 1.

Power = (Amperes) x (Voltage) x (PF)
Amperes = Power/Voltage x (PF)
Amperes = 6000W/240V = **25 Amperes**

This calculation indicates that a slave relay with contacts rated for at least 25 amps is required.

When the *Stargate's* Relay Output is OFF, the Relay Output is open, which de-energizes the 12V DC relay coil to allow the 240V rated contacts to return closed (water heater ON). When the *Stargate's* Relay Output is ON, this will energize the 12V DC relay coil, which opens the 240V rated contacts (water heater OFF). To clarify this control function, the water heater can not be powered to heat water until the *Stargate* sends an OFF command. This turns the water heater ON since the relay has (N.C.) contacts.

The water heater programming shown on the next page provides the ability to automatically turn the water heater ON at 5:00 AM every day of the week to begin heating domestic water. In the evening the water heater is automatically turned OFF by the 'Good Night Mode' to save energy. See the 'Good Night Mode' description and programming shown on the next page.

In the 5:00 AM programming, notice that the 'IF' statement requires a 5:00 AM 'Scheduled Time' and a Clear 'Away' Flag before the 'IF' statement is true. This will allow the '**THEN**' statement to turn the water heater ON. The 'Leaving Home Mode' turns the water heater OFF and Sets the 'Away' Flag. A Set Flag will not allow the water heater to turn ON at 5:00 AM ('Scheduled Time') while the homeowner is on vacation or away over night. When the homeowner returns from vacation, the 'Arriving Home Mode' will automatically turn the water

heater ON and Clear the 'Away' Flag. This will also allow the water heater to be turned ON by the next '5:00 AM' 'Scheduled Time' Event.

The homeowner will soon realize the energy savings by not having to heat water when it is not required. This is only one of many electrical loads that are turned OFF when not in use to provide the homeowner with a lower energy bill.

## STARGATE PROGRAMMING:

| | *Description:* |
|---|---|
| EVENT: **WATER HEATER 5:00 AM - ON** | *Feature name* |
| **IF** | *if* |
| Time is 5 : 00 AM .SMTWTFS. | *If the time is 5:00 AM Sun - Sat* |
| and (AWAY FLAG ) is CLEAR | *and the 'Away' Flag is Clear (owner at home)* |
| **THEN** | *then* |
| (RELAY: WATER HEATER ) OFF | *An OFF Relay Output command turns the water heater **ON*** |
| End | |

**NOTE**: The '**THEN**' statement shows a Relay OFF command because the slave relay has (N.C.) contacts.

---

| | |
|---|---|
| EVENT: **GOOD NIGHT MODE** - Water Heater OFF | *Feature name* |
| **IF** | *if* |
| (Good Night Mode) | *If 'Good Night Mode' is selected from a JDS Keypad* |
| **THEN** | *then* |
| (RELAY: WATER HEATER) ON | *Turns water heater OFF* |
| *All other programming lines that make up the 'Good Night Mode'* | |

End

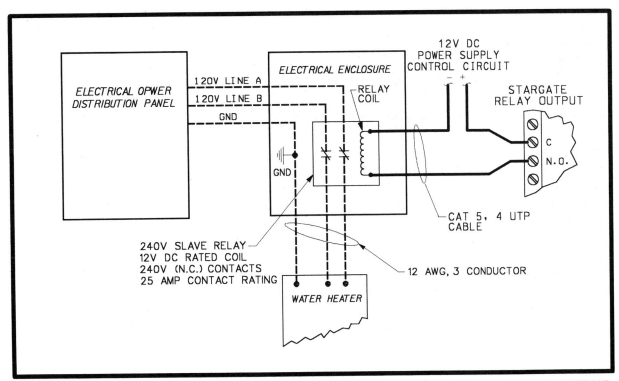

FIGURE 9-3 'EXAMPLE HOME' AUTOMATED WATER HEATER CONTROL USING I/O RELAY OUTPUT AND SLAVE RELAY

**9-12 Automated Water Fountains:** The automated water fountain is located in the front yard of the 'Example Home' and is one of the many mechanical systems controlled by the whole house home automation system. The fountain pump pulls water from the fountain basin and discharges the water through the spray nozzle shown in Figure 9-4. The fountain's mechanical system consists of a circulation pump, system piping, a differential pressure switch, a water level float switch, feedwater solenoid valve and backflow preventor.

The differential pressure switch located across the pump, measures the water pressure difference between the suction and discharge side the pump to prove to the *Stargate* whether the pump is actually ON or OFF. This device is shown in both Figures 9-4 & 9-5. One reason why this is required in the 'Example Home' is to avoid unnecessary ON or OFF commands when the pump is already in an ON or OFF state. In other words, the differential pressure switch proves whether the pump is

actually ON or OFF before the *Stargate* makes control decisions. Also, if the *Stargate* issues an ON or OFF command and the pump does not respond based on the state of the differential pressure switch, the *Stargate* will re-issue the ON or OFF command.

When the fountain pump is ON, the differential pressure switch will sense sufficient differential pressure and close it's internal contacts. This will close the control circuit and initiate 'Digital Input 6' that proves the pump is actually ON. When the *Stargate* senses that 'Digital Input 6' is OFF, it knows the pump is actually OFF. The (DI: 6 DIFF PRESS) OFF state and two other conditions shown in the 'IF' statement of the **'Water Fountain - ON' Event**

shown on page 180, must be true before the *Stargate* will provide an ON command. The differential pressure input is also used to automatically let the homeowner know that the circulating pump has failed, that the control circuit has failed, or the 240V AC power is unavailable at the time. The homeowner will receive notification of a system failure through an audible announcement that is played over the whole house audio system or PA speaker. The **'Announce Fountain Failure'** Event is shown on page 180. For the announcement to be initiated by *Stargate*, the 'Fountain Pump Relay Output' must be ON (pump was turned ON), the differential pressure switch must indicate that the pump is actually OFF, and the 'Fountain Flag' must be Set. This Flag is Set in the 'Water Fountain ON' Event for the 'Announce Fountain Failure' Event to recognize that there was an attempt to turn the pump ON. If all three 'IF' statement programming lines are true, the announcement will be broadcast, *"Fountain has failed"*. The Flag is then Cleared so the 'IF' statement will no longer be true and the message will not be announced over and over again. This particular Event is written to announce the failure only one time per failure no matter if the home is occupied or not. With additional programming, the announcement can be broadcast only if the home is occupied. The *Stargate* will know when the home is occupied because a Flag called 'Away' will be Set by the 'Leaving Mode'. A Clear 'Away' Flag would be part of the 'IF' condition to avoid an announcement when the home is unoccupied. When the programming sees this Flag Cleared by the 'Arriving Mode' the announcement will then be made. This type of control logic can also be used to notify the homeowner of an automated

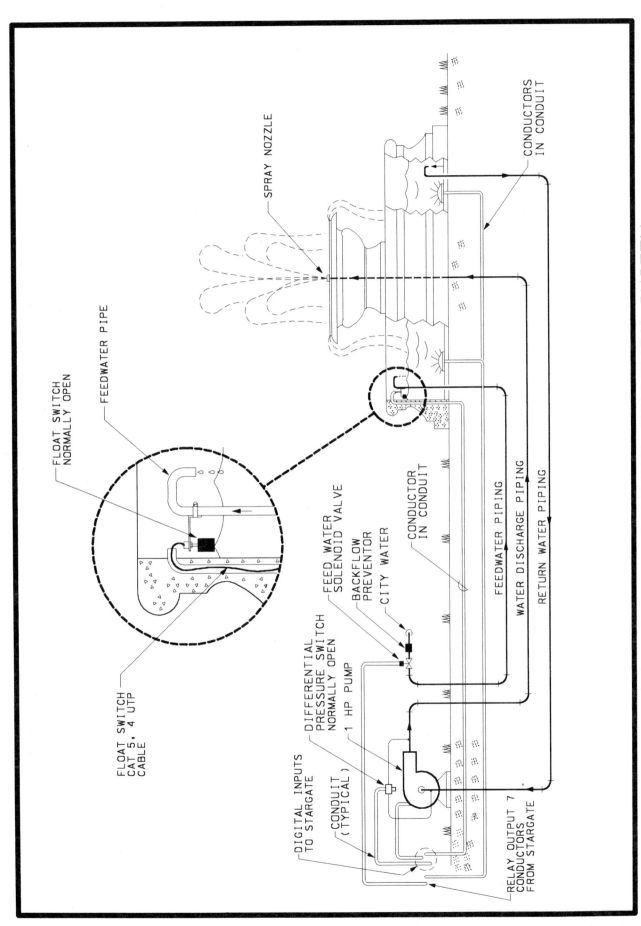

FIGURE 9-4 AUTOMATED FOUNTAIN SYSTEM

177

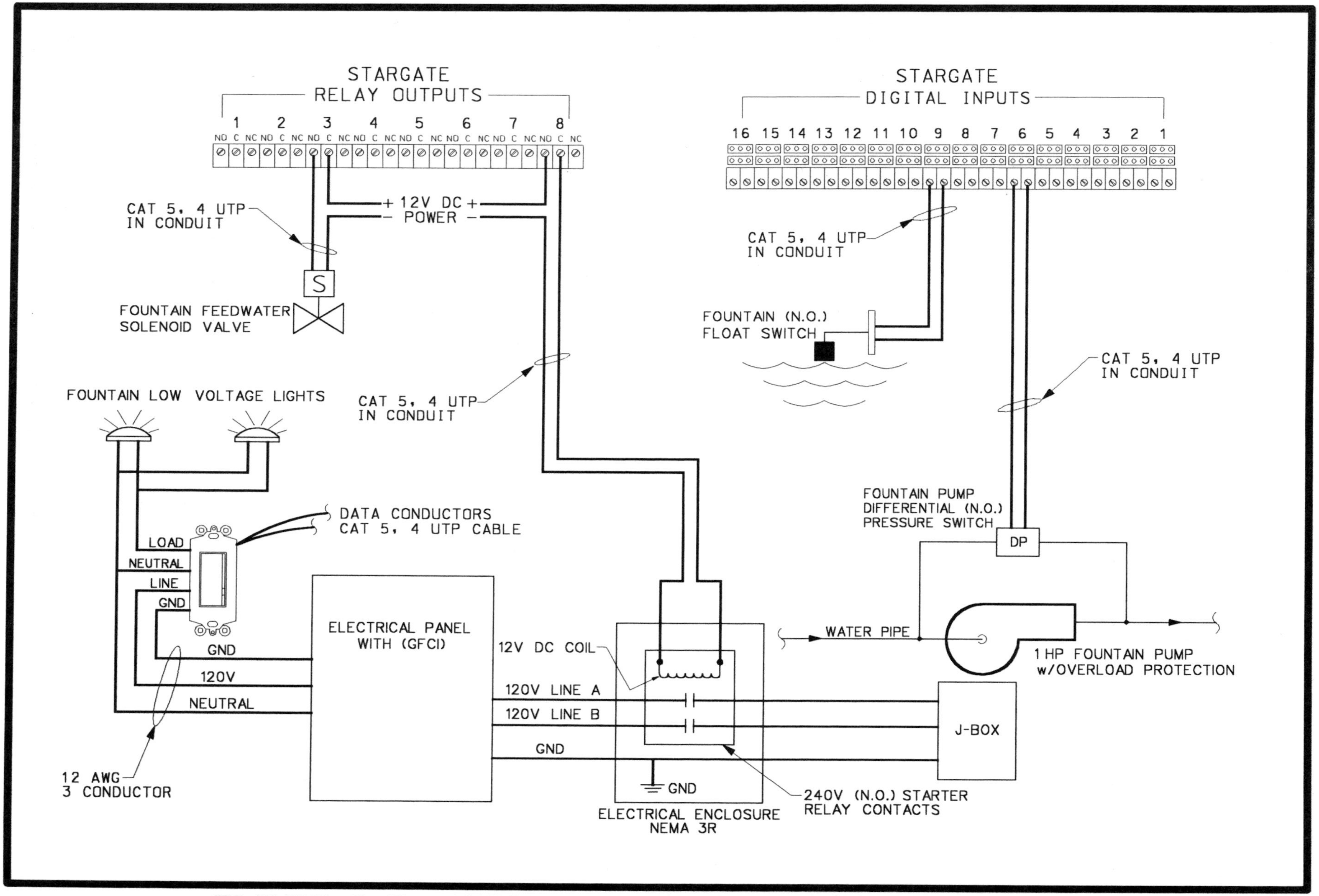

FIGURE 9-5  AUTOMATED FOUNTAIN WIRING DIAGRAM

system electrical load failure at home or any where in the world by telephone.

The fountain pump can be initiated ON and OFF by selecting the 'Fountain ON' or 'Fountain OFF' commands from the *JDS* Keypad located in the Foyer. Another method used to control the fountain is through 'Scheduled Time' Events. Notice the **'Water Fountain ON'** programming shown on page 180. As part of the 'IF' statement, the fountain pump is turned ON at 9:00 AM every day of the week as long as the rain sensor is not detecting sufficient moisture (it is not raining) and the pump is proved to be in the OFF state. The next line of the 'IF' statement reads; **(DI: 6 DIFF PRESS) is OFF**, which lets the *Stargate* know that the pump is not operating. If the pump is running, the *Stargate* will not bother to turn it ON. The next programming line is an 'IF OR' statement' and represents a *JDS* Keypad command called **(Fountain ON)**. Selecting this command will make the 'IF' statement true and allow the THEN' statement to turn the pump ON. In the **'Water Fountain - OFF'** Event shown on the same page, the pump is turned OFF at 6:00 PM each day of the week only when the pump is running, ( DI: 6 DIFF PRESS ) is ON.

The 1 HP, 240V AC pump motor shown in Figure 9-5, is ultimately switched by a slave relay with 240V AC contacts and a 12V DC coil that is installed in a Nema 3R electrical weather enclosure. A (CAT 5, 4 UTP) cable (using 2 conductors) is connected to *Stargate's* 'Relay Output 8' and to the slave relay's 12V DC coil as shown. When the *Stargate's* programming 'IF' statement is true, the 'THEN' statement initiates a command to close (Relay: Fountain Pump ON). This will in turn close the control circuit and supply 12V DC power to energize the coil. This will then close the slave relay's 240V AC contacts to start the pump. When the *Stargate's* (Relay: Fountain Pump OFF) is opened, the coil will be de-energize, which will open the slave relay contacts and therefore stop the pump.

Over a period of time, water in the fountain will evaporate especially when the fountain pump is ON and the spray nozzle is oxygenating the water. When the water level is reduced to a point where the float portion of the float switch

assembly is no longer buoyant, the float switch will close and send a **(DI: 9 FLOAT) ON** signal to *Stargate* as described in the 'Fountain Feed Water Fill' Event shown on page 180. The 'Digital Input ON' state will prove the Event's 'IF' statement true, which will allow the 'THEN' statement to send a **'(Relay FEED VALVE) ON'** command to open the feedwater solenoid valve shown in Figure 9-4. When the water rises to the full level, the float switch will open and send a **DI: 9 FLOAT) OFF** signal to *Stargate* making the 'Fountain Full' Event's 'IF' statement true. This will in turn initiate the **(RELAY: FEED VALVE ) OFF** command to close the solenoid valve. The system designer can also add an Event that will turn the feedwater OFF if it is in the process of filling the fountain and it begins to rain. Another option the designer may incorporate is a differential pressure switch to measure the difference in pressure across the well filter. While the filter is removing debris, the differential pressure will increase until it reaches a maximum setpoint. This will trigger the differential pressure switch closed and send a Digital Input to *Stargate*. *Stargate* will then let the owner know that the filter needs to be cleaned through an audible announcement.

The 'backflow preventor' is a device installed in the feedwater supply line to prevent the fountain water from flowing back into the domestic water system. This device should be installed in all supply water piping that feeds water to mechanical equipment that has the potential of contaminating the water supply.

Category 5, 4 UTP conductors are used to control the pump and feedwater solenoid valve as well as to receive Digital Inputs from the float switch and differential pressure switch. All of these low voltage conductors are routed through conduits shown in Figure 9-4.

The fountain also contains low voltage lighting shown in Figures 9-4 & 9-5. This lighting system consists of a 120V AC transformer, low voltage lighting fixtures, low voltage conductors and a hardwired 'Local Control Switch' as shown in Figure 9-5. Power for the low voltage lighting is ultimately supplied by the home's power distribution panel.

# *STARGATE* WATER FOUNTAIN PROGRAMMING

## *PROGRAMMING:*

**EVENT: WATER FOUNTAIN - ON**
**IF**
    Time is 9:00 AM . SMTWTFS .
    and ( DI: 9 RAIN) is OFF
    and ( DI: 6 DIFF PRESS ) is OFF
           -OR-
    ( FOUNTAIN ON )
**THEN**
    (RELAY: FOUN PUMP ) ON
    (F: FOUNTAIN ) Set
End

## *Description:*

*Feature name*
*if*
*If the time is 9:00 AM Sun - Sat*
*and it is not raining (Digital Input OFF)*
*and the pump is OFF (no differential pressure)*
*or*
*select 'Fountain ON' function on JDS Foyer Keypad*
*then*
*Turn water fountain pump ON*
*Set fountain Flag (See 'Announce Fountain Failure' Event below)*

---

**EVENT: WATER FOUNTAIN - OFF**
**IF**
    Time is 6:00 PM . SMTWTFS .
    and ( DI: 6 DIFF PRESS ) is ON
           -OR-
    ( FOUNTAIN OFF )
**THEN**
    (RELAY: FOUN PUMP ) OFF
End

*Feature name*
*if*
*If the time is 6:00 PM Sun - Sat*
*and if the fountain pump is running*
*or*
*select 'Fountain OFF' function on Foyer Keypad*
*then*
*Turn water fountain pump OFF*

---

**EVENT: ANNOUNCE FOUNTAIN FAILURE**
**IF**
    (RELAY: FOUNTAIN PUMP ) is ON
    and ( DI: 6 DIFF PRESS ) is OFF
    and (F: FOUNTAIN ) is Set
**THEN**
    Voice: "Fountain has failed"
    (F: FOUNTAIN ) Clear
End

*Feature name*
*if*
*Water fountain pump Relay Output is ON*
*and if Digital Input 6 is OFF (No differential Pressure)*
*and if 'Fountain Flag' is Set*
*then*
*"Fountain has failed" is heard over the whole house audio system*
*Clear the Fountain Flag ( to avoid multiple announcements)*

    **Note:** This Event provides the occupant with notification that the fountain has actually failed. The 'Fountain Flag is Cleared so the announcement does not repeat over and over again.

---

**EVENT: FOUNTAIN FEEDWATER FILL**
**IF**
    ( DI: 9 FLOAT) is ON
**THEN**
    (RELAY: FEED VALVE ) ON
End

*Feature name*
*if*
*If the water level in fountain is low*
*then*
*Open feedwater valve to fill fountain basin*

---

**EVENT: FOUNTAIN FULL**
**IF**
    ( DI: 9 FLOAT) is OFF
**THEN**
    (RELAY: FEED VALVE ) OFF
End

*Feature name*
*if*
*When water in fountain basin is filled to a full level*
*then*
*Close feedwater valve (stops feedwater flow)*

**9-13 *Ultraflo* Domestic Water System:** The *Ultraflo* water system is a standard for automated homes for the purpose of providing convenience and water temperature safety for residential occupants. This system also saves water and water heating energy. This system is especially helpful for children and the physically challenged. The proper water flow at the desired temperature is easily achieved by the simple push of a button at the Kitchen sink, Bathroom lavatories, showers, bathtubs and most other water outlet locations. The push button switches are user programmable and include timer functions for one touch hands free operation. Another advantage of this system is that the occupants will never be scalded or chilled in the shower again when someone at another water outlet turns the water ON or OFF. This is because all supply water temperatures are controlled at the central 'Valve Control Panel'.

The core of the *Ultraflo* system is the centralized 'Valve Control Panel' that regulates water temperature and flow. The location of the 'Valve Control Panel' in the 'Example Home' is in the garage as shown in Figure 9-7. This centralized unit contains several banks of solenoid valves. Each valve bank is designed to serve one water outlet. A valve bank consists of a group of solenoid valves joined together to form a water blending unit that mixes hot and cold water to supply the occupants with the desired temperature and water flow on demand. This water blending design allows the use of only one small diameter flexible tube that is routed from the 'Valve Control Panel' to each water outlet location in the home, eliminating the need to install dedicated hot & cold water pipes. By having only one pipe, the desired temperature is established at the 'Valve Control Panel', which eliminates the need to wait for the desired mixing to occur at the faucet, while decreasing water waste. This system also eliminates the need for manual valve water facets that often leak and wear out.

The 'Valve Control Panel' shown in Figure 9-8, is installed within 3-feet of the water heater or other hot water source. Notice that the 'Valve Control Panel' contains an electronic control panel that receives the desired commands from the push button switches located throughout the home. The 'Valve Control Panel' responds by modulating specific banks of valves to promptly serve the families water flow and temperature needs. Manual pre-set flow balancing valves are also part of this panel. These valves are located in each solenoid valve bank to pre-set water temperatures and water flow rates for each water outlet location. The manual flow-balancing valve just down stream of each solenoid valve is used to adjusted the desired water temperature at each water outlet location. After the correct temperature is achieved, a second manual flow-balancing valve located down stream of the first pair is adjusted to provide the desired flow rate for each water outlet location. When the system becomes operational and the desired temperature and flow rate is selected from a push button switch, the results will always be consistent.

A family member at a lavatory, for instance; has the option to have water supplied hot, warm, or cold by selecting the corresponding push button for pre-set temperatures. This push button switch is shown in Figure 9-6.

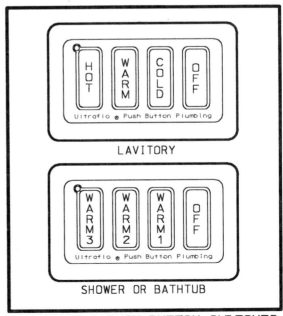

LAVITORY

SHOWER OR BATHTUB

## FIGURE 9-6 PUSH BUTTON SWITCHES

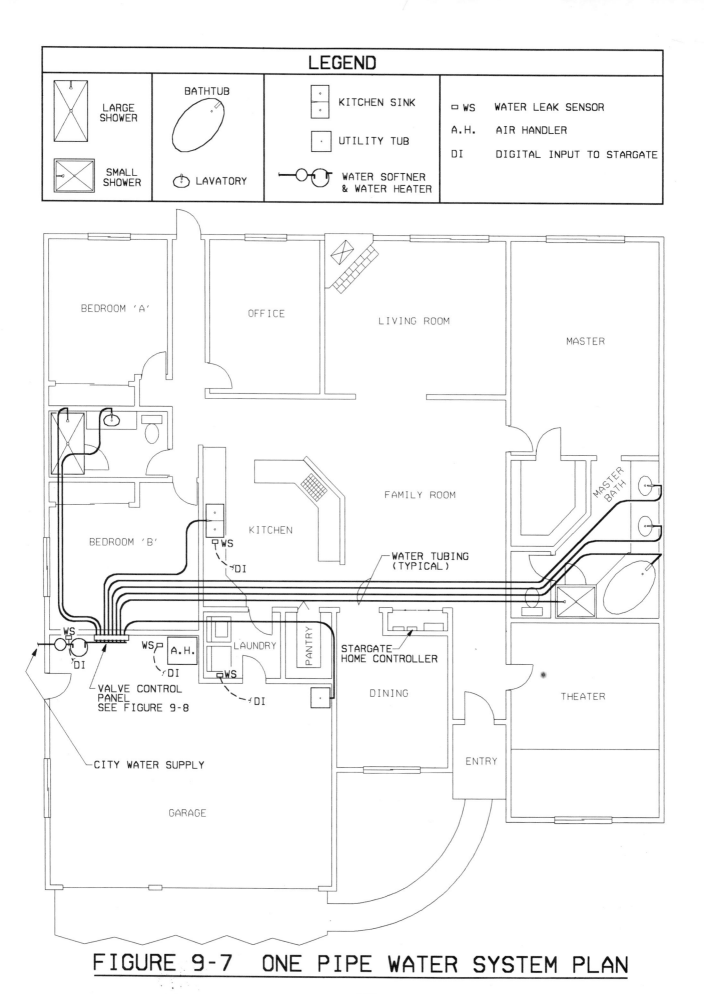

# LEGEND

- **LARGE SHOWER**
- **SMALL SHOWER**
- **BATHTUB**
- **LAVATORY**
- **KITCHEN SINK**
- **UTILITY TUB**
- **WATER SOFTNER & WATER HEATER**
- WS — WATER LEAK SENSOR
- A.H. — AIR HANDLER
- DI — DIGITAL INPUT TO STARGATE

BEDROOM 'A'

OFFICE

LIVING ROOM

MASTER

BEDROOM 'B'

KITCHEN

FAMILY ROOM

MASTER BATH

WS
DI

WATER TUBING (TYPICAL)

WS
DI

WS
A.H.
DI

LAUNDRY

PANTRY

STARGATE HOME CONTROLLER

WS
DI

VALVE CONTROL PANEL
SEE FIGURE 9-8

DINING

THEATER

CITY WATER SUPPLY

ENTRY

GARAGE

# FIGURE 9-7   ONE PIPE WATER SYSTEM PLAN

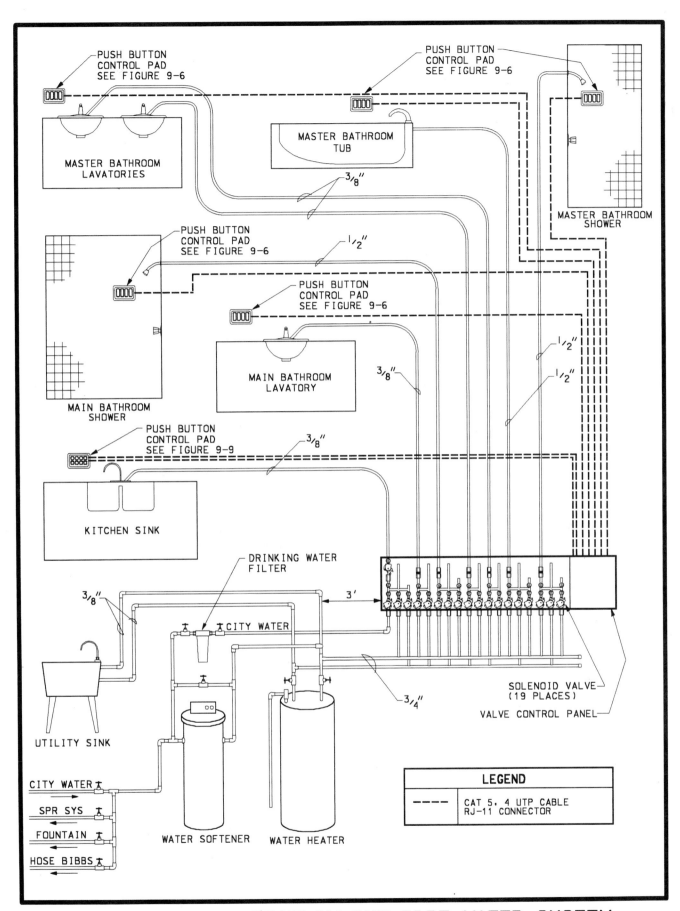

PUSH BUTTON
CONTROL PAD
SEE FIGURE 9-6

PUSH BUTTON
CONTROL PAD
SEE FIGURE 9-6

MASTER BATHROOM
TUB

MASTER BATHROOM
LAVATORIES

MASTER BATHROOM
SHOWER

$3/8''$

PUSH BUTTON
CONTROL PAD
SEE FIGURE 9-6

$1/2''$

PUSH BUTTON
CONTROL PAD
SEE FIGURE 9-6

$1/2''$

$1/2''$

MAIN BATHROOM
LAVATORY

$3/8''$

MAIN BATHROOM
SHOWER

PUSH BUTTON
CONTROL PAD
SEE FIGURE 9-9

$3/8''$

KITCHEN SINK

DRINKING WATER
FILTER

$3/8''$

CITY WATER

3'

SOLENOID VALVE
(19 PLACES)

$3/4''$

VALVE CONTROL PANEL

UTILITY SINK

CITY WATER

SPR SYS

FOUNTAIN

HOSE BIBBS

WATER SOFTENER

WATER HEATER

| LEGEND | |
|--------|--|
| ----- | CAT 5, 4 UTP CABLE RJ-11 CONNECTOR |

FIGURE 9-8   ULTRAFLOW ONE PIPE WATER SYSTEM

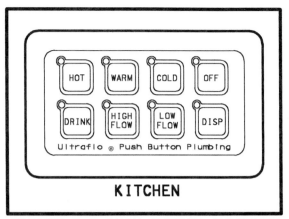

## FIGURE 9-9 PUSH BUTTON SWITCHES

At the shower locations in the home, family members use push button switches that contain the following temperature options: Warm 1, Warm 2, Warm 3 or the OFF button as shown in Figure 9-6. The Kitchen offers the most water flow conditions and temperature options. These include: Hot, Warm, Cold, Drinking Water, High water flow, Low water flow, garbage disposal and an OFF button as shown in Figure 9-9. The drinking water option is only available in the Kitchen. Figure 9-8 shows city water being bypassed around the water softener to the 'Valve Control Panel'. Notice there is an additional solenoid control valve in the Kitchen solenoid valve bank, which is designed to provide drinking water only.

The garbage disposal can also be controlled from the 'push button switch' by installing a garbage disposal module wired to a 120V AC, 60

Hz power source as well as to the disposal. There is an RJ-11 plug-in connector and cable that is pulled from the module to the 'push button switch' in the Kitchen. RJ-11 cables are also used to wire each 'push button switch' in the home to the 'Valve Control Panel'.

Water supply tubing used to serve all lavatories is 3/8" diameter. 1/2" diameter tubing is used to serve showers and bathtubs as shown in Figure 9-8, because of the higher water flow requirements. Tubing is connected from the 'Valve Control Panel' to each facet location using compression type fittings. If plastic tubing is not desired in an *Ultraflo* water system, copper tubing can easily be substituted.

Even though the home has an *Ultraflo* water system, this does not mean that all water outlet locations have to be served by the 'Valve Control Panel'. The utility sink, sprinkler system, hose bibs, water fountain and others are supplied with water directly from the city water supply.

**9-14 Automated Shower:** As part of the 'Morning Mode', the Master Bedroom shower will automatically turn ON and be at the right temperature for the homeowner to conveniently step into. To include this feature as part of the 'Morning Mode', the *Stargate* will need to interface the *Ultraflo* Control system. This can be done by using a Relay Output from the *Stargate*, which will control the Master Bedroom shower solenoid valves 'open' and 'closed' as required. The wiring requirements to interface the two control systems can be supplied by *Ultraflo*.

### *STARGATE PROGRAMMING:*

    EVENT: **SHOWER - ON**
     **IF**
      ( Morning Mode )
     **THEN**
      (RELAY: SHOWER )  ON
      (T: TIMER 10 ) LOAD with 0 : 07 : 00
      *All other 'Morning Mode' programming lines*
    End

### *Description:*

*Feature name*
*if*
*If 'Morning Mode' is selected from a JDS Keypad*
*then*
*Turn Shower ON*
*Start 7 minute timer ( See Time 10 Event below )*

---

    EVENT: **TIME 10**
     **IF**
      ( T: TIME 10 ) is Expiring
     **THEN**
      (RELAY: SHOWER )  OFF
    End

*Feature name*
*if*
*7 minute timer is over*
*then*
*Turn Shower OFF*

**9-15 Automated Sprinkler Systems:** The automated sprinkler system for the 'Example Home' is designed to reduce the quantity of water used and the time required to tend to the lawn. This system has four sprinkler *Zones* and consists of a sprinkler pump and motor ``with starter, solenoid valves, sprinkler heads, water piping, rain sensor and the control capabilities provided by *Stargate* as shown in Figure 9-10. The system water pump draws water from a well and discharges water to the sprinkler heads only when the

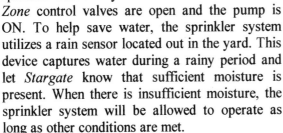

*Zone* control valves are open and the pump is ON. To help save water, the sprinkler system utilizes a rain sensor located out in the yard. This device captures water during a rainy period and let *Stargate* know that sufficient moisture is present. When there is insufficient moisture, the sprinkler system will be allowed to operate as long as other conditions are met.

The sprinkler pump receives it's power from the main power distributions panel located in the garage. In some homes, a separate sub-panel may feed this system. The sprinkler pump uses a starter relay to switch the pump motor power ON and OFF. The starter relay used to control this pump must handle the power requirements of a 1 1/2 HP motor. This means the starter relay must have a 1 1/2 HP continuous duty rating along with a 12V DC coil. Notice in Figure 9-10, how the (CAT 5, 4 UTP) conductors are connected to Relay Outputs of *Stargate*. One is connected to the coil of the pump starter relay. The starter relay coil is energized and de-energized by *Stargate's* (N.O.) Relay Output 4. A (N.O.) starter relay is also used because it will prevent the pump from operating continuously if the control circuit should fail. If the starter relay fails, it will fail open, which will stop the pump. This will avoid the possibility of flooding the landscape. *Zone* 1, 2, 3 & 4 solenoid valve are also controlled by (N.O.) Relay Outputs that will fail open. The control valves selected are all (N.C.) devices. This will allow the valves to fail in the closed position to again avoid flooding.

CAT 5, 4 UTP conductors are shown connected from *Stargate's* Relay Outputs to each *Zone* solenoid control valve. The sprinkler system is controlled ON & OFF by either a 'Scheduled Time' Event or by a push button command from a *JDS* Keypad. Keypads located in the Foyer and next to the Living Room sliding glass door will allow the homeowner to easily select the desired sprinkler *Zones*. When the *Zone* 1 & 2 'sprinkler ON' command is selected from the *JDS* Keypad; for instance, this command will be sent via RS-485 to the *Stargate*. This will prove the programming 'IF' statement true as long as there is insufficient moisture detected by the rain sensor. This will allow the 'THEN' statement to run as shown on page 187. The *Stargate* will first send Relay Outputs to open the *Zone* 1 & 2 sprinkler solenoid valves. Three seconds after the valves are opened, Relay Output 4 will close, which will energize the coil of the pump starter relay and close the starter relay contacts to start the pump.

The rain sensor produces a momentary contact closure each time (.01) inches of rain accumulates in the rain sensor. Notice this sensor located at the top of Figure 9-10. The 'Scheduled Time' Event programming on page 187, shows that different *Zones* of the lawn are watered at 6:00, 6:20, 6:40 & 7:00 AM Monday, Wednesday and Friday for 20 minutes at a time as long as the rain sensor does not detect a minimum of 0.01 inches of moisture.

The conductors used to control this system are pulled from the *'Equipment Room'*, into the attic and over to the perimeter wall to the left of the garage. In wood stud constructed homes, these conductors are then pulled through a 1/2" pre-drilled hole in the top plate of the wall and down to the bottom of the wall. These conductors will then enter a conduit that runs through the exterior wall and exits where the sprinkler pump and solenoid valves are located. These conductors are then terminated to the solenoid valves as well as to the pump starter relay.

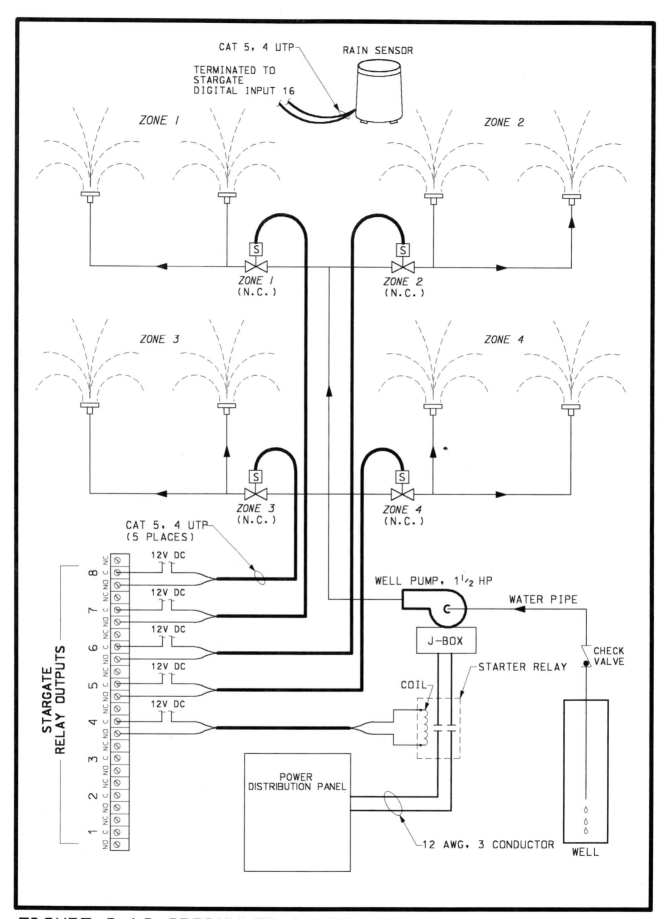

# FIGURE 9-10 SPRINKLER SYSTEM CONTROL WIRING DIAGRAM

# LAWN SPRINKLER - SCHEDULED TIME EVENTS

## PROGRAMMING:

EVENT:  **WATER FRONT YARD 6:00 AM & 6:40 AM**
  **IF**
    Time is 6:00 AM . MWF .
    and   ( F: DI RAIN)  is OFF
            -OR-
    Time is 6:40 AM . MWF .
    and   ( DI RAIN)  is OFF
  **THEN**
    (RELAY: VALVE *ZN 3*)  OFF
    (RELAY: VALVE *ZN 4*)  OFF
    (RELAY: VALVE *ZN 1*)  ON
    (RELAY: VALVE *ZN 2*)  ON
    DELAY  0 : 00 : 03
    (RELAY: WELL PUMP )  ON
End

EVENT:  **WATER BACK YARD 6:20 AM & 7:00 AM**
  **IF**
    Time is 6:20 AM . MWF .
    and  (F: DI RAIN)  is OFF
            -OR-
    Time is 7:00 AM . MWF .
    and  (F: DI RAIN)  is OFF
  **THEN**
    (RELAY: VALVE *ZN 1*)  OFF
    (RELAY: VALVE *ZN 2*)  OFF
    (RELAY: VALVE *ZN 3*)  ON
    (RELAY: VALVE *ZN 4*)  ON
    DELAY  0 : 00 : 03
    (RELAY: WELL PUMP )  ON
    (F: NO RAIN FLAG )  SET
End

EVENT:  **WATER ZONES 1 & 2**
  **IF**
    (SPRINKLER 1 & 2 ON)
  **THEN**
    (RELAY: VALVE *ZN 1*)  ON
    (RELAY: VALVE *ZN 2*)  ON
    DELAY  0 : 00 : 03
    (RELAY: WELL PUMP )  ON
End

EVENT:  **SPRINKLER OFF - RAIN**
  **IF**
    ( F: DI RAIN)  is ON
  **THEN**
    (RELAY: WELL PUMP )  OFF
    (RELAY: VALVE *ZN 1*)  OFF
    (RELAY: VALVE *ZN 2*)  OFF
    (RELAY: VALVE *ZN 3*)  OFF
    (RELAY: VALVE *ZN 4*)  OFF
End

## Description:

*Feature name*
*if*
*If the time is 6:00 AM  Mon - Wed - Fri*
*and water is not present (Digital Input OFF)*
*or*
*If the time is 6:40 AM  Mon - Wed - Fri*
*and water is not present (Digital Input OFF)*
*then*
*Close Zone 3 solenoid valve*
*Close Zone 4 solenoid valve*
*Open Zone 1 solenoid valve*
*Open Zone 2 solenoid valve*
*After 3 seconds perform next line*
*Turn well pump ON*

*Feature name*
*if*
*If the time is 6:20 AM Mon - Wed - Fri*
*and water is not present (Digital Input OFF)*
*or*
*If the time is 7:00 AM  Mon - Wed - Fri*
*and water is not present (Digital Input OFF)*
*then*
*Close Zone 1 solenoid valve*
*Close Zone 2 solenoid valve*
*Open Zone 3 solenoid valve*
*Open Zone 4 solenoid valve*
*After 3 seconds perform next line*
*Turn well pump ON*
*Set 'No Rain' Flag to allow other run times*

*Feature name*
*if*
*If 'Sprinkler Zone 1 & 2 ON' Event is selected from JDS Keypad*
*then*
*Close Zone 1 solenoid valve*
*Close Zone 2 solenoid valve*
*After 3 seconds perform next line*
*Turn well pump ON*

*Feature name*
*if*
*water is present (Digital Input ON)*
*then*
*Turn well pump OFF*
*Close Zone 1 solenoid valve*
*Close Zone 2 solenoid valve*
*Close Zone 3 solenoid valve*
*Close Zone 4 solenoid valve*

NOTES:

# Automated Motorized Systems

**10-1 Automated Window Covering Systems:** Automated Vertical Blind Systems are motorized devices that are designed to provide remote and automatic control of the Verticals for convenience, security and energy management purposes. Most Vertical Blind designs provide complete traverse and rotation of the Verticals to a stacked or closed position. Motorized Vertical Blinds can generally span up to 24 feet when selecting a one-way configuration (one unit) and to a span of 40 feet when selecting a split draw configuration (two units). Verticals are normally opened and closed by low amperage synchronous motors that are powered by 120V or 240V, 60 Hz. Generally a slender motor used on each unit is completely hidden behind the track to provide a clean looking installation as shown in Figure 10-1. The speed of these motors will normally pull Verticals 1 linear foot in approximately 5 seconds. This means that it will take about 30 seconds to completely open or close a set of Verticals installed on a 6-foot window.

Vertical blind systems will normally contain internal limit switches that are designed to automatically stop the blinds once they are fully opened, fully closed, or fully rotated opened and closed. Motors will normally incorporate thermal overload protection that is designed to protect the motor from burning out if an abnormal load is applied or if binding should occur in the tracks.

Motorized Roller Shades shown in Figure 10-2, is another type of automated window covering that is powered by a 120V AC or 240V AC, 60 Hz low amperage compact motor.

A Roller Shade motor is different from a Vertical Blind motor because Roller Shades are designed to reel the shade up or down where as the Verticals Blind motor provides complete traverse and rotation to a stacked position. Roller Shade motors are of a tubular design that conceals the motor within the roller tubes.

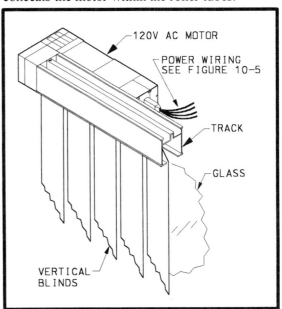

FIGURE 10-1   MOTORIZED VERTICALS

Motorized Roller Shades also contain preset internal limit switches that are designed to automatically stop the shades once they are fully opened and closed. Roller Shade motors also incorporate thermal overload protection to protect the motor from burning out if an abnormal load is applied or if binding of the roller mechanism shown occur.

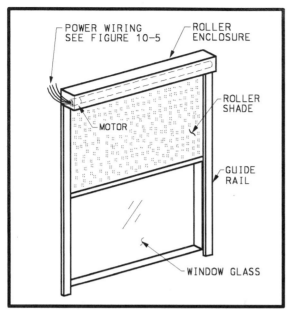

## FIGURE 10-2   ROLLER SHADE

Reference the 'Example Home' automated Window Covering Plan shown in Figure 10-4. This Plan illustrates the location of both the Motorized Vertical Blinds and the Motorized Roller Shades. The majority of the window coverings in the home are Motorized Vertical Blinds except in the Home Theater and Garage. Roller Shades are primarily used in the Theater to block out the sun light more effectively than the Motorized Vertical Blind can, and in the Garage they are used simply because they are less expensive units to install.

Both types of motorized window covering systems can be operated independently or in groups when using the *Stargate* home controller. For independent control, each window covering can be manually controlled by pushing a wall mounted momentary switch located near the entrance of each room as shown in Figure 10-4. This switch is shown close-up in Figure 10-3. Pushing the top of the rocker switch will open the Verticals, pushing the bottom of the rocker will close the Verticals and the middle position turns the unit OFF. This switch controls the Vertical Blinds open with the first motion being a rotation of the vanes and the second being the motion that pulls the vanes back towards the window jam. Closing the Verticals consist of these same two motions

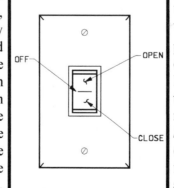

FIGURE 10-3 WALL SWITCH

in reverse. To gain automated control of each motorized window covering, the installer would configure the control system as shown in Figure 10-5. Power required to operate all the Vertical Blind motors as well as the Roller Shade motors is supplied by the 'Example Home' from the main power distribution panel through a dedicated 20 amp breaker. Conductors from this panel are connected to Hot, Neutral and Ground terminal lugs located in a relay electrical enclosure. This will distribute power to all motorized window coverings in the home. A Hot and Neutral are routed from the terminal lugs to two DPDT slave relays. Two slave relays are used to switch 120V AC power and to control the window covering motors forward and reverse. 12V DC low voltage power is used along with *Stargate's* Relay Outputs to actually control the 120V AC relay contacts open and closed as required. All slave relays used to control the motorized window coverings throughout the home are installed in an electrical enclosure located in the *Equipment Room* as shown in Figure 1-8 on page 9.

In Figure 10-5, one slave relay is labeled **'close'**, which is used to close the Verticals while the other relay is labeled **'open'**. Notice that each of these slave relays has one normally open (N.O.) and one normally closed (N.C.) set of contacts. When the *Stargate* receives a command to close the Verticals, it will close the low voltage Relay Output 'A' from the *Stargate*, which will energize the 12V DC slave relay coil (R1). This will close the (N.O) contacts and open the (N.C) contacts to provide power to the Vertical Blind motor. When the Verticals reach the fully closed position, the (N.C.) limit switches contained internal to the Vertical Blind motor will automatically open to stop the motor once it senses resistance to further movement. *Stargate's* Relay Output 'A' will stay closed for a sufficient period of time for the Verticals to fully close plus an additional two seconds. The total time period required to open or close a set of Verticals will depend the its length. This period can be determined by testing and timing.

When the *Stargate* receives a command to open the Verticals, it will close Relay Output

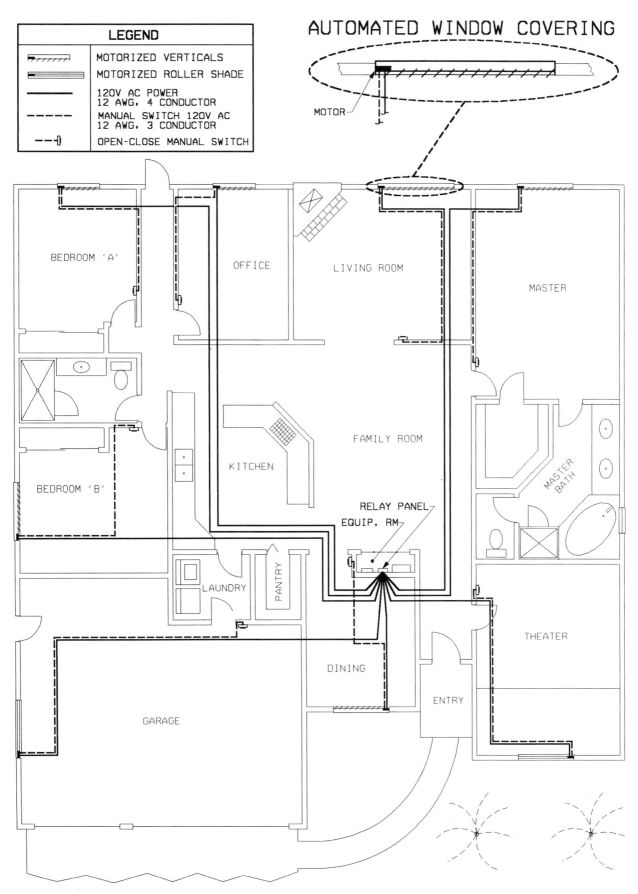

## LEGEND

| | |
|---|---|
| | MOTORIZED VERTICALS |
| | MOTORIZED ROLLER SHADE |
| | 120V AC POWER<br>12 AWG, 4 CONDUCTOR |
| | MANUAL SWITCH 120V AC<br>12 AWG, 3 CONDUCTOR |
| | OPEN-CLOSE MANUAL SWITCH |

AUTOMATED WINDOW COVERING

MOTOR

BEDROOM 'A'

OFFICE

LIVING ROOM

MASTER

BEDROOM 'B'

KITCHEN

FAMILY ROOM

MASTER BATH

RELAY PANEL

EQUIP. RM.

LAUNDRY

PANTRY

THEATER

DINING

ENTRY

GARAGE

# FIGURE 10-4  AUTOMATED WINDOW COVERING PLAN

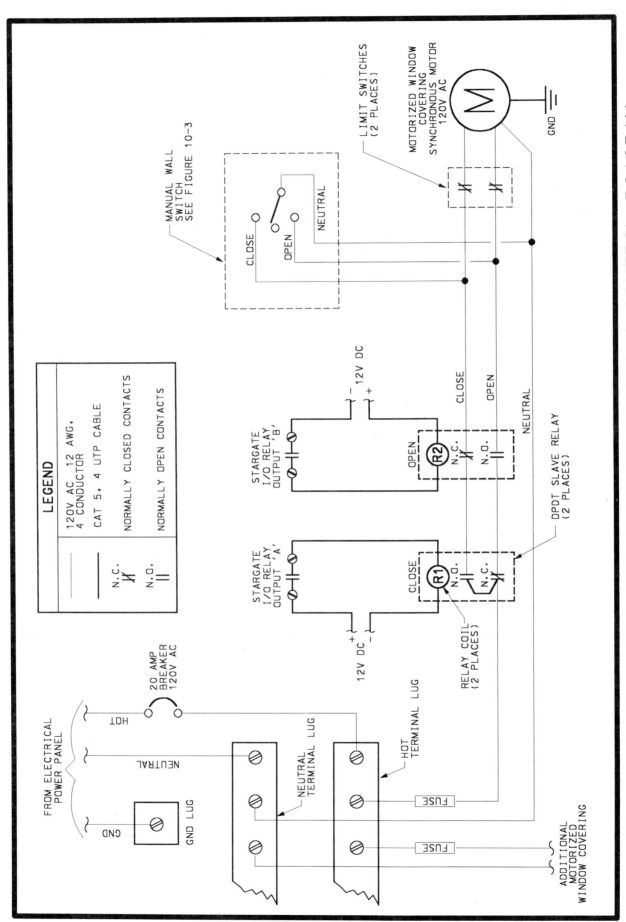

Figure 10-5   AUTOMATED WINDOW COVERING CONTROL DIAGRAM

'B', which will energize the 12V DC slave relay coil (R2). This will close the (N.O) contacts and open the (N.C) contacts to supply power to the motor in order to open the Verticals. When the Verticals reach the full open position, the limit switches will automatically open to stop the motor. *Stargate's* Relay Output 'B' will also stay closed for a sufficient period of time for the Vertical to fully open plus an additional 2 seconds. In Figure 10-5, notice the manual open and close wall control switch that is wired directly to the motor, which essentially bypasses the slave relays. As previously mentioned, the *Stargate* can control each motorized window covering independently, in groups, or all at same time. For instance; as part of the 'Good Night Mode', all or select motorized window coverings are closed by this mode for the night. As part of the control functions contained by the 'Morning Mode', all or just a few of the window coverings are automatically opened while the rest remain closed until at a later time when the other family members normally wake-up.

As part of the 'Vacation Mode', Verticals are periodically opened and closed to make the home look lived in. Now these Verticals do not need to be controlled open to their full open position in one sweep. The *Stargate* can be programmed to incrementally open the Verticals slowly over a period of time by starting a Timer as part of the functions included in the 'Morning Mode'. See the 'Morning Mode' Event programming shown on the next page. If the time is 8:00 AM Sunday through Saturday, this condition will initiate the **'THEN'** statement to run. 'Timer 9' is started and runs for 31 minutes. The Event called 'Timer 9' shown below the 'Morning Mode' Event states in its **'IF'** statement that if 'Timer 9' is running (over the 31 minute period), **'THEN'** the Master Bedroom Verticals will partial open for **5 seconds** by using a 5-second delay before stopping the Verticals. A **6-minute** delay is then used to delay the end of the Event before allowing the 'Timer 9' Event to start over again to perform the next **5-second** closure function. This Event was written for a 6-foot long section

of Verticals. If we use the approximate opening and closure rate of 1 linear foot per 5 seconds, and we use the 5-second opening functions every 6 minutes, the Verticals will be fully open in 31 minutes.

The Verticals or Roller Shades can also be partially closed over a time interval as the temperature increases or decreases, to limit the amount of heat gained or lost by the home. On a hot summer day, window coverings in the closed position will provide an air gap between the inside surface of the window and the window covering. This air gap is an excellent insulator and will decrease the cost of heating or cooling. The use of light colored window coverings will also reflect the heat to help limit the rate of heat gained by the home. The air gap is equally helpful during cold periods of the year, which will decrease the flow of heat from the home.

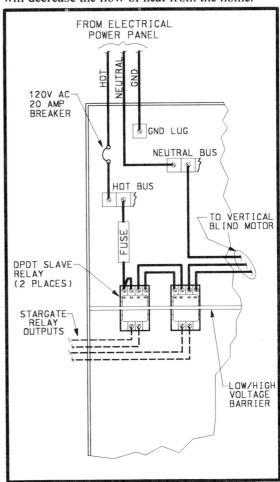

FIGURE 10-6 SLAVE RELAY ENCLOSURE

| *STARGATE PROGRAMMING:* | *Description:* |
|---|---|

EVENT: **MORNING MODE** *Feature name*
  **IF** *if*
    Time is 8:00 AM .S-S. *If the time is 8:00 AM Sunday thru Saturday*
  **THEN** *then*
    **Other lines of programming** *Other lines of programming that make up this mode*
    (Timer 9 ) LOAD with 0 : 31 : 00 *Starts Timer and run it for 31 minutes*
End

EVENT: **TIME 9** *Timer name*
  **IF** *if*
    (T: TIME 9 ) is Running *Timer 9 has not expired*
  **THEN** *then*
    (RELAY: MAS VERT R2 ) ON *(Relay Closed) Open Vertical Blinds in Master Bedroom*
    DELAY 0 : 00 : 05 *delay for 5 second*
    (RELAY: MAS VERT R2 ) OFF *(Relay Open) Stop Vertical Blinds in Master Bedroom*
    DELAY 0 : 06 : 00 *delay for 6-minutes and rerun the 'THEN' statement of 'Timer 9'*
End

EVENT: **VERTICAL BLINDS LIV RM - OPEN** *Feature name*
  **IF** *if*
    (VERTICALS LIVING OPEN ) *Vertical blinds open function is selected on JDS Keypad*
  **THEN** *then*
    (RELAY: LIV VERT R2 ) ON *(Relay Close) Open Living Room Verticals*
    DELAY 0 : 00 : 33 *delay for 32 seconds (time required to open)*
    (RELAY: LIV VERT R2 ) OFF *(Relay Open) Stop Living Room Verticals*
End
    **Note:** Similar Events are written for all other Verticals and Roller Shade systems.

EVENT: **VERTICALS BLINDS LIV RM - CLOSE** *Feature name*
  **IF** *if*
    (VERTICAL LIVING CLOSE ) *Vertical blinds close function is selected on JDS Keypad*
  **THEN** *then*
    (RELAY: LIV VERT R1 ) ON *(Relay Close) Open Living Room Verticals*
    DELAY 0 : 00 : 33 *delay for 32 seconds (time required to close)*
    (RELAY: LIV VERT R1 ) OFF *(Relay Open) Stop Living Room Verticals*
End
    **Note**: Similar Events are written for all other motorized Verticals and Roller Shades in the home.

**10-2 Automated Security Shutters:** Automated Security Shutters are motorized systems that provide a complete solution for the protection of windows, sliding glass doors, standard doors and other types of wall openings against intruders, bad weather, bright sun light and heat gained or lost by the home. High quality Shutters will normally consist of a 'double wall aluminum slat' design that is foam filled for insulating purposes. Aluminum slats generally interlock to completely seal off the wall opening when in the closed (lowered) position as shown in Figure 10-7. When the shutters are opened (raised), they will fully clear the wall opening and roll into a tightly stacked configuration inside an aluminum enclosure.

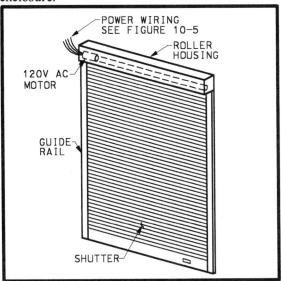

## FIGURE 10-7   ROLLER SHUTTER

When selecting motorized Shutters for the home, the important attributes to look for are units that operate smooth and quite, offer durable construction, are insulated, and are available in an assortment of colors to go with the home.

Roller Shutters are positioned at the window openings of the 'Example Home' as shown in Figure 10-8. The wiring required to power the shutters are represented in solid lines and the manual switch wiring is shown in dashed lines.

The 'Example Home' security system provides multiple levels of security and includes the initiation of the motorized Shutters to close

automatically when an intruder climbs over the fence and breaks an Infrared Beam Sensor. Because this system is automated, it can be considered a primary level of home protection that can actually prevent home intrusions. The wall switches used to control the shutters are the same type used to control the Vertical Blinds and Roller Shades as shown in Figure 10-3. To control the shutters open & closed manually, the owner will push the wall mounted momentary switch located in the entryway of each room. Closing the Shutters by any means will turn a vulnerable wall opening into a protective barrier to provide time until the authorities arrive.

The insulating properties of these Shutters provide a thermal barrier that translates into a significant energy savings. An R-value is a resistance value that relates to the ability or inability to transfer heat that flows into or out of the home. The R-value for single pane windows increases from .8 to 2.4 when using an insulated Shutter. A good portion of this increase in thermal resistance is due to the air space created between the exterior surface of the window or door and the inside surface of the Shutter. The solar heat gained by the home through the window is eliminated because of the Shutter's high shading ability. The insulating properties of the Shutters will also provide an excellent sound barrier from exterior noise.

Shutters are an excellent method of totally darkening an audio/video room or bedroom in order to view video and to gain privacy. The homeowner has the option of positioning a Shutter in the 'dim light' position by lowering it to fully cover the wall open while leaving the slats tilted partially open. When a window or door is left open and the Shutter is positioned for dim light, air is allowed to circulate while maintaining a strong security barrier.

In the southern states, Shutters can in most cases protect the home from hurricanes by preventing flying objects from breaking windows and doors. Openings in the perimeter of the home can cause pressure differences between the inside and outside the home, which can cause severe

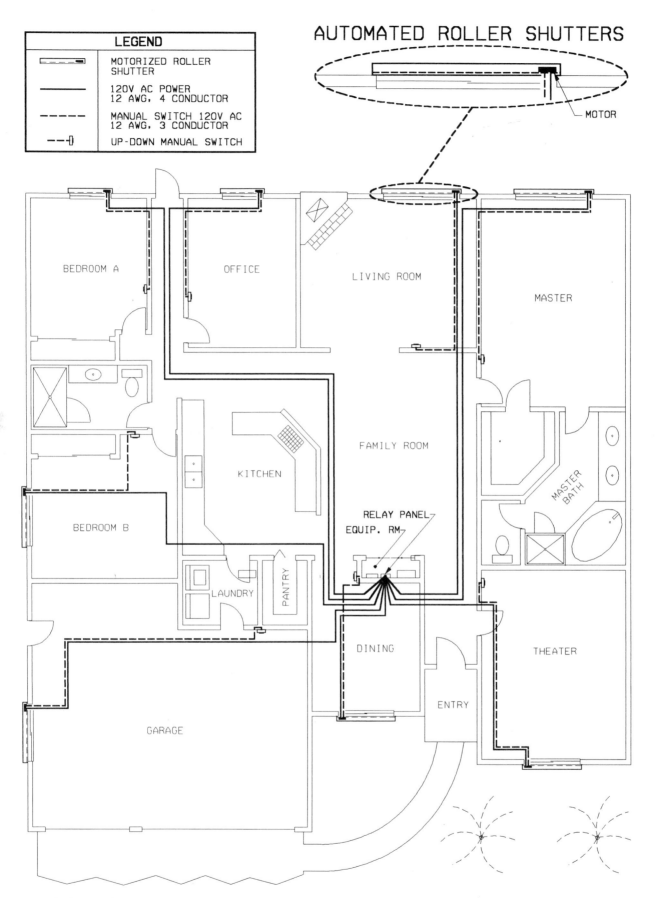

AUTOMATED ROLLER SHUTTERS

MOTOR

**LEGEND**

| | |
|---|---|
| | MOTORIZED ROLLER SHUTTER |
| | 120V AC POWER 12 AWG, 4 CONDUCTOR |
| | MANUAL SWITCH 120V AC 12 AWG, 3 CONDUCTOR |
| | UP-DOWN MANUAL SWITCH |

BEDROOM A

OFFICE

LIVING ROOM

MASTER

FAMILY ROOM

KITCHEN

MASTER BATH

BEDROOM B

RELAY PANEL
EQUIP. RM

LAUNDRY

PANTRY

DINING

THEATER

ENTRY

GARAGE

# FIGURE 10-8  AUTOMATED ROLLER SHUTTER PLAN

damage. By having a means of forming a strong barrier over the wall openings, the home stands a much better chance of surviving severe storms like hurricanes.

Similar to the Vertical Blinds and Roller Shades, Security Shutters are normally powered by 120V AC or 240V AC motors that will in most cases include internal limit switches. Like the Verticals and Roller Shade units, limit switches provide automatic motor shut-off at the full open and full closed positions. Limits can normally be adjusted for sensitivity.

The control system used to operate the Shutters is the same as the Vertical Blinds and Roller Shades shown in Figure 10-5. The momentary wall mounted switch controls the Shutters open or closed by manually pushing and holding the rocker switch down until the desired position is reached. For automated control of the Shutters, the *Stargate* will need to receive an 'open' or 'close' command from any *JDS* Keypad or from any touch-tone phone. Control can also be based on time of day/night or from a sensory input. Motorized Shutters can also be controlled 'open' and 'closed' automatically as part of the home automation system's variety of Modes. These modes may include the 'Morning Mode', Security Mode, 'Vacation Mode', 'Hurricane Mode', 'Tornado Mode' as well as others.

Tornado sensors are designed to detect the signature sound of an approaching tornado. These devices may allow enough time to warn the family to take cover. This sensor may also be used to automatically control the motorized Shutters fully closed to help prevent serious damage to the home. Motorized Shutters will not protect the home if a tornado is in close proximity. The 'tornado sensor' produces a dry contact closure when a tornado approaches the home and will send a Digital Input to the *Stargate*. This input will prove the *Stargate's* programming 'IF' statement true and allow the 'THEN' statement to initiate the *Stargate* to close the Shutters. As shown in the control diagram in Figure 10-5, the *Stargate* closes Relay Output 'A', which energizes the slave relay and closes the power circuit. For a more detailed description of how the sequence of operation is carried out, refer back to the operation of the Vertical Blinds and Roller Shades described in Section 10-1.

The same type of control can be initiated when hurricane level winds are experienced. Motorized Shutters can be controlled closed when; for instance, the wind speed reaches 60 MPH. Wind speeds are sensed by residential weather stations that produce a contact closure (Digital Input) and in some cases an Analog Input that is used to trigger the 'Hurricane Mode'.

## *STARGATE PROGRAMMING:*

| | |
|---|---|
| EVENT: **HURRICANE MODE** | *Description:* |
| | *Feature name* |
| **IF** | *if* |
| (DI: HURRICANE ) is ON | *If wind speed reaches 60 MPH* |
| and (F: HURRICANE) is Set | *and the hurricane Flag is Set* |
| **THEN** | *then* |
| (RELAY: MAS BED R2) ON | *Close Master Bedroom Room Shutters* |
| (RELAY: LIV R2) ON | *Close Living Room Shutters* |
| (RELAY: OFFICE R2) ON | *Close Office Shutters* |
| (RELAY: BED A R2) ON | *Close Bedroom 'A' Shutters* |
| (RELAY: BED B R2) ON | *Close Bedroom 'B' Shutters* |
| (RELAY: GARAGE R2) ON | *Close Garage Shutters* |
| (RELAY: DINING R2) ON | *Close Dining Room Shutters* |
| (RELAY: THEATER R2) ON | *Close Theater Shutters* |
| (F: HURRICANE) Clear | *Clears the hurricane Flag to avoid rerunning the mode* |
| End | |

**Note:** The 'Hurricane Flag' is Set by a separate Event (not shown) that will automatically open all of the Shutters after the 'Hurricane Automatic Close' Event has run and the Hurricane has past.

**10-3 Gate Operators:** Gate operators are manufactured for both residential and commercial applications. These devices are motorized units that mount next to the gate and connect to the gate to slide or pull the gate 'open' and 'closed' upon demand. There are basically two types of gate operators available. One is a 'swing gate' operator and the other is a 'slide gate' operator. A swing gate has conventional type hinges similar to a typical door configuration. To 'open' and 'close' this type of gate, the operator must swing the gate outward to 'open' and swing the gate back to 'close' as shown in Figure 10-9.

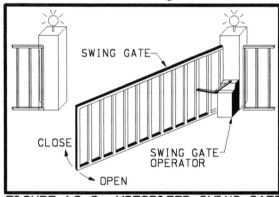

**FIGURE 10-9 MOTORIZED SWING GATE**

This type of operator will normally have an arm located on the top of the motorized assembly that connects to the gate near it's hinge points with the use of additional linkage. As the operator motor rotates one way, the rotating arm **pulls** on the linkage to swing the gate open. When the operator rotates the opposite direction, the rotating arm **pushes** on the linkage to swing the gate closed.

The disadvantage of a swing gate configuration is the room required in front of the gate to swing the gate open. A driver approaching the gate when leaving the property must allow enough space between the car and gate to clear. Some home sites do not have the room required along the length of the stationary fencing to accommodate a '**slide gate**' configuration, so the swing gate may be their only option.

Some manufacturer's offer swing gate operators with linkage that crosses over the

rotating arm and can create a dangerous scissor type action. Other manufacture's offer configurations that eliminate the scissor action and reduces the risk of injury. Consumers should be aware of the possible hazards that a motorized gate assembly may pose to children and pets before making their final equipment selections.

Most gate operators are powered by 120V AC motors; however, there are residential and light commercial units that offer DC motors powered by 12 volt circuits and utilize 7-10 amp hour batteries. Charging the battery is accomplished through a plug-in transformer or an optional small solar panel that mounts on a stand close to the operator. These DC operators are generally smoother and quieter devices while operating compared to units powered by 120V AC motors. A DC powered unit is most convenient when a 120V AC power failure occurs because this will provide the homeowner will uninterrupted service. 120V AC operators can be powered by an uninterrupted power supply (UPS) system in the event that the primary power source is unavailable; however, this is an expensive option. The UPS system normally offers the option of opening the gate automatically (one time) after power is interrupted and will return the gate to the closed position when primary power is restored. The homeowner can also select an option that will

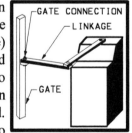

FIGURE 10-10
SWING GATE OPERATOR

maintain the gate closed during a primary power failure until opened by a keyswitch or button.

Slide gate operators are mounted in the approximate location of the 'Example Home' configuration shown in Figure 10-11. Slide gate operators rotate a sprocket that pulls a chain back and forth in order to 'open' and 'close' the gate. As previously mentioned, this type of gate does require space along the stationary portion of the fence to allow the gate to slide back to the full open position as shown in Figure 10-12.

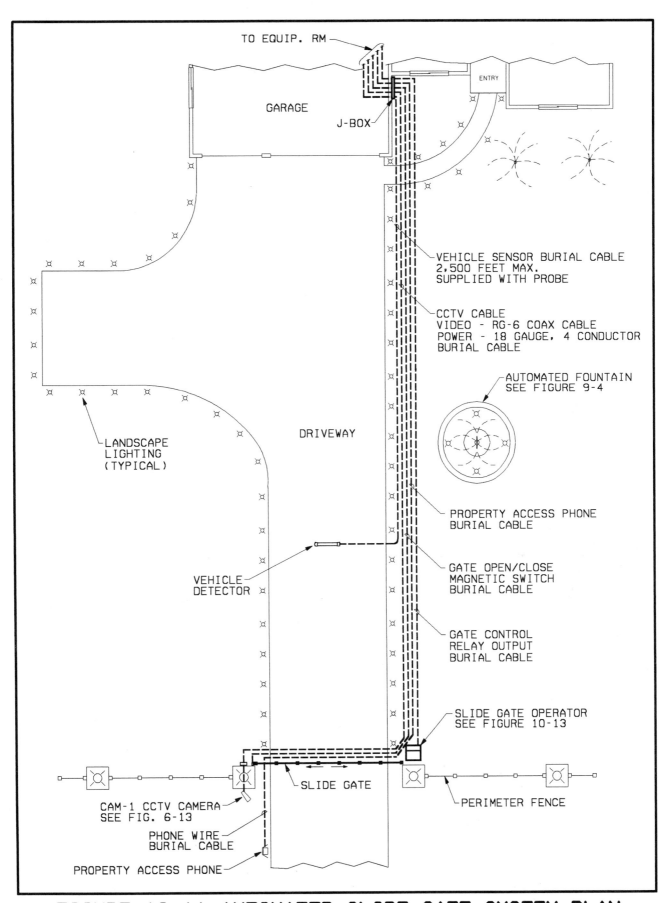

TO EQUIP. RM

GARAGE

J-BOX

ENTRY

VEHICLE SENSOR BURIAL CABLE
2,500 FEET MAX.
SUPPLIED WITH PROBE

CCTV CABLE
VIDEO - RG-6 COAX CABLE
POWER - 18 GAUGE, 4 CONDUCTOR
BURIAL CABLE

AUTOMATED FOUNTAIN
SEE FIGURE 9-4

LANDSCAPE
LIGHTING
(TYPICAL)

DRIVEWAY

PROPERTY ACCESS PHONE
BURIAL CABLE

GATE OPEN/CLOSE
MAGNETIC SWITCH
BURIAL CABLE

VEHICLE
DETECTOR

GATE CONTROL
RELAY OUTPUT
BURIAL CABLE

SLIDE GATE OPERATOR
SEE FIGURE 10-13

SLIDE GATE

PERIMETER FENCE

CAM-1 CCTV CAMERA
SEE FIG. 6-13

PHONE WIRE
BURIAL CABLE

PROPERTY ACCESS PHONE

# FIGURE 10-11 AUTOMATED SLIDE GATE SYSTEM PLAN

199

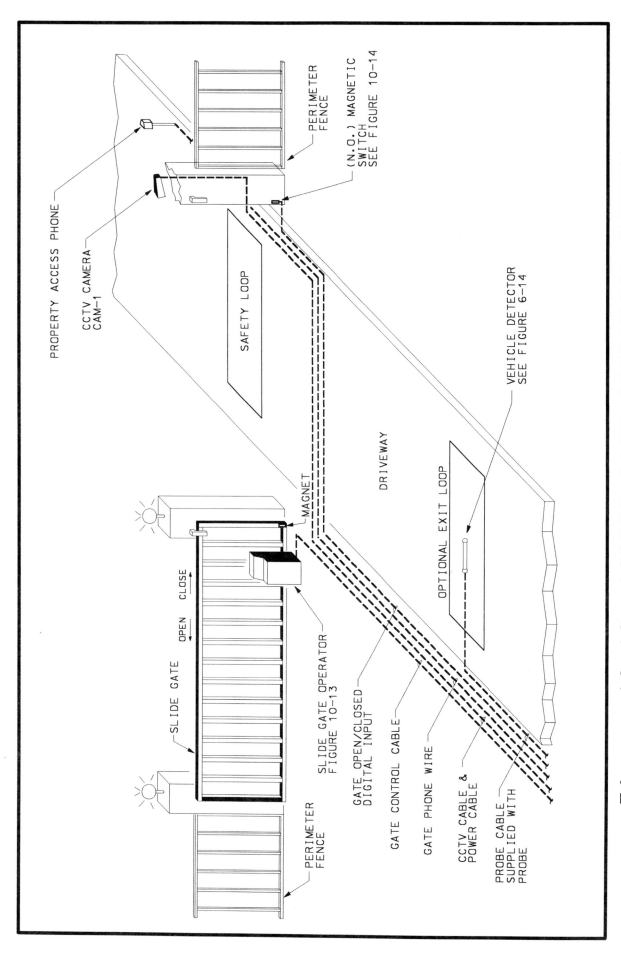

PROPERTY ACCESS PHONE

CCTV CAMERA
CAM-1

PERIMETER
FENCE

(N.O.) MAGNETIC
SWITCH
SEE FIGURE 10-14

SAFETY LOOP

MAGNET

DRIVEWAY

VEHICLE DETECTOR
SEE FIGURE 6-14

OPTIONAL EXIT LOOP

SLIDE GATE

OPEN    CLOSE

SLIDE GATE OPERATOR
FIGURE 10-13

GATE OPEN/CLOSED
DIGITAL INPUT

GATE CONTROL CABLE

GATE PHONE WIRE

CCTV CABLE &
POWER CABLE

PROBE CABLE
SUPPLIED WITH
PROBE

PERIMETER
FENCE

Figure 10-12   ACCESS GATE OPERATING SYSTEM

200

The slide gate is generally a cleaner operating installation compared to the swing gate option; however, each system type has its place when it comes down to specific customer requirements and property configurations.

One possible safety concern of a slide gate configuration is the shearing action that could take place if an individual should put a limb through both the moving and stationary portions of the gate while the system is operating. This could occur if an individual stands on the base rung of the gate for the purpose of riding the gate and accidentally slips. To avoid an incident, most manu-facturers recommend installing a durable decorative aluminum mesh over the face of the gate to eliminate the possibility of someone placing one of their limbs in a vulnerable position.

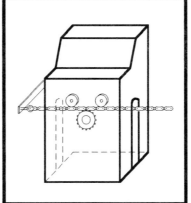

FIGURE 10-13 SLIDE GATE OPERATOR

Emergency gate release functions are also provided by both types of gate operators for the purpose of opening the gate manually for the following reasons: If a mechanical failure should occur, if there is a control system failure, or if there is a power failure and an UPS is not in place. One type of manual system consists of a hand crank or a crank extension tool that fits on a wireless power drill to speed up the operation. Another manual override option is a cable that can be manually pulled to release the chain from the gate so the homeowner can manually slide the gate open. This device is mounted inside a locked box for obvious security reasons.

For fire safety purposes, a fire box is required by most local building codes to allow the local fire department to access control of the motorized gate in case of a fire when the property is unoccupied. This box normally contains a keyswitch that must be turned to open the gate in an emergency condition.

Both types of gate operators must be installed on a concrete pad located on the interior side of the gate. Both types of operators offer an option called 'Safety Loops' that are designed to prevent the gate from closing on a vehicle while it is exiting, while it is entering, or stopped in the path of the gate. 'Safety Loops' consist of twisted wire lengths that are laid into a small vertical cut in the driveway surface approximately (1/4" wide x 1 1/2" deep). After the wire is installed, the cut in the driveway is filled with sealer to protect the conductors. 'Safety Loops' work by sensing a magnetic field when a large metal object is present and sends a control signal to the operator to stop the gate. These loops are positioned in the driveway as shown in Figure 10-12. This safety system is independently controlled by the gate operator and is not controlled by *Stargate*.

An 'Exit Loop' is installed in the driveway on the inside of the gate as shown in Figure 10-12. The 'Exit Loop' senses a vehicle leaving the driveway and automatically opens the gate. The Exit Loop is installed in a similar fashion as the 'Safety Loop'. The 'Exit' loop function is also controlled independently by the gate operator and is not controlled by *Stargate*.

Another control option is the use of a photoelectric cell that detects a vehicle breaking the beam and initiates the gate open. This type of detection device is not as dependable as the control loops because children, pets and birds can trigger the gate open or closed when the homeowner least expects it.

The homeowner has the choice of opening the gate when arriving home by several means. These methods include: A hand-held transmitter and receiver combination, a keyswitch, a card reader, a single push button, a three push button combination keypad, a telephone entry system, and an outdoor intercom system. All of these options ultimately provide an input to the *Stargate* to initiate a low voltage Relay Output that will open the gate. Another input device used to control the gate automatically is a 'Vehicle Identification Tag' and an in-road mounted reader. This system is used to control the gate 'open' and 'closed' automatically only by specific vehicles that carry the tag. This identification tag mounts to the undercarriage or to the front of the vehicle similar to an E-Pass used at tollbooths. The in-road receiver is installed in the pavement or concrete driveway and receives a signature identification of the vehicle as it passes within 32 inches of the reader at speeds of up to 25 mph. Systems of this type should be kept confidential. This is because someone that is aware of how the system works could potentially steal the homeowner's car to get onto the property. They would also easily enter the home if another system was used to automatically open the garage door as well.

The homeowner of the 'Example Home' uses a simple but popular hand-held radio transmitter and receiver combination for herself and the family. When visitors arrive, a telephone entry system is used as part of the features offered by the Panasonic Hybrid Phone System described in Chapter Eight. This telephone entry system uses an 8-conductor burial cable that is routed under ground to a J-Box that is mounted on the exterior wall of the home shown in Figure 10-11.

Remote control of the gate by *Stargate* requires 2-conductors of the 8-conductor burial cable. A (CAT 5, 4 UTP) cable is pulled to an exterior wall J-box from the *Stargate* located in the *Equipment Room*. This cable allows the *Stargate* to control the gate 'open' and 'closed' using a *Stargate* Relay Output. This allows the homeowner to remotely control the gate from inside the home or away from the home as well. These control inputs originate from any *JDS* Keypad, touch-tone phone, IR or RF hand-held remote as well as others.

In the 'Example Home' design, there is an over head door type magnetic switch that is mounted on the column where the gate closes up against as shown in Figure 10-12. This is a normally open (N.O.) switch (when magnet is next to switch) that maintains the control circuit open while the gate is in the closed position. This magnetic switch is wired to a Digital Input of *Stargate* in the same way that an identical device is wired to control the garage doors of the home. A closer look at this magnetic switch used for the property access gate is shown in Figure 10-14. This device is used to prove whether the gate is actually 'open' or 'closed' to allow *Stargate's* programming to make the proper control decisions. When the gate is control to an 'open' position, the magnetic switch will close and

create continuity in the circuit. Continuity is detected by the *Stargate* as a 'Digital Input ON' condition. When the gate is in the 'closed' position, the *Stargate* will detect a 'Digital Input OFF' condition. The use of these inputs will be demonstrated in a moment. The control circuit is wired in series with a security system *Zone* similar to the configuration shown for the garage door control in Figure 10-16. This wiring is used to avoid the installation of another over head door type magnetic switch for security purposes only. Normally a security system uses (N.C.) magnetic switches; however, in this dual

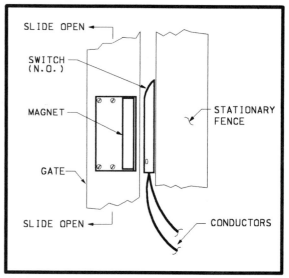

FIGURE 10-14   GATE MAGNETIC SWITCH

purpose case, it is best to use a (N.O.) switch to keep the *Stargate's* Digital Input OFF when the gate is closed since this is the position of the gate the majority of the time. In this wiring configuration, the security system controller will need to be programmed to accept a (N.O.) switch for the specific security *Zone* used. In other words, while in the armed state, instead of having the alarm activate when a (N.C.) switch opens, it must be programmed to activate the alarm when the security panel sees the switch close. The disadvantage of using a (N.O.) switch is the possibility of an intruder cutting this *Zone* cable, which will not be detected by the security panel. If the cable can be reached from outside the gate, then a standard (N.C.) magnetic switch should be used. This will provide detection of a cut cable; however, it could also shorten the life of *Stargate's* Digital Input.

When a visitor approaches the front gate and it is in the closed position, the visitor can contact an occupant in the home by using the property access system provided by the Panasonic Phone System. Once the visitor reaches an occupant and entry is approved, the occupant has the option of

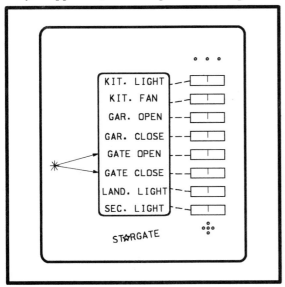

**FIGURE 10-15 KITCHEN JDS KEYPAD**

selecting the 'Gate Open' command by punching *9 on the touch-tone phone. Button 5 on the *JDS* Keypad shown in Figure 10-15, can also be used to open the gate. These two methods of opening the gate will Set the 'Open Gate Flag' shown in the 'Set Gate Open Flag' Event on the top of page 204. This Flag must be Set and the gate must be in the closed position (Gate Digital Input is OFF) before the 'IF' statement of the 'Gate-Open' Event shown below is true. Once this occurs the 'Gate-Open 'Event 'THEN'

statement will open the gate. The 'Digital Input OFF' state is useful if an occupant accidentally pushes the 'Gate Close' button when a 'Gate Open' function is actually desired. If the 'Digital Input is ON, it would not allow the gate to open.

This same control logic is used in the 'Gate-Close' Event shown on page 204. The 15 second delay at the end of the 'THEN' statement of each Event is to avoid having the gate controlled prematurely by accidental multiple pushes of the 'Gate Open' or 'Gate Close' buttons.

When an occupant pushes the 'Gate-Open' button and wants confirmation that the gate has actually opened, the Gate Digital Input must be ON and the 'Open Gate Flag' must be Set for the 'Announce Gate Open' 'IF' statement to be true as shown on page 204. This Event will then announce "**Gate is Open**" over the whole house audio system. The same control logic is used to receive audible indication that the gate has closed when an occupant initiates the close function.

When an occupant selects the 'Gate Close' command using the phone or *JDS* Keypad and the gate is proved open, the 'Gate Close' Event will initiate the gate close function. Now when the gate actually ends up in a fully closed position, the Gate (Digital Input OFF) state and a Set 'Close Gate' Flag will make the 'Announce Gate Closed' Event 'IF' statement true and announce "**Gate is Closed**" over the whole house audio system.

Also notice in the 'Gate-Close' Event on page 204, that the gate is automatically closed at 10:00 PM Sunday through Saturday in case the homeowner accidentally leaves the gate open.

### STARGATE PROGRAMMING

| | **Description:** |
|---|---|
| EVENT: **GATE - OPEN** | *Feature name* |
| **IF** | *if* |
| ( F: OPEN GATE ) is Set | *'Open Gate' Flag is Set by 'Set Gate Open Flag' Event on Pg 204* |
| and (DI: GATE ) OFF | *and Digital Input 'Gate' is OFF (Gate is Closed)* |
| **THEN** | *then* |
| (RELAY: GATE ) ON | *Opens the gate* |
| DELAY 00 : 00 : 15 | *allow 15 seconds for gate to fully open before new command* |
| End | |

**Note:** Button number 5 will open the gate only if Digital Input (DI) is OFF, which means the gate is closed. The homeowner cannot accidentally 'open' the gate with the 'close' button because Digital Input 'Gate' must be ON, which is not the case when it is in the closed position. *9 received by the Panasonic Telephone Controller to directly perform the gate open function. (See page 153). 'Set Gate Open Flag' Event shown on page 204 initiates the 'Gate Open' Event shown above.

EVENT:   **SET GATE OPEN FLAG**                                    *Feature name*
  **IF**                                                                        *if*
    ( XSEQ: G1  G-ON )  Received within 4 seconds   · *JDS Keypad or Phone initiates X-10 G1-ON command*
  **THEN**                                                                    *then*
    (F: OPEN GATE )  Set   *Sets the 'Open Gate' Flag to make 'Gate-Open' Event on Pg 203 IF statement true*
End

---

EVENT:   **SET GATE CLOSE FLAG**                                   *Feature name*
  **IF**                                                                        *if*
    ( XSEQ: G1  G-OFF )  Received within 4 seconds   *JDS Keypad or Phone initiates X-10 G1-OFF command*
  **THEN**                                                                    *then*
    (F: CLOSE GATE )  Set   *Sets the 'Close Gate' Flag to make 'Gate-Close' Event below IF statement true*
End

---

EVENT:   **GATE - CLOSE**                                          *Feature name*
  **IF**                                                                        *if*
    ( F: CLOSE GATE ) is Set               *'Close Gate' Flag is Set by the 'Set Gate Close Flag' Event*
    and (DI: GATE )  ON                         *and Digital Input Gate is ON (Gate is Open)*
        -OR-                                                  *or*
    Time  is 10:00 PM .S-S.                      *If it is 10:00 PM Sunday thru Saturday*
    and (DI: GATE )  ON                         *and Digital Input Gate is ON (Gate is Open)*
  **THEN**                                                                    *then*
    (RELAY: GATE )  ON                          *Close the gate*
    DELAY  0 : 00 :15              *allow 15 seconds before another command is accepted*
End

  **Note:**   Each night of the week the *Stargate* will make sure the gate is not left open accidentally by
        closing it automatically at 10:00 PM Sunday through Saturday.

---

EVENT: **ANNOUNCE GATE OPEN**                                     *Feature name*
  **IF**                                                                        *if*
    (DI: GATE )  ON                           *If gate is proved open by the magnetic switch*
    and (F: OPEN GATE )  is Set       *and the Open Gate Flag is Set (The 'Gate Open' command was initiate)*
  **THEN**                                                                    *then*
    Voice: "Gate is Open"            *"Gate is Open" is heard over the whole house audio system*
    ( F: OPEN GATE ) Clear       *Clears Flag so 'Gate Open' command does not run over and over*
End

  **Note:**   This Event provides the occupant with confirmation that the gate has actually opened.

---

EVENT: **ANNOUNCE GATE CLOSED**                                   *Feature name*
  **IF**                                                                        *if*
    (DI: GATE )  OFF                          *If gate is proved closed by the magnetic switch*
    and (F: CLOSE GATE )  is Set     *and the 'Close Gate Flag' is Set ('Gate Close' command was initiate)*
  **THEN**                                                                    *then*
    Voice: "Gate is Closed"           *"Gate is closed" is heard over the whole house audio system*
    (F: CLOSE GATE ) Clear        *Clears Flag so 'Gate Close' command does not run over and over*
End

  **Note:**   This Event provides the occupant with confirmation that the gate has actually fully closed.

**10-4 Automated Garage Door Control**: In the 'Example Home' the garage door is controlled by several methods. The homeowner can select 'Garage Open' or 'Garage Close' functions from any *JDS* Keypad in the home or from a touch-tone phone anywhere in the world. When the homeowner wants to control the garage door 'closed' from within the house or from a remote location, it is important to assure that the door actually closes without having to check it visually. Since the garage door opener is

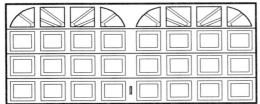

controlled by a momentary switch closure that incorporates a reversing relay, it does not offer separate 'open' and 'close' functions, which can create a control problem. For instance; the owner may intend to close the garage door at a time when the door is half-way open. Initiating the door closed could actually move the door to the full open position and not close it at all. The owner would not know this, which could pose security concerns. To resolve this problem the installer can use a normally open (N.O.) magnetic switch and configure the control wiring in series with a *Stargate* Digital Input along with the security system *Zone* terminals as shown in Figure 10-16.

When the homeowner initiates a 'close' command from a remote location, the *Stargate* will automatically initiate a second 'close' command 30 seconds later, only if the door is conformed 'open' by a (Digital Input ON) condition detected by *Stargate*. This is shown in the 'Close - Garage Door' Event and the 'Time 4 'Check Closed' Event shown on page 207. This control feature will continue to check the door closed until it is actually confirmed closed when *Stargate* detects a (Digital Input OFF) state. At the moment the door is fully closed, the (N.O.) magnetic switch will open and create an open circuit, which turns the Garage Digital

Input OFF, (No continuity in circuit). As shown in the 'Open - Garage Door' Event on page 107, the door will now be allowed to open when the 'Open - Garage Door' function is selected and the when the Garage (Digital Input OFF) condition confirms the 'IF' statement true.

The same (N.O.) magnetic switch is used as part of the security system to notify the homeowner and monitoring service of an intrusion when the system is in an *Armed* state. Security systems will in most cases use (N.C.) magnetic switches. The reason for this is to avoid the possibility of an intruder cutting the magnetic switch conductors to evade detection during an intrusion. This scenario may be possible in certain cases, however, it is also improbable in others.

The reason for using a (N.O) magnetic switch in this case is to avoid having the Digital Input circuit hot (Digital Input ON) for long periods of time. This would be true in this case because the door is left in the closed position most of the time. When wiring a (N.O.) magnetic switch to a specific security *Zone*, the *Zone* will need to be programmed to initiate the alarm when the circuit goes closed (door pried open by an intruder). Now if the garage door is controlled opened when the security system is *Armed*, the (N.O.) switch will 'close' and the alarm will also be activated.

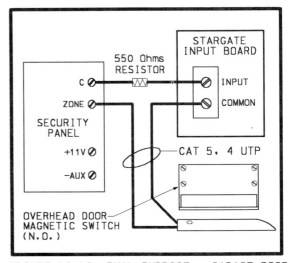

FIGURE 10-16 DUAL PURPOSE - GARAGE DOOR SECURITY & GARGAGE DOOR CONTROL

Wiring the security system in series with a *Stargate* Digital Input is unnecessary when a *Caddx* NX8-E or NX8 security system is connected to *Stargate* through their RS-232 interface. When using this configuration *Stargate* can read what security *Zones* are open or closed and what state the security system is in at any particular time. In this case, *Stargate* will know when the garage door is actually open or closed. This will replace the second line condition of the 'IF' statement in each garage door Event shown on page 207. For instance, The second line 'IF' condition for the 'Close - Garage Door' Event would read as follows: 'IF' '**Zone 1 is faulted**' (Garage Door Open), THEN close the door and set a timer to initiate another close command in 30 seconds. See the *Stargate* software Window shown in Figure 5-8 on page 113.

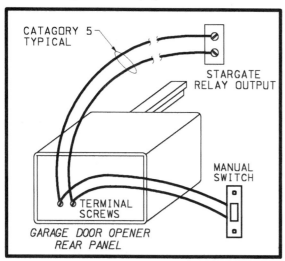

FIGURE 10-17   GARAGE DOOR CONTROL

Since the garage door opener requires a momentary contact closure to operate, no matter what method of control is used, *Stargate* needs to simulate a momentary contact closure by using a 1-second delay in the Event's 'THEN' statement. Notice in all three garage door control Events shown on page 207, that the Relay Output will first close and then open 1-second later. This is how we create a momentary switching function. The Relay Output from *Stargate* is connected to the garage door opener as shown in Figure 10-17. (CAT 5, 4 UTP) conductors are connected to the same terminal screws on rear panel of the garage door opener as the manual momentary wall switch conductors as shown.

The second method of opening the door is to select the 'Leaving Mode' from the *JDS* Keypad located at the Laundry Room entrance. This Mode will open the garage door, turn OFF all the lights, ceiling fans, audio/video equipment, close select window Verticals and Roller Shades, change the air conditioning temperature set-points and what ever else the homeowner desires all by the push of one button.

The third method used to open the door is to press buttons *43 on any touch-tone phone. (*) designates an 'open' command and #43 is used for a 'close' command. 4 = 'G' as labeled on the phone Keypad for 'garage' and 3 = 'D' for 'door' as shown in Figure 10-18. This is an easy method of remembering the correct button selections.

The forth method controls the door open as one of many functions provided by the 'Arriving Mode'. The 'Arriving Mode' will first turn the receptacle power ON that the garage door is plugged into before the door can open. This Mode is initiated by using a long range (200 feet minimum) radio frequency (RF) push button transmitter and receiver combination that provides (N.O.) and (N.C.) contacts. The (N.O.) contacts are connected to a Digital Input of *Stargate*. When the homeowner approaches the house, she will press the button, the receiver will close the circuit and *Stargate* will sense continuity as the (Digital Input goes ON). This will prove the programming 'IF' statement true and initiate the 'THEN' statement of the 'Arriving Mode' Event shown on the next page.

The fifth method of controlling the garage door is to use the standard momentary push button supplied with the garage door opener. In the 'Example Home', this switch will be used only during an automated control system failure.

FIGURE 10-18   PHONE KEYPAD

| | |
|---|---|
| EVENT:  **OPEN - GARAGE DOOR** | *Feature name* |
| **IF** | *if* |
|   (OPEN GARAGE) | *'Open Garage' function is selected on any JDS Keypad* |
|   and (DI: GARAGE ) OFF | *and Digital Input 'Garage' is OFF (garage is closed)* |
| **THEN** | *then* |
|   (RELAY: GARAGE ) ON | *(Relay Contacts Closed) momentary switch* |
|   DELAY 00 : 00 : 01 | *Delay 1 second* |
|   (RELAY: GARAGE ) OFF | *(Relay Contacts Open) garage opens* |
|   DELAY  00 : 00 : 10 | *allows 10 seconds for door to fully open before new command* |
| End | |

| | |
|---|---|
| EVENT: **CLOSE - GARAGE DOOR** | *Feature name* |
| **IF** | *if* |
|   ( CLOSE GARAGE) | *'Close Garage' function is selected on any JDS Keypad* |
|   and (DI: GARAGE ) ON | *and Digital Input 'Garage' is ON (garage is open)* |
| **THEN** | *then* |
|   (RELAY: GARAGE ) ON | *(Relay Contacts Close) momentary switch* |
|   DELAY 00 : 00 : 01 | *Delay 1 second* |
|   (RELAY: GARAGE ) OFF | *(Relay Contacts Open) momentary switch (garage closes)* |
|   (T: TIME 4 ) LOAD  with  0 : 00 : 30 | *Start 30 second Timer to re-check door closed* |
|   DELAY 00 : 00 : 10 | *Allow 10 seconds for garage to fully close before new command* |
| End | |

| | |
|---|---|
| EVENT: **TIME 4  CHECK DOOR CLOSED** | *Timer name* |
| **IF** | *if* |
|   (T: TIME 4 ) is Expiring | *When 30 second timer has expired* |
|   and (DI: GARAGE ) ON | *and Digital Input 'Garage' is ON (garage is open)* |
| **THEN** | *then* |
|   (RELAY: GARAGE ) ON | *(Relay Contacts Close) momentary switch* |
|   DELAY 00 : 00 : 01 | *Delay 1 second* |
|   (RELAY: GARAGE ) OFF | *(Relay Contacts Open) momentary switch (garage closes)* |
|   DELAY  00 : 00 : 10 | *allow 10 seconds for garage to fully close before new command* |
| End | |

| | |
|---|---|
| EVENT:  **ARRIVING MODE** | *Mode name* |
| **IF** | *if* |
|   (DI: ARRIVING 3 )  is ON | *A Digital Input is triggered by remote control receiver* |
|   and (F: AWAY FLAG )  is SET | *and the 'Away' Flag is Set* |
| **THEN** | *then* |
|   (X: RECPT GAR DR  H-6 )  ON | *Turn Garage door power receptacle ON* |
|   (X: LIGHT  GARAGE  H-5 )  ON | *Turn Garage lights ON* |
|   (RELAY: GARAGE )  ON | *(Contacts Closed) momentary switch* |
|   DELAY 00 : 00 : 01 | *Delay 1 second* |
|   (RELAY: GARAGE )  OFF | *(Contacts Open) momentary switch (garage open)* |
|   *all other lines of Arriving Mode programming* | *programming lines are not shown for simplicity* |
|   "          " | *"          "* |
|   (F: AWAY FLAG) Clear | *Clears the 'Away' Flag to avoid rerunning of Mode* |

# Automated Door Locks

**10-5 Automated Door Locks:** Electric door locks are used in entry and exit areas to help secure the home and to avoid possible intrusion if the homeowner forgets to manually lock the doors. These devices externally look like standard door locks and are available with lever or ball type knobs. These locks are easily automated by using a control method that will apply and remove 12V DC power to lock and unlock the door.

Electric door locks can be locked and unlocked from remote locations by initiating a command from any *JDS* Keypad. These locks can be controlled individually or in groups by programming an Event for *Stargate*. One way of controlling these locks is through the 'Good Night Mode'. This mode is normally initiated from a push button Keypad or by a 'Scheduled Time' Event. As part of the 'Good Night Mode', doors are automatically locked, lights are turned OFF, the security system is *Armed*, etc. There are two types of electric door lock control configurations to choose from. One is a 'Fail Safe' unit and the other is a 'Fail Secure' model. 'Fail Safe' door locks, lock the outside door handle when power is applied and unlocks when the power is removed. The disadvantage of the 'Fail Safe' model is that if the AC power fails, the lock will automatically unlock. These units can always be locked or unlocked from the outside with a key. The inside doorknob will always allow the occupants to exit the home normally or in case of an emergency.

'Fail Secure' models will unlock the outside door handle when power is applied and locks the door when power is removed. This unit can also be locked or unlocked with a key from the outside. The advantage of this model is that the door will remain locked even if the AC power

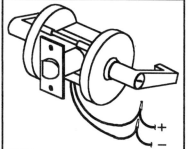

should fail. The door cannot; however, be controlled 'open' during a power failure and will always allow the occupants to exit safely.

Each electronic door lock installation requires a 22 GA, 2 conductor unshielded cable connected to a Relay Output of the *Stargate* as shown in Figure 10-19. Conductors are routed from the *Equipment Room,* into the attic and over to the electric door lock locations. The wires will then need to penetrate the top plate of the wall through a ½" diameter pre-drilled hole above the hinged side of the door. The cable is then pulled down through the wall to the center door hinge area. A small hole will also need to be pre-drilled in the wall stud and door casing to allow the wires to be pulled through. These conductors are then connected to an electrified door hinge that is used to essentially hide the wires underneath the hinge plates. Separate conductors are routed from the electrified door hinge to the door lock. This is accomplished by drilling a small hole through the door with a long security type drill bit. Wires are then terminated to the door lock and the installation is complete.

Electric door strike devices are also available to take control of the doors in the home. Electric door strikes are used along with a standard door lock. A standard door lock needs to be manually placed in the locked position to extend the bolt outward so it can be captured by the door strike. When power is applied to the electric door strike, the strike will open and the door can then be pushed open. The disadvantage of this type of arrangement is that the door will need a spring return to automatically close the door fully to allow the electric door strike to recapture the door lock bolt. The door can always be locked and unlocked using the key from the outside and can be opened manually from inside the home as well. The advantage of this type of electric door lock is that it alleviates the installer from having to drill a hole through the inside of the door for the wires. An electric door handle or knob type lock; however, is a cleaner looking installation because there are no signs that the door is electronically controlled and will manually work like a standard doorknob.

Another type of lock is the electric deadbolt. This device is used when even greater security is desired. There are also 'Fail Safe' and 'Fail Secure' versions available. This unit is installed by pre-drilling a 1 3/8" diameter hole, 3 1/2" deep in the door jamb. A 22 GA, 2-conductor cable is then terminated to the deadbolt to provide power to the internal solenoid actuator. The last step is to mount the deadbolt to the doorjamb using wood screws. The disadvantage of this type of locking device is that the 'Fail Secure' version should not be used on exit doors because the door can not be opened manually from inside the home in an emergency. This is a significant disadvantage in most applications for obvious safety reasons. It is however, one of the best means of securely locking doors.

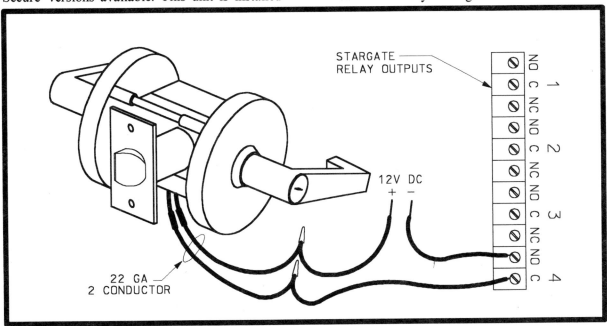

## FIGURE 10-19 ELECTRIC DOOR LOCK

*STARGATE PROGRAMMING:*

*Description:*

EVENT:  **FRONT DOOR - LOCKED**
  **IF**
    (FRONT DOOR LOCK )
  **THEN**
    (RELAY: FRONT DOOR)  ON

End

*Feature name*
*if*
*If the JDS Keypad selection is – lock front door*
*then*
*Lock front door ('Fail Safe' door lock)*

EVENT:  **FRONT DOOR - UNLOCKED**
  **IF**
    (FRONT DOOR UNLOCK )
  **THEN**
    (RELAY: FRONT DOOR)  OFF

End

*Feature name*
*if*
*If the JDS Keypad selection is – unlock front door*
*then*
*Unlock front door ('Fail Safe' door lock)*

# NOTES:

# Glossary of Terms

**AC (Alternating Current)** – The available current from electrical power systems in the USA and other countries. An electric current that reverses its direction sixty times per second or 60 Hz.

**A/D** – Analog to Digital converts analog voltages into a digital representation compatible with the *Stargate*.

**AHCS** – An Abbreviation for Automated Home Control System. A residential home control system that provides automatic & remote manual control of electrical loads for purposes of convenience, safety, security, energy savings, water management and more.

**Ampere** – A unit of electrical current equal to one volt across one ohm of resistance. Abbreviated as amp or A.

**Analog Input** – A linear voltage from 0-5V DC received by the *I/O-Xpander* or *Stargate* to base control decisions on.

**A/V** – Refers to audio/video equipment that may include, audio receivers, amplifiers, *Kustom 6* units, CCTV cameras, modulators, VCRs, DVDs, Tape players, TVs, etc.

**AWG** – American Wire Gauge. This is the standard measuring gauge for non-ferrous conductors. Gauge is used as a measure of the diameter of a conductor or the thickness of the cable.

**Bandwidth** – The range between the lowest and highest frequencies of a transmission channel. Describes the amount of data that can be transmitted through a given channel.

**CAT 5, 4 UTP** – Category 5, 4 pairs of unshielded conductors that are used for telephone service inputs, telephone extensions, other data communications and controls.

**CFM** – Cubic feet of air per minute. CFM represents units for an air flowrate to identify how much air is entering or exiting a space.

**Circuit** – The complete cyclic path of an electric current that includes the source of electric energy.

**CO** – (Central Office). A Telephone Company facility where subscriber's lines are linked to switching equipment for connection to each other for both local and long distance calls.

**Coaxial Cable** – Is used for high-speed data, CATV, Satellite Digital Signals, Internet and Ethernet data applications.

**Conditioned Space** – The volume of air in the home that receives heating, cooling & ventilation.

**Conductor** – Refers to an electric wire that provides a path for current to flow.

**Contacts** – Electrical conductive points or sets of points that open and close electrical circuits that ultimately controls electrical loads.

**Connector** – A device that connects conductors to electrical equipment or other wires and cables.

**CPU** – Central Processing Unit used to control a Home Control System as referred to in this manual.

**Current** – The flow of electrons through a conductor.

**Cycle** – 1 revolution of a 60 Hz sine wave from zero degrees back to zero degrees.

**Daisy Chain** – A wiring method that configures each telephone jack in a home where the conductors are wired in series from the previous jack. It is not the preferred method because a break in a conductor will disable all jacks down stream of the break.

**DC** – (Direct current). An electrical current that flows in one direction.

**Digital Input** – D/I or DI; closing of a circuit that produces a voltage differential of 4-24V DC across a set of Digital Input terminals of the *Stargate* or *IO-Xpander* that is sensed by *Stargate* to base control decisions on.

**Dolby ProLogic** – An enhanced process of the Dolby Surround decoding system that provides "logic" circuitry for the purpose of improving sound. Dolby ProLogic Systems use two front speakers, a center channel speaker and two rear speaker channels for ambiance reproduction.

**Drop** – A cable end pulled from the *Distribution Panel* location to each room in the home. This is generally where wall jacks are installed.

**DPDT** – Refers to double pole double throw contacts in this manual. Includes (N.O.) & (N.C.) contacts as part of a relay.

**Dry Contact** – Metal points that close to complete a circuit or open to break a circuit.

**Duct** – An air passageway made of sheet metal, fiberglass, PVC or ductboard material. Used to convey conditioned air to conditioned spaces. Ductwork is also used to return air back to the air handler and to convey air from outside to the air handler as fresh air.

**Ethernet** – A local area network used to connect personal computers, printers and other peripherals within the home. An Ethernet system can operate over (CAT 5, 4 UTP) cable, coaxial cable or fiber optic cable.

**Exfiltration** – Is an air conditioning cooling load. This load refers to the lost of conditioned air through cracks in walls, ceilings and around doors and windows.

**Exit Delay** – This allows a person to *Arm* the security system and leave through a protected entrance without causing an alarm condition.

**GA** – Refers to the word gauge, which is used to identify the size of a conductor.

**GND** – Refers to a home's ground wire(s) or grounding rod.

**Hardwire** – Refers to the use of hard conductors or wiring that is connected from Analog or Digital Input sources to the I/O, and from a I/O Relay Output to a controlled device.

**Heat Gain** – An increase in the amount of heat contained by a space resulting from solar heat gain, infiltration, heat flow through walls, windows, roof, including internal loads which consists of heat rejected from people, lights, equipment, and other sources.

**Heat Loss** – A decrease in the amount of heat contained in a space resulting from the flow of heat through walls, windows, roof, and from the exfiltration of warm air.

**Heating Load** – The rate at which heat must be added to a space to maintain the desired heating temperature setpoint.

**HVAC** – An abbreviation for Heating, Ventilating, & Air Conditioning. A mechanical system that provides heating, cooling & fresh air ventilation for the home.

**Home Run Wiring** – A wiring topology that connects each sensor or contacts directly to the control panel instead of wiring two sensors or more in series away from the panel.

**Hub** – A device located in the *Distribution Panel* where all associated cables are connected. Hubs are useful for their centralized management capabilities that allow the user to redirect signals to alternate *Zones* as required.

**IAQ** – (Indoor air quality). Generally refers to the quality of the air we breath inside homes and buildings.

**Infiltration** – Is an air conditioning cooling load. This load refers to a quantity of outside air that flows into the home through cracks in walls, ceilings and around doors and windows.

**(in-wg)** – (inches of water gauge). Refers to pressure. $1/27^{th}$ of a pound per square inch is equal to 1 in-wg.

**Internal Load** – Is a source of heat from inside the home that is considered when calculating the required HVAC cooling capacity. These loads often include heat rejected from people, appliances, computers, etc.

**I/O** – Input/Output communications in reference to Analog & Digital Inputs or Relay Outputs.

**Jack** – A receptacle used in conjunction with a RJ type plug to make electrical contact for communications.

**Keyswitch** – Opening or closing a low voltage circuit to perform a control function. This method is used to *Arm* and *Disarm* a security system, or to initiate a safety release that will open a driveway gate in an emergency.

**kHz** – 1 kHz = 1000 hertz. Hertz is a unit of frequency equal to one cycle per second.

**Kilowatt (kW)** – 1 kW = 1000 watts. A unit of power.

**KW-HR** – Kilowatt – Hour. A unit of energy used by the electrical power companies to charge their customers. KW-HR(s) is equal to power in Kilowatts (kW) x (Hours used). Electric companies generally charge the public between 6 & 10 cents per KW-HR.

**kOhm** – Kilo-ohm = 1000 ohms, A unit of electrical resistance.

**LAN** – Local Area Network. A network within a home or building used to link together computers and peripheral devices for the purpose of sharing system resources.

**Load** – The amount of power (Watts) required by an electrical device to operate.

**Magnetic Switch** – A sensory component used to detect movable objects such as windows & doors for security purposes and to initiate modes. It consists of two separate parts, a magnetically activated switch and a magnet. Moving the magnet causes the switch mechanism to open or close.

**Mbps** – MegaBits per second or one million bits per second.

**MH** – Man hours. Refers to the total hours spent to complete a task.

**Modular** – Equipment is modular when it is made up of plug-in units, which are assembled together to make system components larger.

**mV** – Is equal to 1000$^{th}$ of a volt

**(NIC)** – Ethernet Network Interface Card that is required in each computer to operate on an Ethernet network.

**Neutral Wire** – A grounded conductor that completes a circuit by providing a path back to the power source. Is normally identified by a white insulator over the conductor.

**(N.C.) Normally Closed** – A circuit or switch in which the contacts are **closed** when the device is de-energized.

**(N.O.) Normally Open** – A circuit or switch in which the contacts are **opened** when the device is de-energized.

**NOS** – Network Operating System. This system is used to provide a means for computers to access an Ethernet network.

**Number Code** – A number code can be any number 1 thru 16. Number codes are the second portion of an X-10 Receiver address or transmission code.

**O.A.** – Outside Air intake of an air condition system. This air is required to make up fresh air inside the home for its occupants.

**O.C.** – (On center). Is generally used in a distance measurement between the centerlines of two objects.

**Off-Hook** – When the telephone handset is lifted from the cradle.

**On-Hook** – When the telephone handset is resting on the cradle.

**Patching** – A means of connecting circuits using patch cords and connectors that can be easily connected and reconnected at another point.

**PBX** – Private Branch Exchange. A small privately owned version of the Telephone Company's larger telephone central switching office.

**PGM** – Programmable security system panel outputs.

**PLC** – Power-line Carrier: A home automation system protocol that provides the transmission of digital X-10 signals over the power lines in the home for purposes of communicating to Receiver Switches in the system that ultimately respond to control electrical loads.

**Polarity** – A term used to describe which side of an electric circuit is positive of negative.

**Protocol** – A specific type of home automation form of communication and technology as used in this manual.

**Radio Frequency (RF)** – An electro-magnetic wave frequency located between infrared frequencies and audio frequencies used for the purpose of providing radio transmissions.

**Relay** – An electromagnetic device used for remote control purposes. This device is activated by power in an electrical circuit to operate electrical loads in a different circuit.

**Relay Output** – *Stargate's* (N.O.) or (N.C.) 1 amp @ 24V DC rated contacts as part of the I/O used to close or open a circuit for the purpose of controlling an electrical load.

**Resistance** – A property of a conductor opposing the passage of electric current.

**Ring** – As in Tip and Ring. The second of the two wires needed to set up a telephone connection.

**RJ** – Registered Jack. RJ identifications are telephone and data jacks registered with the FCC. For example, RJ-11, RJ-45, etc.

**R-Value** – A unit of thermal resistance used for comparing insulating values of different materials. The higher the R-value of a material, the greater its insulating properties are, which slows down the flow of heat through the material.

**'Scheduled Time' Event** – A section of *Stargate's* programming that controls electrical loads based on time of day. The time of day is used as an 'IF' condition that needs to be proved before the Event can control a load. 'IF' it is 1:00 PM, THEN turn light ON.

**Set-Back Temperature** – A temperature set-point selected for the cooling mode, which is higher than the design set-point for energy conservation purposes. In the heating mode the set-point temperature will be lower than the heating design setpoint for the purpose of also saving energy.

**Service Entrance** – The location where telephone, CATV and other service inputs interface the home's *Structured Wiring System*. These enclosures are generally located near the 60 Hz power meter outside the home.

**Solar Heat Gain** – Heat added to a space from direct sunlight (solar energy).

**Thermostat** – An automatic control device designed to be responsive to changes in temperature. This device is used to maintain a set-point temperature by controlling the appropriate HVAC mechanical equipment.

**Tip** – The first wire in the Tip/Ring wire pair. It is the Telephone Company's equivalent to a ground wire in an electrical circuit.

**Topology** – The geometric and electrical configuration of a local communication network. Example topologies are 'Home Run' and 'Daisy Chain'.

**TP** – Twisted Pair

**Twisted Pair** - Two insulated copper conductors that are twisted around each other to reduce interference from one wire to the other. For example, Category 5 includes 4 twisted wire pairs, (CAT 5, 4 UTP).

**Volt** – Electromotive force equal to the difference of the potential between two points. Abbreviation for volt is V.

**Watt** – A unit of measure of electrical power at a point in time, as capacity or demand. A watt equals 1 Joule of energy per second.

**Zones** – A region or area set off as distinct from surrounding areas.

> More Than
< Less Than

# Popular Home Automation Websites

- Smarthome.com – www.smarthome.com
- Home Controls, Inc. – www.homecontrols.com
- EH Publishing, Inc. – www.electronichouse.com
- HomeTech Solutions – www.hometechsolutions.com
- Smart Home Systems USA – www.smarthomeusa.com
- Worthington Distribution – www.worthdist.com
- JDS Technologies – www.jdstechnologies.com
- Electronic House Magazine – www.electronichouse.com
- Home Automation Association – www.homeautomation.org
- Leviton – www.leviton.com
- Advanced Control Technologies, Inc. (ACT) – www.act-solutions.com
- SwitchLinc – www.smarthome.com
- HomePro – www.smarthomepro.com
- X-10 Pro – www.x10pro.com
- X-10 (USA), Inc. – www.x10.com
- Residential Control Systems (*RCS*) – www.resconsys.com
- Home Automation, Inc. – www.homeauto.com
- Digital Security Controls (DSC) – www.dsc.com
- Xantech – www.xantech.com
- Winland Electronics, Inc. – www.winland.com
- Street Smart Security – www.streetsmartsecurity.com
- Home Director – www.homedirector.com
- Aprilaire – www.aprilaire.com
- Compose PLC – www.composeplc.com
- Powerline Control Systems (PCS) – www.pcslighting.com
- Caddx Security Systems – www.caddx.com
- Elk Products, Inc. – www.elkproducts.com
- ADI – www.adilink.com
- Aqualine – www.aqualine.com
- asiHome – www.asihome.net
- Home Automator Magazine – www.homeautomator.com
- Home Toys – www.hometoys.com
- *i*Automate – www.iautomate.com
- Somfy – www.somfy.com
- Automation and Security Technology – www.homeautomationnet.com
- FutureSmart – www.futuresmart.com
- Broadband Utopia – www.broadbandutopia.com

# LATEST TECHNOLOGY OF AUTOMATED HOME CONTROL

## SYSTEM DESIGN MANUAL USING X-10 & HARDWIRED PROTOCOLS

By: Robert N. Bucceri

## Learn How to Design Home Automation Systems

**Includes the Following Automated Sub-Systems:**

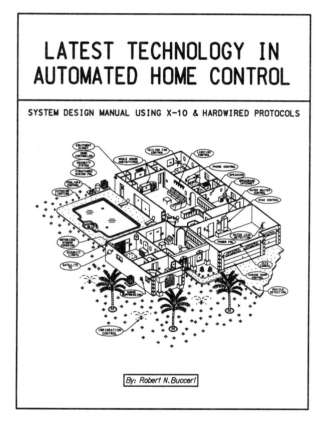

- **Lighting Control Systems**
- **Ceiling and Attic Fan Control**
- **Multi-Zone HVAC Systems**
- **Multi-Zone Whole House A/V Systems**
- **Multi-Zone Sprinkler Systems**
- **Integrated Security Systems**
- **CCTV Camera Surveillance Systems**
- **Energy Management Systems**
- **Pool and Spa Control Systems**
- **Drapery and Verticals Control**
- **Water Heater Control**
- **Water Leak Detection Systems**
- **Property Access Gate Control**
- **Garage Door Control**
- **Vehicle Detection Systems**
- **Appliance Control**
- **Security Light Systems**
- **Telephone Control Systems**
- **Electrical Noise Suppression Systems**
- **RF and IR Remote Control Systems**
- **Surge Suppression Systems**

**Also Includes:**
- **X-10 Trouble Shooting Methods**
- **X-10 Signal Coupling Methods**
- **Home Controller Programming of Multiple Modes**
- **X-10 Signal Blocking Methods**
- **Home Automation Equipment Specifications**

ISBN 0-9700057-2-5

# HOW TO AUTOMATE BOTH NEW & EXISTING HOMES

## FEATURES X10 & HARDWIRED TECHNOLOGIES

### By: Robert N. Bucceri

## ILLUSTRATES OVER 140 HOME AUTOMATION SYSTEM FEATURES

**Includes the following and much more:**

- Access Control Over the Internet
- Controlling System by Phone
- Automatic Arm/Disarm Methods
- Automated Surveillance Systems
- Automated Lighting Systems
- Automated Multi-Zone HVAC Systems
- Automated Pools and Spas
- Automated Sprinkler Systems
- Automated Window Coverings
- Automated Garage Doors
- Vehicle Detection Systems
- Water Leak Detection Systems
- Energy Management System
- The Economizer Mode
- Leaving Home Mode
- Automatic Arriving Home Mode
- Good Morning Mode
- Good Night Mode
- Entertainment Mode
- Vacation Mode
- Pool & Spa Modes

## Also Includes:

- Measuring X10 Signal Strength
- Finding Electrical Noise Sources
- X10 Signal Coupling/Amplification
- X-10 Signal Blocking Methods
- Home Automation Equipment Specifications

ISBN 0-9700057-3-3

NOTES:

# NOTES:

NOTES: